Darwinian Happiness

DARWINIAN HAPPINESS

Evolution as
a Guide for Living and
Understanding Human Behavior

by

Bjørn Grinde

The Darwin Press, Inc.
Princeton, New Jersey

Library of Congress Cataloging-in-Publication Data

Grinde, Bjørn, 1952-
    Darwinian happiness : evolution as a guide for living and understanding human behavior / by Bjørn Grinde.
        p. cm.
    Includes bibliographical references and index.
    ISBN 0-87850-159-2 (alk. paper)
    1. Genetic psychology. 2. Behavior evolution. 3. Sociobiology. 4. Happiness. I. Title.

BF701 G69 2002
155.7--dc21

                                                2002074108

Photos and figures by Bjørn Grinde.
Design by Darwin Productions.

Frontispiece: When looking for guidance, the church may be of help, but so can the theory of evolution. (From a monastery in Armenia, the first nation to become Christian.)

Published by: The Darwin Press, Inc. Princeton, NJ 08543-2202 USA
Printed in the United States of America

CONTENTS:

ILLUSTRATIONS

FOREWORD

Human intelligence enables us to contemplate a state of being whereby we could be happier than we presently are. Hence many thinkers have tried to grasp conditions for happiness. In spite of much thought and writing on the subject, their efforts have left us little wiser.

One of the reasons seems to be that they have been looking in the wrong direction. Happiness has long been seen in an "idealistic" perspective—that is, in the way life fits our ideas about how it should be—but since ideals differ, this approach does not lead to any universally accepted guidelines. Philosophers keep on quarreling about which ideal should be at the basis of true happiness. Moreover, there is growing evidence that happiness does not stem from any intellectual "real versus ideal" comparison, but rather depends on unreasoned affect, on how our innate repertoire of emotions and feelings are activated.

A "naturalistic" perspective promises a much better understanding. In this view happiness depends on the degree to which we live in accordance to our nature. It is assumed that evolution shaped us in ways that added to the survival of our ancestors, and that these imprints of the past still have a drastic effect on our happiness under present-day conditions, even though we do not recognize the imprints consciously. In psychology a related view is known as the "need" theory, and in sociology it is referred to as the "livability" explanation.

This approach requires that we get to know what human nature is like. That is what this book is all about. It presents a concise state-of-the-art in human behavioral biology and shows how this knowledge can be used to promote human happiness. Bjørn Grinde has done a wonderful job in crossing disciplinary boundaries and presenting this complicated matter so eloquently.

Ruut Veenhoven
Professor of Happiness Studies and
Editor of *Journal of Happiness Studies*
Erasmus University Rotterdam
The Netherlands

ACKNOWLEDGMENTS

Some people say that writing is a lonely job, but it is not necessarily so. When writing about science you need the advice and help of others; thus, writing this book involved interacting with a number of people. I would like to thank those who have helped me, but I should add that the text is solely my responsibility.

Thanks go to Marina Butovskaya, Bente Clausen, Alison Coulthard, Jan Erik Dahl, Asbjørn Flemmen, Turid Vogt Grinde, Tove Gulbrandsen, Arild Haugan, Olav Hungnes, Fran Johnsen, Tom Øystein Jonassen, Paul Levinson, David Lykken, Randolph Nesse, Jaak Panksepp, Janne Reseland, Randi Skaug, Brynjulf Stige, Bernhard Strasser, Ruut Veenhoven, Torfinn Ørmen. And finally, a special thanks to Ed Breisacher, my editor at the Darwin Press, for believing in the project and for invaluable help in executing it.

CHAPTER 1

Introduction:
On Genes and Gurus

Machhapuchhre—the mountain that was never climbed.

The Price to Pay

Human beings appear to be the most adaptable species on earth: We are farmers, industrial workers, nomads, and professional golf players. We survive everywhere, from deserts to the frozen tundra, from mega-cities to solitary caves. We have even left our footprints on the moon. But are we really as adaptable and versatile as this suggests?

Certainly we can exist under the most difficult of situations, but survival does not necessarily imply that we can thrive under any and all circumstances. The question we should ask is: Are people happy? A closer look suggests that our present situation is far from ideal: Depression, anxiety, and other mental disorders have reached epidemic proportions. People suffer from eating disorders, obesity, and drug abuse; they have insomnia and evidence aberrant sexual habits. Societies are riddled with aggression and crime. Wars are on-going and result in the mass slaughter of our own species—one of the features distinguishing us from most non-human animals. Humans even commit suicide, which ranks among the ten leading causes of death in the United States. From a biological point of view suicide is a most bizarre act, and an obvious indicator of maladjustment.

Even those who appear to be healthy may not be happy. The absence of disease may not indicate well-being. Many people are lonely and bored, lacking purpose in life. Living becomes a daily routine, with tedious jobs of limited relevance, and mental isolation even when surrounded by a large crowd.

The lists of societal problems and disorders are sometimes described as "the diseases of civilization." The point is that many, if not most, humans do not seem to be content, despite all the advantages of an industrialized society. The big question is, why?

Animals living under natural conditions do appear to be content, but various symptoms related to those described above are also observed in animals held in captivity. Household pets and animals in zoos or on farms often exhibit behavioral disturbances, particularly those under the control of people who are not qualified to take care of them. For example, they perform stereotypical behavior, like striding back and forth at a particular location in the cage; in fact, similar repetitive behavior is common in a variety of human mental disorders. To my mind, the crux of the matter is that these animals are subjected to conditions that differ from those for which their genes have actually prepared them.[1]

To some extent modern societies resemble a zoo, in that we are confined to conditions that are different from those for which we are biologically adapted. Given our current behavior, our "zookeepers," that is to say, politicians and government officials, have every reason to be alarmed. If they were good managers, they would try to change our living conditions to better suit us. Just as it is possible to design zoological gardens where animals actually thrive, it is also possible to do something about human conditions. The key to success is to adjust the environment as far as possible to suit the biology of the species in question.

In other words, I believe one important cause for the problems facing mankind is that we are losing sight of our biological inheritance: Our genes not only carry instructions for the development of arms and legs; they also contain a blueprint—though a less precise one—for our mental capacity. We should take a closer look at this blueprint, as I am convinced that knowledge about mankind's biology will help us make better choices, both in our personal lives and in designing our societies. The principle is the same as the intuitive recognition that insights into the biology of dogs help owners offer proper care for their pets. Yes, we are versatile, but there is a price to be paid for stretching the limits.

The Biological Perspective

In this book I take a biological perspective on the quandaries of society and the happiness of its citizens. I believe that an understanding of how our bodies and minds are designed by our genes holds an untapped resource for improving our way of living. To be a Stone Age creature in a Jet Age zoo tends to cause problems—the "diseases of civilization" mentioned above. I believe that biology offers a possible cure. While I do not claim that our Stone Age ancestors had a better life than what it is possible to achieve today, I do believe that there are things we can learn from our tribal past. It should be possible to construct a way of living that surpasses both ancestral tribal life and what most present people experience. This book is an attempt to tap that potential by looking into our genetic heritage, and I use the term *Darwinian Happiness* for the doctrine that underlies this attempt. (The concept will be presented in more detail in Chapter 3.)

Darwinian happiness does not hold the answer to all our problems. It is neither the sole principle to guide us in our quest for a good life, nor is it some magic formula. A biological perspective cannot offer a "do it yourself," ten hints for instant happiness. Nevertheless, I believe that such a perspective holds promise for improving the living conditions of mankind, and that it is possible to extract from it specific advice, primarily by offering insight into how the human brain works. How great or small that benefit may prove to be is still too early to tell.

That Little Extra Something

We all rely on a pinkish-gray, jelly-like mass to run our lives. It operates by means of a dual mechanism involving electrical and chemical communication. We call that mass the brain, and it is our body's greediest organ. Although the brain accounts for only two percent of our body weight, it receives 15 percent of our blood supply and consumes 25 percent of the oxygen carried by our blood. A newborn baby's brain is even more voracious, demanding 60 percent of the energy the baby consumes.[2]

There is no doubt about it: The brain is in charge. True, the brain depends on the rest of the body, and it receives a lot of important input from all the other organs; yet, it is fair to say that these other organs, including the much-vaunted heart, have the emotional and intellectual power and significance of a potato.

True, the heart does create a rhythmical beat, a beat that soothes us and can change according to our state of mind. Without these prosaic properties, however, we would no more have put our heart on a pedestal than we would have placed our liver or kidneys there. The mammalian brain, on the other hand, is the most fantastic miracle created by evolution, and we are equipped with the deluxe version. Or are we?

Technically, our brains are no more advanced than those of mice. The general design of a mouse brain is very similar to that of the human brain, and its functions are based on the same mechanisms. The largest mammals in fact have brains that are larger than ours, and a variety of animals have brains that exceed ours in their ability to accomplish a number of tasks. For example, bats can map their surroundings from sounds, dogs have a richer olfactory life, pigeons have keener vision, and who knows what goes on in the head of a dolphin. Although the differences in sensory functions are reflected in the design of the sensory organs, it is the corresponding sections of the brain that allow these animals to carry out such tasks.

Chimpanzees actually have brains that include most of the features associated with humans: They invent tools, and they acquire knowledge and hand it down from one generation to another—a property we generally refer to as culture.[3] They even sport self-awareness. This can be demonstrated with the mirror test: A budgie or parakeet will look in a mirror because it desires company, while a chimpanzee demonstrates self-awareness by removing a speck of dust on his forehead. Without the realization that he is the one in the mirror, the chimpanzee would not have tried to remove it. He really knows who he is.[4]

Normal decency should prevent us from bragging about more than one particular feature of our brain: During the later part of our evolutionary history we evolved an unparalleled cognitive capacity. This singular aspect made us what we are today—the masters of thinking and talking. Evolution sometimes acts that way, producing minor improvements that may lead to drastic changes. The development of legs from the fins of fish allowed vertebrates to colonize land; thus legs changed the face of the Earth. That little extra something added to the human brain has had even more drastic consequences: It is altering the Earth at an unprecedented pace.

Granted, human activity influences the Earth more than the activities of any other animal, but this does not mean that we are fundamentally different from them. It merely indicates that we are a particularly interesting biological phenomenon, but a noteworthy phenomenon nevertheless.

The brain is only an instrument and the body is actually no more than a frail wrapping. Both are products of a set of genes that exist for the simple purpose of reproducing themselves. In other words, the brain is not a computer that responds rationally to instructions; your genes "knew what they wanted" when they developed your brain. Genes did build versatility into the design, and as a consequence we can influence our actions by virtue of our free will. But most features of the brain serve the genes' purposes more directly. Our emotions reflect such features. For instance, we fall in love because it is in the interest of our genes that we find a mate.

The human brain is not just a fantastic feat of biological engineering. When designing it, evolution included something more valuable than anything else in nature. The genes have bestowed upon us a most wonderful gift, a feature so precious, yet so mundane, that few people ever stop to think about it: Our genes offer us the prospect of happiness. This book is about how to take care of that present.

The Whispering Guru

Roughly speaking, you can consider your personality as consisting of three parts: The first part is the genetic influence common to all humans. Since this is the most important contribution, I would allocate to it three out of a total of five "units." The second part (one unit) is the genetic influence peculiar to you. The final part (another unit) is how you are molded by the environment surrounding you.

Of the three parts, the first defines the limits of human behavior: We are simply not equipped to follow a scent like a dog, and we will never fly like a bird. The next two parts—how your specific environment interacts with the unique characteristics inherent in your genes—will mainly result in quantitative modifications. In other words, various aspects of a personality will predominate to a greater or lesser degree. For example, we all occasionally get angry, but some people hardly ever raise their voices, while others explode at the slightest provocation.

This book primarily deals with the first part, the one that defines human behavior in general.

The zoologist David Barash has dubbed the way our brain is designed by the genes to influence behavior as the "the whisperings within."[5] A knowledge of biology helps us understand the whisperings, and helps us recognize the forces involved in directing our thoughts, emotions, and actions. Biology opens up windows to our minds. What is more, I believe the acquisition of a knowledge of human biology can be compared to consulting a guru. Like the sages of India, this guru offers insight into the mysteries of life, as well as practical advice to guide you in your quest for contentment. As with any sage, not everything your internal guru whispers is worth listening to, but you should keep in mind that the guru is an expert on that gift of happiness the genes have bestowed upon us.

The guru does not offer fixed answers for behavior. Your acquired attributes, as well as the characteristics of the culture to which you belong, are equally important for the choices you make in life. Furthermore, the guru does not demand blind obedience, your conduct is your own choice—and your own responsibility. For example, in most cases the guru will tell you to be nice to others; fortunately for us, evolution has molded the human species into a social animal. Without our gregarious instincts, modern societies would be in much deeper trouble than they actually are. Accordingly, one of the messages from the guru is "Be nice to your comrades." But even in situations where this message is not being conveyed, you may still choose to be nice. The advice of the guru is not always worth following, but it is well worth considering. This book is about how to decipher the whispering, and how to evaluate the hints.

My own, somewhat antiquated book on social convention states that a courteous human should behave like a well-groomed product of culture, having no functions in common with animals. The "whispering guru" is skeptical: Most categories of emotions *are* shared with animals. Social life would not just be boring if natural functions were excluded; it would hardly make any sense at all. We ought to accept the repertoire of feelings with which evolution has equipped the human species, rather than try to compete with robots.

Plate 1. The great Buddha of Kamakura. For thousands of years people have sought the sages and gurus of the East for spiritual enlightenment. Some of the answers may be in our genes.

A Few Words on Terminology

A glossary at the end of this book explains the most important technical terms. These terms are printed in **bold** the first time they appear in the text, and the list is short. *Italics* are occasionally used to emphasize significant concepts that are not included in the Glossary.

The first question in science is whether or not a theory has explanatory power. The next question is whether the theory may benefit mankind. A variety of novel ideas have come out of the recent interest in understanding the human psyche in an evolutionary perspective—a disci-

pline I prefer to call **human behavioral biology**. I believe many of these
theories comply with both questions. They are not just interesting but
also have applied perspectives: They can be used to help the individual in
his or her pursuit of happiness, and to create a better society. In this book
I shall try to outline current knowledge, and suggest ways to exploit this
knowledge.

The idea of listening to your internal "guru" certainly does not imply
that you should yield to any desire or instinct. Neither do I claim that our
common genetic inheritance ought to dictate political or personal decisions. Personal choices are nobody else's business but your own, and choices
regarding society should be best settled by political mechanisms. Human
behavioral biology is only a tool that can help us make intelligent decisions.

To some people *sociobiology* is synonymous with the biological study
of human behavior.[6] For me the term "human behavioral biology" seems
more useful because it does not appear to restrict itself to social interactions, but includes activities and emotions of single individuals, too. Other
popular terms that stand for much the same are *evolutionary psychology*,
evolutionary anthropology, and *human ethology*.[7] The psychological perspective stresses the importance of cognitive processes—that is, thoughts,
feelings, and other mental activity that does not necessarily lead to ob-
servable behavior. Anthropology, on the other hand, is primarily concerned with cultural issues, while ethology focuses more on overt behavior.

I view our mental capacity as part of our biology. Thus, human behavioral biology covers everything that involves our brain, from contem-
plating the meaning of life to muscle reflexes. The subject may be described as the study of the brain's role in the biological **adaptation** of
human beings.

An *innate* or *inherent tendency* means that your **genes** try to influence
behavior in a certain direction. This is the whispering of the guru. It is
important to note that the strength of that whispering can vary considerably from one individual to another. For example, most people experience
a fear of falling when looking down from the top of a cliff, and the mes-

sage of caution helps you keep a safe distance from the edge. The fears of some people develop into phobias, while others are able to rationalize and suppress their anxiety. Yet, we all have a guru inside us whispering a warning when we approach the edge.

The main task of human behavioral biology is to describe how our inherent tendencies affect us.

Summary of Chapters to Follow

The following chapters expand on the approach outlined in this chapter.

In order to appreciate the remaining text, it is essential to have at least a rudimentary grasp of the principles guiding the evolutionary process; thus, Chapter 2 offers a brief introduction to the theory of evolution. In Chapter 3, I shall present a Darwinian approach to an evolutionary understanding of the concept of happiness. This is the pivotal theme of the book. In other words, I take a biological approach to the question of the quality of life. I believe our present knowledge of human behavioral biology is sufficient to extract meaningful suggestions. It should help us devise recommendations not only for alleviating diseases of civilization, but also for increasing pleasure, and for giving future generations a chance to live a good life.

Chapter 4 introduces additional background information relevant to the study of human behavioral biology. I have tried to reconstruct the evolution of key human features, and to discuss the types of information on which our knowledge of innate tendencies is based.

The remainder of the book describes various aspects of human behavioral biology, focusing on how the individual or society may relate to them. As a starting point, Chapter 5 describes the principles of brain function. The brain is the main organ of interest for any question related to Darwinian happiness. To understand how it ticks has a bearing on most of the issues raised in this book. Chapter 6 discusses some examples of how we can recruit the brain for our personal benefit.

In Chapter 7 I take a closer look at consciousness and free will as well as the annoyances and delights of emotions. A central question is to what extent we are in charge of our feelings.

Our brains are equipped with a variety of more or less distinct features, such as the capacity to learn a language, to coordinate limbs, and to experience love or hate. A comprehensive list of features should, among other things, include our complete repertoire of feelings, as exemplified by pain, hunger, delight, sorrow, and compassion. It is theoretically possible to compile a complete list of all the features required to perform as a human, although the task is difficult—for two reasons: First, they are difficult to categorize since the features to be described are often interrelated (such as our desires for love and sex); and second, we still lack a perfect understanding of the human repertoire.

This book does not attempt to cover all aspects of human behavior, but concentrates on the features where I believe the Darwinian perspective to be particularly valuable. Moreover, it will not focus on behavior that has a well known impact on health, such as smoking, choice of food, or ergonomics, but rather look at aspects of human behavior that may affect our quality of life without necessarily causing overt disease. Chapters 8 through 11 will therefore cover various aspects of human interactions. Elements such as the distress associated with freezing or hunger are less interesting: Their adaptive functions are obvious, and we intuitively know how to deal with these situations. On the other hand, our innate social tendencies are complex, not very well understood by the average person, and of the utmost importance for the quality of life. I believe most people will benefit from acquiring a biologically based understanding of attributes such as love, friendship, and hate.

Chapter 12 deals with the strange phenomenon of religiousness.

Chapters 13 and 14 discuss some features of the mind that presumably were not important in the evolution of mankind, but which have an innate component and have come to prominence in modern society: Chapter 13 deals with art and visual aesthetics; Chapter 14, with music. These features are included because they are interesting, and because I believe there is potential for increasing their value, and thus improving the quality of life through a deeper understanding of their innate components.

The final chapter offers visions of the future.

A different type of font style is used for supplementary text; that is to say, material that I believe will help the reader but that is not absolutely essential in order to follow the main theme of the book. Here the reader will find more technical details, or a treatise of subjects that complement the remaining text.

Each chapter ends with a short section where I try to summarize the main purpose of the chapter.

Caution

When reading the text you may feel that I consider nature to be paramount, and nurture to be irrelevant. I would like to stress that this is not the case. It is simply that this book concentrates on the aspects of human behavior that involve the genes, for this is the constituent I wish to address and which I feel qualified to discuss.

The purpose of the book is to explain human behavioral biology, because I believe this science can help us make decisions, and thus improve the quality of our lives. The purpose is not to moralize, nor is it to tell the reader how to behave or what to do. Whatever messages your genes may whisper, or even cry out loud, there is nothing in biology that needs to stop you from using your measure of free will. There are no fixed answers to the many problems of life, and decisions should always be made by balancing the pros and cons.

This book is aimed at a general audience, but biologists and practitioners in mental health care or the social sciences may also find some of the observations worthy of reflection.

Our present knowledge offers only a simplified version of reality, and the content of this text is but a further simplification of our knowledge. Thus the reader should be aware that any description of human nature, whether by a biologist or a social scientist, will inevitably be colored by both personal views and particular scientific traditions. I am convinced that the main concepts I describe are correct, and I have tried to add qualifiers where appropriate, but at times I do try to paint pictures from fragmentary evidence. Furthermore, in cases where the scientific community adheres to more than one conflicting theory, I will tend to focus on the one I consider to be better, rather than trying to present them all. Also, in order to convey my message, it may be necessary to paint a picture more distinct than justified when taking the evidence at our disposal into account. And, finally, although I would claim that the advice I offer is based on science, it obviously falls outside the realms of descriptive science.

* * * * * * *

In this introductory chapter I have attempted to give you a sense of what the book is about, and what you may expect to gain from reading it. The Oracle of Delphi bears the inscription "Know thyself." I try to present you with one part of yourself—the influence on mentality and behavior exerted by our common genetic inheritance. Thus, it is more about mankind than about you personally, but I expect that much of what I write could apply, more or less, to you as well. In my mind, knowledge of our innate tendencies is definitely valuable regarding questions about how to shape a society and, I believe, also of value for the individual in his or her pursuit of happiness. We are designed with a propensity for contentment and joy. Knowing yourself, and understanding that propensity, should help you find it.

CHAPTER 2

Evolution:
The Theater of Life

Watching Theater Earth—overlooking the Mariana Trench, the deepest point known.

The Green Stage

If alien observers had been able to follow the history of life on Earth, they would have witnessed a remarkable and dramatic play. The performance is based upon a script entitled "Evolution" and began some three to four billion years ago. It is a kind of experimental drama in which the script merely provides a set of obscure rules as a guide through an eternal happening.

The main plot is about survival and propagation, so it is hardly surprising that the play has so far starred a formidable number of actors. The majority of these have disappeared, but quite a few are still with us. The show may last a few more billion years, presumably until the sun consumes the Earth; however, to the fascination of present spectators, the drama is currently approaching a climax.

Quite recently, only a couple of hundred thousand years ago, a new character made his appearance. His peculiar properties have left the scene open for a variety of future scenarios. We are still unsure whether the new character is a hero or a villain, but there can be no doubt that the role he plays is a leading one. This player has not only caused enormous repercussions within the rules allowed by the script, but is now even challenging the whole principle on which the script is based: With the aid of biotechnology he is no longer aspiring to be only a mere character in the play; now he wants to be a co-director. His name is *Homo sapiens.*

The outcome of human actions remains open. Perhaps we will bequeath a globe that is as dull as Mars or Venus, where occasional collisions with comets are the only action an onlooker may hope for; but then again we may be able to pass across the stage in pristine condition to the benefit of future actors. Judging by his performance so far, man appears to be the villain, but the uncertainty regarding the qualities of this character is what makes the present act so exciting—we must hope that he will prove to be a champion struggling to overcome his inherent weaknesses, similar to the typical heroes of modern fiction.

Plate 2. Are we just puppets in the theater of life, moved by the strange forces of evolution? If, on the other hand, we do have the power to direct the action on the stage, how are we to fulfill that task?

The point is that by understanding the rules of the play, and, equally important, understanding ourselves, we can alter our role. We basically know what is required in order to retain the world as a green stage, and we are all members of the cast.

In this chapter I shall offer an outline of the script.

Earth: a Brief Chronology

The current universe presumably began with the "big bang" that occurred some 15 billion years ago, after which the earth formed less than five billion years ago. As depicted in the accompanying figure (Figure 1), once conditions allowing life had been established, life soon emerged— initially in the shallow waters of an earth lacking oxygen, and in the shape of simple cells extracting energy from chemical reactions. Since then, evolution has created a myriad of life forms, but they are all composed of the same types of molecules and use pretty much the same biochemistry. Some of the milestones in the theater of life that I refer to are indicated in Figure 1; their exact timing is controversial, but the chronology is probably correct.

Note that the creation of life appeared to be a rather obvious consequence of a proper chemical and physical environment. We have, therefore, every reason to expect that some of the other trillions of planets out there also support life, probably based on pretty much the same biochemistry as life on earth. However, the creation of an organism capable of understanding what the universe is—and what life is—was not an obvious event and, indeed, took another four billion years. Yet, the presumed number of planets supportive of life, and the time offered since the start of the universe, suggest that there are, or have been, some life forms out there who would enjoy the Earth's version of the theater of life—and maybe even empathize with the fate of the leading character. Sadly, they are beyond reach.

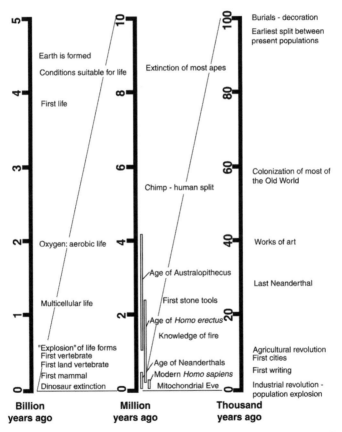

Figure 1. A brief history of Earth. From left to right: Major events since the formation of our planet some 4.5 billion years ago; a chronicle of the last 10 million years; and the history of 100,000 years of human activity.

The Script

Evolutionary theory has made it possible to organize our knowledge of life on Earth. Like an enormous jigsaw puzzle the various pieces of information gained from observations and/or experiments are now falling into place.

For example, in one experiment, a dog and a squirrel are each tied to a separate tree. Food is potentially positioned within their reach, but the ropes are wound around the trunks of the respective trees. If the animals run straight for the food bowls, without first unwinding the rope, they will not reach them. The strange thing is that the dog, which we generally regard as the more intelligent of the two, will tend to strain and pull on the rope with pleading eyes and dribbling jaws, while the squirrel, on the other hand, will find its way around the trunk and reach the food.

The theory of evolution, as first described by Charles Darwin in 1859, helps us understand these patterns of behavior.[8] The explanations are to be found in what kind of qualities evolution has bestowed upon these animals. By adapting to different **niches**, or ways of living, animals have developed different strategies for obtaining food: While the dog visually hunts his prey or seeks a meal by following a scent, the squirrel searches for food by running around in a more whimsical way. These differences explain the observed behavior, but how did they arise?

The script of evolution has two core elements: **variation** and **selection**. In the first place, **species**, such as dogs, orangutans, or humans, consist of individuals that are genetically different. The variability derives from the fact that there are spontaneous changes in the genes, called **mutations**, as well as a reshuffling of the parental genes that takes place each time a child is conceived. Therefore, with the exception of identical twins, two individuals are always genetically dissimilar.

The gene that determines which ABO blood group you belong to offers a slightly complex, but nevertheless illuminating example: The blood group is determined by a gene whose function is to place sugar molecules on the surface of our red blood **cells**. The A type of the gene adds one specific molecule, the B type a slightly different molecule, while type O (an inactive variant of the gene) does not add any molecule at all. A long time ago there was only one version of this gene: For argument's sake let us assume that this was type A. The gene then mutated to create the B and the O versions.

We all carry two copies of all our genes, including the ABO gene—one inherited from our mother and one from our father. Your blood group

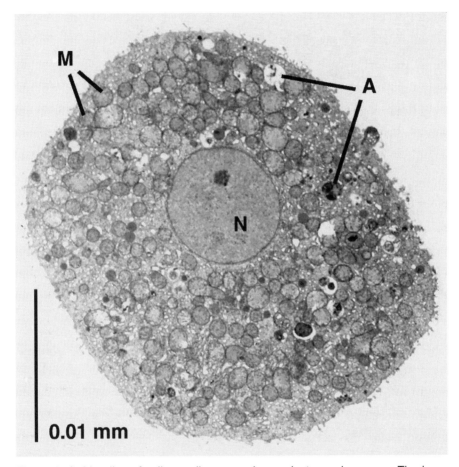

0.01 mm

Figure 2. A thin slice of a liver cell as seen in an electron microscope. The large structure in the middle is the nucleus (N), where all the chromosomes, with their DNA, are located. Most of the remaining easily visible structure are mitochondria (M), the power stations of the cell. This cell has been removed from the environment it is designed for—that is, the liver. As a consequence, it does not thrive and has started to eat itself from the inside, a process that can be seen in the form of autophagic vacuoles (A). As indicated by the bar to the left, the diameter of the cell is about 0.025mm.

is determined by the combination of these two genes in the following manner: If you inherit two As, then you are blood type A; an A and an O will still make you type A; two Bs and you are blood type B; a B and an O will also make you type B; an A and a B will make you type AB; while two Os will give you blood type O. Thus, if your father is blood type A, carrying an A and an O gene, and your mother's blood is type B, carrying a B and an O gene, you may end up with any of the four possible blood types, namely A, B, AB, or O; it all depends on the lottery when genes are randomly picked from your father and mother. In other words, you may possess inherited qualities not expressed in either parent!

The second element is the selection of those individuals with the "most favorable" genes. These individuals will reproduce themselves more often than others; that is, they will procreate more offspring. The number of favorable genes in the population will therefore gradually increase.

For example, our interest in blood types is primarily related to the problems that can arise after blood transfusions. If a person with type A receives blood from a type B person, his immune system will attack the foreign cells and cause a life threatening condition. If donor-blood were not tested prior to injection, blood transfusion would exert a selective pressure. The winners in such a situation would be people with blood type AB, because they can receive blood from any donor. However, you need not worry if your blood type just happens not to be type AB, since this particular selection pressure is avoided as long as we do not give patients the wrong blood. As far as we know, in the absence of blood transfusion there is no obvious advantage of having either type A, B, AB, or O red blood cells. Only infrequently do mutations cause a disadvantage, and even more rarely do they result in an improvement.

It is important to note that "favorable genes" in the above context apply to those that make an individual better equipped for survival and reproduction. Occasionally a reproductive advantage may actually constitute a disadvantage as far as survival is concerned. Moreover, it should be noted that evolution can only improve traits across the range of environments actually experienced by the species, and the process is unable to predict what environmental constraints the future may bring. For these two reasons, as exemplified below, evolution does not necessarily progress in the direction of consistently "better"—or more functional—individuals.

Evolution has equipped the peacock with beautiful plumage; yet a conceited crow has little reason to envy the peacock—however concerned with ornamentation it might be. Big, colorful feathers are a dangerous investment: They give the bird extra weight to carry around, and also make the bird more likely to be discovered by predators. The fact that such plumage nevertheless exists is due to the preference of female birds for males with gaudy feathers.

Tail feathers are important for flight control, but in the evolution of peacocks they probably started to grow bigger than normal because the larger feathers made an individual look big and powerful—and a large male tends to dominate other males. At some point the females came to prefer oversized, colorful feathers, and from then on their size increased even more. The males carrying genes specifying the "right" feathers got the opportunity to mate with several females, and thus produced more progeny.

As a species, the peafowl might have been better designed for survival if the peahen had taken an interest in features that do not impose such a burden on the male—for example, the quality of his song. Peahens are not alone, however, in making seemingly irrational partner-choices —a point you may already have noted by observing family and friends. The criteria that control the choice of spouse are often different from those that make an individual good at survival. We therefore tend to differentiate between *natural selection* and *sexual selection*.[9] The two mechanisms often point in different directions, and only the former can be trusted to improve a species' ability to survive. The irrational choice of sexual partner may actually be an Achilles heel in the evolutionary process.

There are several examples demonstrating that sexual selection can exert a strong influence on the direction the evolution of a species is taking. However, although certain features such as plumage may be extenuated to the absurd, this process is less likely to hit on totally new ideas. The peacock, for example, had a reason for developing large tail feathers—in that the overall larger size made them more frightening. Yet, the present size of the tail feathers is presumably more a consequence of sexual selection than the result of an arms race.

The moas, which were wingless birds that used to run around in the forests of New Zealand, provide an example of another problem that restricts evolution in the quest for forming the ideal organism: The genes of the moa were well adapted to life on those peaceful islands. That is, until humans arrived. This significant change in the birds' environment caused their extinction; the moa's genes made the "mistake" of not considering the possibility of having to cope with human predators. Without the capacity to fly, they were easy prey.[10]

In biology we use the word **habitat** for the specific environment a species is adapted to. Environments, and thus habitats, are in a state of constant change, but fortunately, in the absence of human activity, not often as rapidly or as drastically as in the case of the moa. Given sufficient time, the process of evolution might have replaced the wings presumably lost by the moa's predecessors, making the birds able to escape the threat.

Our own distant ancestors offer another example. After the apes split with the monkeys some 25 million years ago, the ape lineages proved highly successful while the monkeys were comparatively rare. Then, some 10 million years ago, almost all the apes vanished; they became extinct. The lineage leading toward gorillas, chimpanzees, bonobos, and humans was one of the few that barely survived. Apparently what happened was partly a change of climate (the world cooled off) and partly that we were "outsmarted" by monkeys: They evolved the capacity to eat unripe fruit (they were able to deal with the tannins that are added to the fruit by the plant in order to avoid its premature consumption). The apes were bigger, but that did not help them when the fruit had vanished from the trees before they had a chance to fight for it. Thus the climate and the activity of monkeys changed the habitat of our distant forebears in a way that almost crushed them.[11]

The important point is that evolution does not necessarily result in species that are better, at least not in any general sense of the word. Evolution is solely concerned with adapting species to deal with currently prevailing conditions. Only a few of the species that have tried their luck in life's theater are still with us; most have fallen by the wayside because they were unable to adapt to changing environments.

For example, dark-skinned people have more pigment in their skin than white people; the additional pigmentation protects them against damage caused by UV-radiation from the sun and thus reduces the risk of skin cancer. Where there is limited sunshine, as in northern climates, it is advantageous to have less pigment. The reason is that, in the absence of sunlight, our production of vitamin D is diminished. The molecule ergosterol, which is made by both dark-and white-skinned people, requires sunlight to be converted to vitamin D; however, light-skinned people are able to absorb more of the available sunlight as compared to those with darker skin. One would expect that there has been a process of selection for dark skin in Africa, where there are greater amounts of sunlight and, conversely, for light skin in Northern Europe. If depletion of the ozone layer continues to allow more UV-radiation to reach the surface of the Earth, we would anticipate selection in the direction of greater pigmentation (owing to the protection it affords for preventing cancer). Thus, if you are a white person, you might consider the expected evolutionary advantage of adding genes for heavier pigmented skin to your offspring when choosing a partner.

A Success Story

There is an anecdote about two sages who were attacked by a tiger. When one of them started to run, the other one said, "Why run? You cannot outrun a tiger!" The first one threw a quick glance over his shoulder and answered with what is the central element of evolutionary doctrine, "That doesn't matter, as long as I can outrun you."

Evolution is nature's way of solving problems. The main problem to be solved is how to design an organism that survives long enough to reproduce, as in the above example by being able to outrun others when attacked. The main tools of evolution are genetic variation and selection. Although the central element of evolutionary doctrine is easy to understand, it takes a lot of knowledge to comprehend how the tools are applied to different organisms. I shall introduce a few more concepts, as well as a couple of examples that further illustrate the strengths and weaknesses of the evolutionary process.

In biology, the term **fitness** indicates an individual's or a species' ability to pass on genes to the next generation. If each individual produced on average one new individual, the population would be stable. However, all species—plants, animals, and humans—are designed with a tendency to produce a surplus of offspring. (Humans living in affluent societies constitute an interesting exception to this rule.) Since the particular niche a species inhabits can only support a limited number of individuals, the "strongest"—i.e., those with the best, or most fit, genes—will prevail over the others.

In the Americas white people displaced the Native American Indians because they had better weapons and technology—which is to say that they were more fit, but which, of course, says nothing about whether what the white man did was morally right or not. Correspondingly, one species may displace another that is less fit, which is what happens when weeds take over your garden.

For a biologist the term *success* is closely related to fitness. A species (or an individual) with high fitness is by definition successful. The total number of individuals comprising a species, or the total number of progeny an individual has produced, can be used as indicators of either fitness or success. If you want to compare the fitness of unrelated species, such as flies and elephants, it's considered appropriate to compare their **biomass**. The biomass of a species is the combined weight of all the individuals.

Most biologists consider **genes**, encoded in the sequence of **DNA** molecules, to constitute the central unit in biology. The rest of the body is merely the wrapping—designed and constructed with the objective of allowing the genes to reproduce themselves. As the biologist Richard Dawkins has stressed: If adaptations are to be treated as being for the good of something, then that something is the gene.[12] Thus, in order to measure fitness or success, we might look at the number of copies of the species' genes, or, preferably, **genomes**, which are the total package of genes required to produce an organism. However, a kilo of flies contains roughly the same number of genomes as a kilo of elephants, making it easier to simply measure the biomass.

The human species is a shining example of biological success: The reason for our prosperity lies in our ability to find new ways of exploiting the environment. By means of agriculture and industry we can extract a living from our surroundings much more efficiently than our animal competitors; in addition we have learned to protect ourselves against dangers. In other words, we have expanded our niche, largely at the expense of other species. This has brought about an enormous increase in the number of individuals. It is possible that the Earth contains more flies than humans, but I believe no animal species surpasses us when it comes to biomass.

I doubt whether there is any other example in the history of evolution of a single property with such an impact in terms of fitness as human intelligence. Intelligent parents were able to foster more children, resulting in the spread of genes governing intelligence. Over a period of just a few million years a staggering development of the brain's function took place. Yet this is just another example of how the process of evolution is played out on Earth following the rules of variation and selection. (The evolution of humans is the theme of Chapter 4.)

You may think that evolution, in its quest for survival, would try to produce individuals that live forever. It does not. We are selected to survive long enough to reproduce, but preferably not too much longer: If each individual should hang around forever, it would just impede the evolutionary process. In order to create new variants that can survive in an ever changing environment, it is important to have a reasonable turnover of individuals. Species that went for the Methuselah approach would stagnate and eventually lose ground to more adaptable species.[13]

Compared with other animals, humans actually have a rather long life expectancy. You may thank your grandchildren for that: Evolution presumably gave us some extra years because our children need extensive care, and because grandparents can improve the fitness of their children and grandchildren—and thus their own fitness—by helping out.[14]

On Flying Elephants

Evolution leads a species toward adaptation in a particular habitat, but evolution is no perfectionist. Individual species are, as a rule, not optimally adapted, and this is not just due to the problems of sexual selection and a changing environment. As the "designer of life," the process has other weak points as well. The fact that biological success is measured in terms of survival and reproduction—not excellence—allows evolution sometimes to get away with designs that would cost a human engineer his job. Which is why several features of your body are well past their "sell-by-date"-stage. We would probably be better off without such things as toenails and our remnants of a tail. Moreover, our spine is certainly not optimally constructed, and the best that can be said regarding our appendix is that it serves as a source of income for surgeons.

Both the spine and the appendix are consequences of our evolutionary background. Vertebrates started their development with a spine that had the relatively simple task of providing structural integrity for the bodies of fish. The next step involved the horizontal spinal column of the four-legged amphibians and reptiles. Only humans made the dubious transition to a completely upright position. Seen in the light of our background, evolution has done a decent job with our backbone (although back complaints abound), and the appendix now rarely causes any real problems (thanks to modern surgery). An engineer, however, would easily have found room for improvements here.[15]

If nature had used cockroaches as a point of departure for the evolution of mankind, we would have been spared both back pain and appendicitis, but would probably have had to contend with completely different problems.

The point is that evolution operates in a world with obvious restrictions. It has to choose from a finite menu of options. Two main factors are involved in imposing limitations upon what evolution can produce: First, further development necessarily builds upon the existing genes of the species; and second, any modification will have to obey the laws of genetics. Both factors imply that progress must occur gradually.

The ancestors of bats were small animals that made long leaps, gliding from tree to tree. They developed the ability to fly because the air provided greater access to food in the form of insects as well as better security against predators. Had the point of departure not been a small, light animal with skin stretched between the fingers, then evolution would never have been able to produce a flying mammal. Thus you will never see a flying elephant, other than in cartoons, no matter how much food suitable for elephants can be found in the air. The gulf between today's elephants and flying versions is too great for evolution to be able to bridge.

Another important characteristic of the script of evolution is that genes may, in an indirect way, influence fitness. Parent birds do not feed their young because they recognize them as newly packaged versions of their own genes; it is the sight of a gaping mouth and the sound of the associated screeching that stimulates the bird's brain so that it goes hunting for food and returns to push it down the hatchling's throat.

Many parent birds do not even differentiate between their own and

Plate 3. Elephants are likely to remain on the ground because evolution can only install small changes at a time, and because each intermediate form needs to be sufficiently adaptive to survive.

others' young; if a baby cuckoo hatches in the nest, it will be fed with the same enthusiasm, to the detriment of the host's offspring and genes. The point is that the mother bird does not need to know anything about genes, or even recognize her own young. Under normal circumstances all that is required to propagate her genes is to procure more food as a reaction to gaping mouths.[16]

The evolutionary process has no heart and no brain; it does not care whether a species is perfectly adapted to an environment or not. The only issue at stake is whether the species has the qualities required for survival. If it does not, it will either evolve or disappear.

Dead as a Rock—yet the Core of Life

Qualities that are "good" increase the fitness of an organism; that is to say, they increase its ability to survive and reproduce, and will thus be selected.

The principles of evolution apply to behavior as well, meaning that behavioral biology is based upon the following rule of thumb: *Animals behave in such a way as to maximize their fitness.* In other words, behavior reflects a strategy for survival and reproduction. If you find a connection between a type of behavior and fitness, you have a possible evolutionary explanation as to why the relevant behavioral pattern exists. Revealing such connections is an important objective of behavioral biology.[17]

The previously mentioned experiment involving the dog and the squirrel provides an example of such an explanation: Under normal conditions, fitness for the dog means following its nose, while the squirrel is better off by adopting a "searching" behavior.

The example of the dog and the squirrel also illustrates another important point: It is easy to associate evolution with the development of wings, skulls, and other physical structures, but evolution does not only control anatomy; behavioral modes, such as strategies for finding food, have developed in accordance with the same principles. In fact, all behavioral characteristics are influenced by genes, and are thus subject to selection. It is, however, more difficult to follow the evolution of behavior because our thoughts and actions—in contrast to teeth and bone—rarely create fossils.

Although the principles are uncomplicated, comprehensive biological knowledge is required to sense the course evolution has followed to produce the features we observe. Uncovering the most likely explanations for behavioral characteristics is often difficult. It is important to have an intimate understanding of the process of evolution, as well as detailed knowledge of both the species in question and the specific type of behavior, in order to arrive at the correct answers.

I believe it is worthwhile to seek the evolutionary explanations for human behavior, because they suggest in what direction and how strongly our genes influence us, and that is what this book is all about. However, a rich flora of evolutionary explanations, or "just so" stories, have reached print. With a bit of imagination there seems to be no limit in terms of suggestions, and unfortunately many of the proposed explanations have no foothold in biology. On the other hand, there is not necessarily just one cause for the evolution of a specific trait: For example, some say we evolved social behavior as a defense against predators, while others believe that it was a question of becoming predators ourselves.[18] It is not so much a question of which of these explanations is correct—both probably have a bearing on the evolution of human social behavior. The more appropriate questions are: How much influence in shaping our genes can be attributed to each of these explanations or assumptions, and what are the concomitant consequences in terms of inherent tendencies? Rather than making sweeping statements of the type "this trait evolved for that function," one should try to paint realistic evolutionary scenarios, where many factors act jointly in putting together the complex dispositions of a species.

In discussing human biology, I may sometimes give the impression that genes have souls. They do not, of course. The use of expressions such as "the genes wish you to" or "evolution decided to" is simply a way of describing how evolution has shaped genes to influence us in a particular way. I should stress that it does not imply that genes (or DNA) have any desires of their own.

True, DNA is the core of life, yet when isolated in laboratory tubes, DNA molecules are as dead as rock.

Summary

To understand how evolution works is somewhat like mastering a language; it is relatively easy to learn some words and a bit of grammar, but to really comprehend all the fine nuances requires a lifetime of dedication. The simplified ideas of evolution—such as "survival of the fittest," and the view of a process leading to optimal, or ideal, species—can sometimes be misleading. Although the evolutionary drive towards fitness maximization is a real force, when it comes to explaining behavior, it should be treated as no more than a rule of thumb. This is particularly true when dealing with a species—such as ours—for which the environment recently has changed drastically. Our genes are in many ways simply not adapted to the present environment.

The evolutionary process has neither heart nor brain, and it does not know what perfection is; the process is merely a consequence of the genetic nature of all living things. Moreover, when it comes to anatomy and physiology, we know pretty well what evolution has been up to, but regarding behavior and mental capacity, whether in humans or animals, it is a lot more difficult to describe what the genes really have evolved to specify.

This chapter introduces some important concepts, such as *species, mutations, genomes, biomass, cells, natural selection, sexual selection, variation, habitat, fitness* and *success*. Mastering them and having some understanding of how evolution works should be enough for a critical reading of the remaining part of the text.

In the next chapter I shall try to explain the pivotal theme of the book: how knowledge of the way evolution has shaped our own species can be applied to bear on our quality of life. This biologically based view on happiness has helped improve my own quality of life, and I believe most people have something to gain by listening to Darwin and his disciples.[19]

CHAPTER 3

Darwinian Happiness:
Why We Should Listen to Our Genes

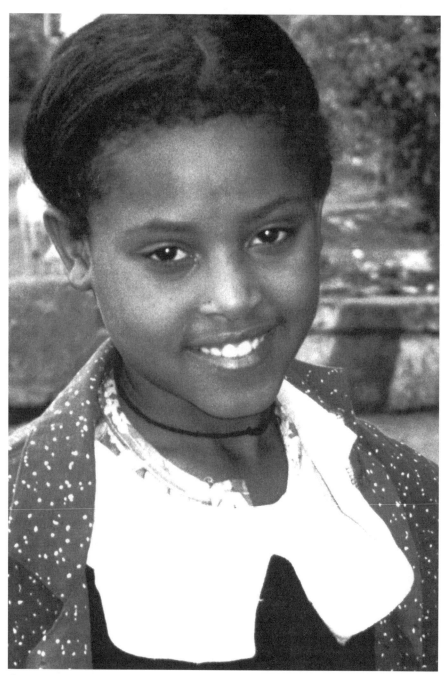

Contentment: a young Ethiopian woman.

Where to Look for Advice

Happiness is not a typical subject for biological investigations; in fact, not even social scientists seem to take much interest in this topic. They prefer misery, which makes sense: People seek help regarding their problems, not their joy. The only professional group that actually takes bliss seriously is the clergy—your priest will care for you in times of both joy and sorrow. I am sure that an intelligent minister can guide you in your pursuit of happiness, and, I believe, so can Darwin.

Actually some social scientists have recently taken an increasing interest in the good life, a field sometimes referred to as "positive psychology," and a few scientists such as David Buss, Jerome Barkow, and myself, have even considered happiness in an evolutionary perspective.[20] This book does not try to cover all the research carried out in this field, nor does it attempt to compete with all the popular self-help books that are available. Certain observations, however, are of particular interest in regard to the perspective on happiness that I shall present.[21]

David Myers and Ed Diener are among those who do take a critical look at joy. Surprisingly, they find hardly any correlation between happiness and factors such as riches, educational level, race, and age. In the poorer countries, income does correlate with emotional well-being, but in a country such as the United States even the very rich are only slightly happier than the average person. It is fascinating to note that in places where the basic requirements of life are reasonably secure, the money you spend does not make you more content. These and other results led David Lykken to suggest that the brain might have a setpoint for happiness, just as it has been claimed that there is a setpoint for your body weight. But as in the case of weight, many factors, including personal choices, influence our score.

Happiness is for those who know how to nurture it. While economic pursuits do not appear to be an efficient way of establishing a good life, I believe it *is* within the power of biology to help us. But how?

The term "success" may be as close as biology comes to indicating that something is desirable. Biological success, however, is measured in biomass or in number of offspring, and neither gaining weight nor breeding an extraordinary number of children is likely to secure eternal joy. True, happiness is relevant for biological success, to the extent that the state of mind influences fitness, but biological success is not required for happiness.

In order to extract meaningful advice from a knowledge of biology, we need an approach quite different from that of traditional biology. We need to consider concepts other than success and fitness. The purpose of this chapter is to introduce the concept of Darwinian happiness.

The Rose Doesn't Care

If you wish to discuss the quality of life of a plant, there is not much else to consider than biological success. Given optimal conditions, that is, conditions adjusted to its biological requirements, a plant will thrive. A plant that thrives will grow and produce lots of seeds, which again translates into progeny. Thus, the quality of life of your rose is straightforward to explain and easy to measure. However, as pointed out above, the same criterion does not make complete sense when discussing the quality of human life.

Evolution has provided mammals, and man in particular, with a feature that allows a somewhat different view on the quality of life: We have a brain that registers a good mood, and Darwinian happiness depends on this particular feature. The magic of the brain is that it provides us with feelings, and thus with the possibility to cherish more than mere survival. We can enjoy life!

Your rose thrives under the right conditions, but lacks the nerve circuitry required to appreciate the difference between blooming and withering. The owner rejoices when admiring the flower, and may even assume that the flower is happy; but, for all practical purposes, the rose couldn't care less.

Both human genes and rose genes are designed for particular conditions of living—both thrive when offered these conditions. In the case of humans, however, the advantage is not just a question of achieving biological success: When offered appropriate stimuli and environments, we also tend to *feel* better. Proper living conditions are one element in the concept of Darwinian happiness, but it should be stressed that what matters is the mental effect of adjusting the conditions of living to human nature, and not the potential effect on procreation.

In animals with an advanced nervous system, agreeable sensations do not depend solely on living in an environment resembling what the genes are designed for, since both positive and negative sensations can be evoked by various stimuli relatively independent of living conditions. This points to a second element in the concept of Darwinian happiness: In order to improve our quality of life, we ought to nurture the pleasant sensations, and avoid negative feelings.

These two elements are closely related, but are dealt with separately below in order to ease the discussion. They can be combined in a somewhat naïve rule of thumb: "You should listen to the whispering of your internal guru."

Discord or just Mismatch

I shall refer to the two elements included in the principle of Darwinian happiness respectively as *stress* and *rewards*. Briefly, the key principles are (1) to avoid stress by adjusting the conditions of life to our innate tendencies, and (2) to utilize the brain's potential for rewarding sensations.

That should be easy. All you need is a pile of brownies, a comfortable sofa, and a remote control for the TV. But, is that all? Although the principles may *sound* straightforward, they are not—unfortunately. In order to convey the correct impression of what Darwinian happiness stands for, I need to use this rather lengthy chapter to clarify the notion.

To begin with the first element, research on animals has taught us that living under unnatural conditions has detrimental effects.[22] "Unnatural" in this context applies to conditions different from those the animals are designed to live in; and it applies to physical conditions, such as nutrition or temperature, as well as behavioral conditions. The focus of this book, however, will be on the behavioral or, if you prefer, mental environment. For example, if you isolate a baboon from its flock, this will result in tension, and the animal may eventually develop behavioral disorders. A tension also occurs if you force several adults of the naturally solitary orangutan to live together. In both cases, you are offering the animals conditions that are not in tune with the behavioral biology of their respective species, and the consequences are hence likely to be detrimental.

Some scientists use the term **Environment of Evolutionary Adaptation**, or **EEA**, for the kind of conditions our genes expect.[23] I should mention that our genes were not shaped in one particular environment, but rather over millions of years of interaction with various conditions. Our basic emotions, for example, which will be discussed in more detail in Chapter 7, did not appear in the Stone Age, but rather entered the brains of our ancestral animals some two hundred million years ago. Subsequent evolution, all the way up to modern humans, has modified our emotional setup, but the alterations have had to comply with the rules governing the evolutionary process.

Furthermore, present humans are adapted to diverse environments. The Inuits of Greenland are fit for a climate different from that of the African Bantus. These variations in climatic adaptation, however, do not matter that much for the present discussion: The more salient features of human EEA are not so much a matter of the physical environment, but are rather a question of the social environment; and although Inuit and Bantu societies are organized in different ways, the genes that influence their social inclinations are presumably much the same.

Even though it is dubious whether a single environment can accurately describe our "ideal" environment, for present purposes it is practical to use the concept of a human EEA. We are all adapted to a set of more or less vaguely defined conditions, but the one and only EEA probably never existed; yet, the Stone Age conditions of some 50,000 years ago are presumably a rather good approximation.

In order to illustrate possible detrimental effects of the non-EEA qualities of our present environment, let us first consider two examples from anatomy, involving our eyes and teeth. Why are modern societies plagued by near-sightedness and the necessity of dental work?

Tribal peoples rarely need eyeglasses. While 80 percent of the 18-year-old men of Singapore are near-sighted, only one percent of the rural population of Nepal has the same problem. Two environmental factors may help explain why so many individuals in industrialized societies suffer from myopia: One is the tendency of infants to spend long periods of time focusing at fixed, close ranges, and rarely having the opportunity to look at anything far away. The other factor is the exposure to light during nighttime very early in life; keeping the lights on in the bedroom is a common practice in modern societies.[24] The growth of both eyeballs and lenses is affected by light, as well as by how the eyes are used. Our genes are neither adapted to books nor to electricity; the expansion of the eyeball may therefore end up not matching the shape of the lens and, as a consequence, the focus is off. We need spectacles.

Similarly, while the size of teeth is genetically determined, the size of jawbones depends somewhat on how vigorously they are used for chewing purposes. The food we give our children today is not exactly designed to be workout equipment for building jaw muscles and bones; there was no baby porridge for sale in the Stone Age.[25] Sales statistics for chewing gum reflect our inborn desire to exercise our jaws; the wires attached to adolescent teeth may partly reflect the failure of infants to do so.

The above two examples illustrate possible consequences of a lifestyle different from that for which our genes have prepared us. We do, of course, invent remedies, but I assume your teenage daughter would prefer not to walk around with her mouth looking like a Frankenstein monster construct. And although some people claim that eyeglasses are sexy, most people would rather do without.

Teeth and eyes are physical features. The genes have designed both physical features and mental functions to develop as we age, and correct maturation relies on appropriate external stimuli in both cases. The question is: Do we provide the emotional settings our genes are adapted to or do our emotions face the same problems as our eyes and teeth?

Experiments with monkeys and apes demonstrate that bringing up infants without motherly care, or away from the social life of a group, causes serious behavioral problems when these juveniles mature to adults. Humans are more versatile, yet most experts agree that similar gross deprivations cause problems in our species as well. It should be pointed out that it is particularly detrimental to offer children inappropriate conditions, since the effects on development may have lasting consequences.[26]

The stress associated with an unnatural way of life is not restricted to children. We are, for example, designed to be active during the day and to sleep at night, and deviations from this situation can cause stress, as so many people have experienced with jet lag or when working night shifts. Ordering people to work at night is a bit like throwing them into the sea and asking them to live like a dolphin. Yes, we can survive in the sea, but we are not designed to live there. (I am using the word "stress" for the detrimental effects of living under unnatural conditions, but I want to emphasize that this is a particular way of using the word: The meaning differs from the classical concept, which is associated with the "fight-or-flight" response.[27] While classical stress can be either a possitive or a negative experience, present use focuses on negative aspects. (I use the term in a broader sense, somewhat like "strain.")

The good news is that the brain is a particularly adaptable organ: With the right effort, it is theoretically possible to alleviate most psychological problems. The bad news is that both near-sightedness and mental diseases are reaching endemic proportions, and that it is a lot more difficult to cure anxiety than to find the right pair of glasses. Moreover, it is easier to identify aberrant eyesight than it is to recognize an aberrant psyche.

The difference between how we live and what our genes are adapted to is commonly referred to as a *mismatch*.[28] I believe mismatches are often associated with stress, but in many cases they are not. For example, to sleep on a modern mattress probably creates less stress on your body than sleeping on the ground, even though spring mattresses were not available in the Stone Age. This book is concerned with situations where mismatches can have negative effects, and it is important to have a concept that covers these situations. I have chosen the word **Discord** (with a capital "D") as short for *"discord between environment and genes."* Thus, while a mismatch can be entirely beneficial, a Discord implies a situation that in most, or at least some, people causes an element of distress.

Discord situations may well have troubled our ancestors in the Stone Age as well—for instance, when a natural catastrophe ruined the local environment or when a child was orphaned. A Discord situation should therefore be defined as a deviation from optimal conditions, rather than a deviation from a particular habitat that occurred sometime in our evolutionary history. The important point is that we are better off if we can avoid unnecessary Discords.

We are all different, and what can be defined as being a Discord for one person can be quite harmless for another. Furthermore, a Discord need not necessarily even be all that bad, since the stress factor involved may be compensated for by various advantages. Driving a car, as opposed to walking, may be considered to be a Discord, but it does enable you to go places your feet would never take you.

On the other hand, there probably are negative consequences of a Discord life that we are not at all aware of: The cumulative effect of various Discord conditions may cause mental disease or decrease our quality of life, without anybody realizing the reason for the distress. In a majority of cases we know very little about what causes mental problems. Even if most of the Discord situations have little impact on most people, each type of situation may add a slight harm to a certain percentage of the population, and be responsible for a lot of misery.

In the above examples, near-sightedness and troublesome teeth are consequences of a Discord situation. The science of *Darwinian medicine*, as described by Randolph Nesse, George Williams, and others, addresses such issues.[29] This field of medicine focuses on the clinical implications of a Discord lifestyle, while the notion of Darwinian happiness is meant to help people improve their lives regardless of clinical symptoms. My contribution to Darwinian theory will concentrate on mental well-being rather than on diseases.

The Sweetness of Sugar

Why are certain sensations considered pleasant while others are so clearly deemed unpleasant?

Have you ever watched a child offer to share its candy with a cow? Both usually end up disappointed. Humans find sugar delicious because fruit was an important part of the diet of our ancestors; cows, on the other hand, eat grass, and they appreciate being offered something salty, while they do not care much for the sweet taste of candies.

It is in the interest of plants that their fruits are eaten, because this is one of the modes by which seeds are dispersed; however, the fruit should not be consumed until it is ripe and the seeds ready. Sugar is nutritious and is added as the fruit ripens; it entices us. The sweet sensation registered by our brain is there to make sure we take advantage of what the plant is offering. Certain species of animals, including humans but not cows, have this symbiotic relationship with fruit-producing plants, much the same way bees help flowers. Sugar is "sweet," but is only regarded so by the animals in question. In other words: *The pleasant sensation induced by sugar is one example of a general principle developed by evolution for the purpose of influencing our behavior.*

We are equipped with a complicated set of feelings designed to induce us to take actions conducive to the propagation of our genes. These sensations, as well as any other feeling the individual may regard as positive or desirable, are what I refer to as rewards. The brain offers a variety of rewards and punishments in the form of agreeable and unpleasant sensations; the results are what you might expect: We try to obtain the rewards and to avoid the pain. (The neurology of rewards will be discussed in Chapter 5.)

As in the following example, rewarding sensations can take many forms. Climbing a mountain or participating in a sports competition gives you an "adrenaline high." These stressful situations feel good, because when you encounter a dangerous situation, it is not in the interest of the genes to be part of a depressed individual with a low level of self-esteem. To ensure that whatever resources you may have are mobilized, the genes have connected the classical stress response to a positive sensation. The delight of the adrenaline "rush" feels quite different from the sweetness of sugar, but both are examples of rewards offered by the brain. I might add that the former pleasure depends on the assumption of being in control of the situation; if you slip and fall while climbing, the experience becomes rather unpleasant.

Research conducted by the physiologist Michel Cabanac suggests that the capacity to have some sort of awareness of pleasure and displeasure evolved between the amphibian and reptilian stage of vertebrate evolution.[30] A reptile seeks pleasurable stimuli, such as sunbathing, and it is possible to measure a physiological response in the sunbathing reptile.

Plate 4a. Happiness is not always displayed, but sometimes it is very obvious.

Plate 4b. Happiness can be found anywhere.

The response is actually somewhat similar to what we can measure in humans when they are engaged in positive experiences. Fish and amphibians do not show the same response; their behavior is presumably more instinctive and less influenced by sensations.

I believe humans possess the most pronounced positive and negative sensations. This assumption is based on the fact that we have the largest measure of free will, and that free will is a two-edged sword for the genes: An ant will always follow the will of the genes; a human may choose to take actions that are not in the interest of his or her genes. (Just consider, for instance, the recent decline in birth rates. If it had not been for the recent invention of contraceptives, the intensity of the rewards associated with sexual activity would have kept the babies coming.) In order to retain their influence on behavior, it seems plausible that the genes would enhance the intensity of agreeable and punishing sensations.

Darwinian Happiness

A good life is a question of how we feel. The propensity to experience various feelings is laid down by the genes; thus, biology is relevant for a discussion about the quality of life. The concept of Darwinian happiness is an attempt to describe the biological contribution.[31]

Two main principles are pertinent to the Darwinian approach that I advocate: One is that living conditions should be adjusted to suit our inborn tendencies in order to avoid stress brought on by a sub-optimal environment. The second is that agreeable sensations offered by the brain should be pursued while unpleasant sensations ought to be avoided. *Darwinian happiness is a question of how successfully we follow these principles.* In order to employ the former we need knowledge about human EEA; for the latter, we want to know more about the sensations provided by the brain, and the stimuli that elicit them. This defines the purpose of later chapters of the book; the rest of the present chapter will further clarify what the two principles are about.

A Guide for the Keeper of the Human Zoo

The point of this book is not to say that we should throw our clothes and TV out the window, and head for the nearest cave. Modern society has too many obvious advantages. In many ways we live in astonishing comfort compared to what our ancestors had to put up with, and we possess tools that can be used to prevent many diseases and to ameliorate the symptoms of others. The point is that the apparent comfort does not mean there is no room for improvement.

The concept of Discord, moreover, is relevant when discussing possible improvements, and I shall use this section to illustrate further what Discord stands for, with the help of a few examples.

City-dwellers come face to face with many strangers every day. A meeting with an unknown person calls for our attention; the mind is inquisitive and alert. Our natural response typically involves a mixture of curiosity and fear of possible hostile intentions. Such encounters, in comparison, were rare in the tribal community of our ancestors, and the response was appropriate. In modern cities we tend to avoid eye contact with strangers; we are taught that it is not proper to be inquisitive, and we do not have the time, either. Any anxiety generated by unfamiliar faces needs to be suppressed, or it will quickly reach an intolerable level. Meeting strangers involves stress in the classical meaning of the word, because it tends to cause a measure of fear; it is also an unnatural situation to which we are not able to respond in the way our inborn tendencies would prefer. The latter is an example of Discord and causes stress in the present sense of the word.

Certain jobs involve facing a large number of unfamiliar persons—for example, serving as a hospital nurse or working as a shop assistant. We are all different and we are also adaptable. Some people learn to adjust to the situation and may even find it stimulating; after all, we are rewarded for satisfying our curiosity, and fellow humans are normally considered interesting. For others, the situation is unpleasant and tiring. However, even for those who appreciate seeing strangers, there may be an unrecognized element of stress related to the experience that may cause harm, just as reading books as a child could contribute to your near-sightedness even if you never felt that you strained your eyes.

The "fight-or-flight" type of stress is a natural response, and as such not necessarily negative for your measure of Darwinian happiness. Many of us enjoy riding a roller coaster or seeing a horror movie—thrills that give us a much more intense kick than the typical encounter with a stranger. The Discord effect arises from the number of encounters, a feeling of not being in control of the situation, and the fact that the inborn tendency to respond is inappropriate. Moreover, the psychological changes associated with classical stress are designed for coping with short-term situations; sustained over time, they begin to break down the body. It is well known that overdoses of stress in its classical meaning can cause a long list of ailments, and the same may be true for the stress associated with Discords. Stress can compromise the immune system and induce a range of complaints such as headaches and muscle pain. It is also implicated in emotional problems, such as depression, nervousness, aggression, and social maladjustment.[32]

Although the social strain of modern living may have a larger impact on Darwinian happiness than the physical strain, the physical environment is also important. For instance, sitting in an office chair all day tends to cause various muscle problems. We can alleviate the symptoms by making the workplace ergonomic, but some strain will inevitably remain, as the situation is too different from what the human body is designed for. The subsequent muscle pain does not improve our quality of life.

Environment is important in other ways, too. We are adapted to being in the proximity of plants; their absence may very well be a stress factor even if you do not recognize that you miss them; and they may improve your mood even if you do not notice that they are there. The typical office environment is barren. Research by the urban ethologists Lisa Oberzaucher and Karl Grammer suggests that humans thrive better and improve in cognitive tasks if there are plants present. Thus, a yucca for your office may be an excellent investment.[33]

The main point I am trying to make in this section is that Discords are a question of disturbing a delicate balance. We are sufficiently flexible to survive out of balance, but only at a cost. If you throw sand into a complicated machine, it may not stop, at least not immediately, but you are certainly unlikely to improve its function. I believe Discords are like sand in the human emotional machinery and, as such, are an important contributor to the diseases of civilization. (How Discord conditions can affect your brain will be further discussed in Chapter 7.)

There are several biology-based handbooks available to help the farmer, the dog owner, and the zookeeper—books that help them devise the best possible conditions for various animals. When it comes to humans, however, the available literature is far less abundant. You may think that such a book would be easy to write, since we know a lot more about humans than we do about any other species. Personally I would consider a book on humans to be more important; after all, we are most concerned about the well-being of our own species. But then humans tend to have a more complicated emotional life than cows or dogs. Moreover, human emotions are a very emotional subject for humans.

For both the farmer and the keeper of the human zoo, the main priority is not to create EEA conditions: For the dairy farmer the objective is to have cows that produce as much milk as possible; an appropriate environment becomes an issue if it influences milk output. However, to the extent that it is practical, the farmer will prefer to offer the cows conditions resembling what their genes have designed them to live in, because well adjusted cows produce more milk than stressed cows. Similarly, we should try to reduce human Discord, because society adjusted to our genes is expected to boost happiness—whether measured by psychological tests of subjective well being, as in the research of Myers and Diener, or in terms of Darwinian happiness.

The Average Human

Our understanding of human behavioral biology applies to the typical person. We are shaped not only by universal inborn tendencies, but also by our particular set of genes and by the environment; the individual may thus differ drastically from the typical human. The behavior of an average human in an average Stone Age society reflects our common genetic inheritance, and this fictive character is what the science of human behavioral biology refers to when discussing our innate tendencies.

Acting against our personal biases may involve a measure of stress in the same way as not adjusting to innate tendencies. The concept of adjusting life to the biology of mankind is therefore of more value for a community than for the individual members of that community. Furthermore, it is not just the individual who deviates from what the human behavioral biologist would expect; the same can be said for entire cultures. The cultural constraints should be kept in mind: Inflicting change on a community puts its members under stress, even if the changes are in tune with our knowledge of human biology.

And, of course, it should be kept in mind that what is natural is not always desirable. Leprosy is a natural consequence of an infection with *Mycobacterium leprae*; the use of antibiotics to stop the bacteria is not.

On Reward and Punishment

Now, to return to the concept of positive and negative sensations: Why is the brain designed to harvest rewards and endure punishments?

Sensations evolved for the purpose of influencing behavior. As a gross approximation, we can divide all sensations (which here include feelings and emotions) into being either pleasant or unpleasant; and the reason why they tend to fall into these two categories is because they evolved either as an incitement to encourage a particular behavior or for the purpose of discouraging a certain type of behavior. I use the words *reward* and *punishment*, respectively, to represent these two possibilities.[34] Thus, most sensations can—with some deliberation—be classified as either rewarding or punishing; yet the use of these concepts is like painting a black-and-white picture of a more complex reality. Bearing these limitations in mind, I believe the concepts of reward and punishment to be useful for a discussion of happiness.

It should be mentioned that, while I use the term "reward" for any sensation considered to be agreeable, neurologists often use "brain reward" (sometimes referred to as pleasure drives) in a more specific sense: The activation of partly characterized nerve circuitry involved in delivering some of the more distinctive pleasurable sensations.[35] There will be a more detailed discussion on brain rewards in Chapter 5, and I shall restrict myself here to a few comments:

Evolution shaped the human brain as a tool for survival and procreation; sensations are therefore designed to promote behavior, not to contribute to our quality of life. Thus, the categorization of sensations as either positive or negative is an artificial approximation; and even though the approximation is reasonably clear-cut in most cases, the distinction is not always obvious. Certain sensations that you may consider negative, I will argue, can contain an element of reward, as will be exemplified in the next section. Furthermore, even sensations for which the negative label should be obvious, such as pain, are somehow desired by certain people: There are those who appear to enjoy banging their head against a wall. The point is that for the average person the distinction will, in most cases, be relatively easy. True, most of your time may be spent in the absence of strong sensations, but when specific feelings do pop up, it is usually possible to distinguish between plus and minus.

There is another problem of classification that needs to be discussed: Feelings such as hunger and fear start out in the basal parts of the brain. We know quite a bit about the neurology of these basal processes, but when the conscious cognitive mind starts to deal with them it tends to get more complicated. Sensations require an involvement of cognitive functions, which means that whether feelings such as hunger and fear are conceived as pleasant or unpleasant depends a lot on the processing at this higher level. The cognitive modulation is based on past experiences, on personality, and on expectations; thus closely related situations may sometimes be considered rewarding, while at other times they may be experienced as being punishing.

For example, I have pointed out that a dangerous situation can rapidly switch from a positive thrill to a frightening encounter, as when a climber loses his grip. Similarly, a slight hunger can be experienced as pleasant: It entails an anticipation of food related rewards, and can intensify the pleasure of eating. Too much hunger, however, is unpleasant, particularly in a situation where you are unable to obtain any food. While the *annoyance* of hunger is there to discourage you from ending up in a situation where no food is available, the *pleasure* of hunger is there to encourage you to enjoy a meal. Your cognitive functions can actually turn the sensation around rather swiftly, as when somebody snatches the last sausage from the plate.

Thus, in my vocabulary, feelings such as hunger and fear can turn out as either rewarding or punishing. This may seem like an inconsistency, but, as pointed out above and below, it makes evolutionary sense when analyzed in more detail. We perceive fear as either pleasant or unpleasant, depending on whether we assume we are in control or not, because these two modes of experiencing fright serve different biological purposes: The brain is designed to induce us to take chances, otherwise we would never have risked confronting a dangerous prey or ventured into uncharted land; but it is also designed to stop us from causing harm to ourselves.

Another point that should be made is that many of the rewards generated in the brain are much less obvious than the sweetness of sugar, or the pleasure of an orgasm. They may just be vague stimulations that gently influence behavior—for example, the awareness of being with a friend. However, even rewards that are too "weak" to be consciously recognized as such can influence your mood and exert a positive effect on your quality of life.

Some people are more clever than others when it comes to sensing pleasures: When offered an apple, they will first appreciate the sight and the smell of it, then slowly eat it while savoring the taste. Others simply devour the apple and experience nothing. It is possible to tune into the delights the brain offers: *The rewards are for those who learn how to harvest them.*

In the long run it is difficult to be happy on an empty stomach. In order to enjoy life, our need for food, shelter, and health must be attended to; freezing is unpleasant, so both lizards and humans enjoy sunbathing. By satisfying basic requirements, we both avoid stress and elicit rewards. In other words, it is of obvious importance for Darwinian happiness to provide the requirements for sustaining life.

Once the basic needs are satisfied, the other most significant external factor appears to be our social life. The importance of having somebody to turn to emphasizes the social nature of human beings. To enjoy life we need to get along with family and friends. If we are able to avoid the problems of Discord, fulfill our needs, and have a satisfactory social life, we ought to obtain a high score on Darwinian happiness. Moreover, we will then have a proper foundation for enjoying the more "luxurious" utilities at our disposal, such as art and music. (See Chapters 13 and 14.) Actually we are equipped with a variety of talents and interests that are worthwhile engaging. Those of us who are not keen on concerts may play soccer, or take pleasure in the process of learning by studying the movement of distant stars. There are plenty of opportunities.

To obtain a good life, you do not need to engage in every activity associated with possible rewards. A certain diversity is advantageous, as the quality of life tends to be higher if you are able to appreciate a variety of stimuli. The most important principle to consider may be: *Engage your mind and body in tasks for which they were designed, and learn to enjoy whatever rewards the brain offers while doing so.*

The Pleasure of Crying

Why do people flock to films reputed to make them cry? Apparently even sadness and grief may be perceived as something positive. To understand this paradox, it is important to distinguish between a harmful event and the associated response. The former is something to be avoided; the latter a natural emotion.[36]

The loss of a spouse, for example, may be tragic for the genes; but, since misfortunes occasionally occur, the genes have prepared the brain to cope with the problem. Once your spouse is gone, the genes are presumably best served by implementing a mechanism that helps you master the situation; the normal response includes grief and sadness. The response may elicit compassion and help. It makes sure you keep a low social profile and thus avoid conflict with others at a time when you are vulnerable; and it may improve your mental recovery, and thereby increase your chance of finding a new spouse.

The point is that, to the extent grief is adaptive, the brain should encourage you to entertain this feeling; and the only encouragement available is in the form of an agreeable sensation. The principle of engaging your mind in tasks for which it is designed applies to mourning as well.

A situation of grief thus typically involves both negative and positive emotional elements; the negative ones are there to make sure you try to avoid a similar situation in the future, while the positive ones are there to help you make the best of the present situation. When watching a film, we can concentrate on the positive side; we can identify with the characters and enjoy sorrow without personally having to go through the harmful event. The loss of a spouse is presumably something most people want to avoid, but if you can stimulate the compensatory response with the help of a fictitious person on a screen, you avoid the misfortune and reap the benefit. You go for the joy of melancholy. You delight in the compassion you feel for the characters, and in the grief you share with them.

Similarly, you feel pain if you cut your finger because the event is harmful for your genes, which appreciate the utility of an intact hand. However, if you should hurt yourself, there is no reason to suppress the feelings aroused: It is natural to scream, and your internal guru advises you to express natural feelings.

Our tendency to scream aloud may actually serve particular functions. We scream to attract attention when injured and thereby to obtain help; we scream to warn others of danger; and we scream to scare off predators. As an adaptive response, you would expect load vocalization to be rewarding. In densely populated modern society loud voices are considered uncivilized. The positive side of screaming is reflected by the fact that people seem to enjoy the opportunity when social restraints are removed. You can observe the effect at sports events, but screaming is also a part of certain therapeutic and meditative practices.

The term reward may seem odd when applied to sadness and screaming; for most people, grief has a negative connotation. The main point is to distinguish between sensations designed for aversion and sensations involved in coping. According to the present vocabulary, the former is a punishment, while the latter is something you are urged to engage in, and thus potentially rewarding.

My Delight or Yours

There is one obvious quandary associated with the philosophy of Darwinian happiness: The pursuit of happiness for one person is sometimes in conflict with what is good for others. For example, rape may involve a positive sensation for the rapist, but be a completely negative experience for the victim. The problem of social versus anti-social behavior is discussed in Chapters 10 and 11, and I shall here restrict myself to a brief comment.

Humans are fortunately gregarious; our brain rewards us for the approval we receive from comrades. Those who cause unnecessary harm to others risk expulsion from the group, and banishment will most likely ruin their quality of life. Furthermore, our sense of morality tends to inflict punishing sensations upon those who violate accepted rules of conduct. Unfortunately, the Discord quality of modern society does not provide optimal conditions for relying on these mechanisms to make people behave. We have therefore devised laws and accompanying penalties, the purpose of which is to guide individuals in directions beneficial to the society as a whole. Whereas the individual should be expected to pursue his or her Darwinian happiness, society should try to promote Darwinian happiness for everybody.

When to Dupe the Genes

You and your genes do not necessarily share interests. While biology advocates the case of your genes by pointing to the principle of fitness, the concept of Darwinian happiness stands up for your rights. And, as I shall discuss below, you are in a position to dupe your genes.

All mammals presumably have brains capable of experiencing pleasure. It is, therefore, not surprising to find that animals will indulge in stimulants when offered the opportunity. As previously suggested, humans possess possibly the most powerful reward mechanisms. We are also unique in another way; we have the brainpower to realize what it is all about, and to exploit the situation.

Not only can we choose from a variety of naturally occurring rewarding stimuli, we have also created a number of substitutes. Artificial sweeteners and pornography are typical examples, but if you have the money, you can buy products catering to any conceivable type of reward available in your brain. Abuse has become easy. Fortunately, we also have the power of mind to make intelligent choices, and can therefore decide not to abuse stimuli. We can choose to go for the long-term benefits rather than gorge ourselves on short-term delights, since even the most determined hedonists realize that endless bounty is not necessarily that desirable.

The problem is that our intellect and our desires are rather delicately balanced. A further understanding of what our brains are up to should help the intellect make intelligent decisions, which is one of the objectives of this book.

Although any stimulant that triggers rewards is a commercial gold mine, the amount of gold recovered does not necessarily correlate with long-term improvement of Darwinian happiness. Most commercial stimulants have obvious negative consequences: Too many sweets destroy your teeth (a condition that may be appreciated by your dentist, though neither by you nor your genes). Some people become alcoholics, and end their lives with a defective liver. Others eat too much fat and die from coronary diseases. And then there are those who are sexually super-active, and end up with nothing else to keep them company than an assortment of sexually transmitted germs.

To counteract these problems we invent substitutes that elicit rewards without jeopardizing our health. The most obvious examples are in the field of nutrition: Evolution gave us a craving for whatever is nutritious, and the craving is particularly strong for nutrients that were important in the diet of our ancestors. The consumption of such food is, of course, linked to powerful brain rewards, which is why we have artificial sweeteners, alternatives for ordinary table salt, and a substance called olestra that gives food a fatty taste. These products are all designed to harvest rewards while avoiding adverse effects of over-consumption. They are designed to dupe the genes, but may actually benefit both you and your genes.

What makes food consumption a troublesome Discord, particularly in present societies, is that the default state of mind is to wish for more. Except when the stomach has recently been filled to the brim, the neurochemistry responsible for eating behavior tends to make you want to take another bite. In the natural setting of the Stone Age, this was not a problem because the trouble of obtaining food put a limit to consumption, and because the food items available where not designed to hyper-stimulate your taste buds. But in our society, obesity and its concomitant medical and mental problems are unfortunate consequences.[37]

Using stimulants and surrogates is a practical attempt at improving Darwinian happiness. Although the over-consumption of certain substitutes can jeopardize health, they do serve the purpose as long as the negative consequences do not outweigh the positive effects.

Why not then settle down on a comfortable sofa with a pile of cookies baked with artificial sweeteners and olestra? Unfortunately, it seems as if the easy solutions always carry drawbacks. The problem is not just a question of obtaining a balanced and healthy diet; a constant repetition of a pleasure-inducing stimulus simply does not work. As even those determined hedonists realize, you reach a point of diminishing returns. The problems of exploiting hardcore pleasure-stimuli are illustrated by the most powerful stimulants we have. We refer to these as narcotics, and their effects will be further discussed in Chapter 5.

There are three main obstacles for those who wish that their yielding to what the mind craves should end up as overall positive experiences: First, the long-term consequences may be harmful (fast food diet is associated with disease). Second, the reward tends to diminish with habituation (the drug abuser requires stronger and stronger doses). Third, the life situation created is not natural and therefore involves an element of stress (commercial sex is not in tune with our innate sexual tendencies).

The reward mechanisms evolved under conditions where the possibility of abuse was negligible. If misuse had been a problem, evolution would presumably have found a solution; the mind would have evolved to compensate. Most animals still live under natural conditions, their reward mechanisms functioning according to the purpose. The problem starts when you create a situation of abundance, such as an affluent human society, which is a Discord condition.

The bottom line is that for the purpose of obtaining a high lifetime score of Darwinian happiness, the advice is to show moderation. It does not mean you should never fool your genes, but you ought to keep in mind that a lifetime score is what matters. The pain of a dental operation may be more than compensated for by the subsequent avoidance of a toothache; the pleasure of heroin easily leads to pain; and to bear with the bad mood of a friend may be rewarded by a lasting friendship. The present social climate seems to have a tendency to pursue immediate pleasures, with limited regard for long-term consequences—an attitude that is not supported by the concept of Darwinian happiness.

The most potent pleasure centers in the brain are connected with sexuality. The primary purpose of lovemaking is fertilization; no action is more vital to the "wish" of the genes, hence the supreme rewards. But sex is also an illustrative example of how easy it is to fool the genes. The reward system urges you to have intercourse, not to create progeny. Therefore intercourse with a contraceptive may be just as pleasant as one without. Our brains happily deliver rewards for orgasms, even when the individual is conscious of the fact that the orgasm cannot result in conception. In a typical situation of today, such knowledge may actually boost the pleasure, as pregnancy is most often not a desirable outcome. Evolution moves slowly. It has, fortunately, not had the chance to respond to the invention of condoms.

It seems sensible to take some advantage of available gratification. You are advised to deceive your genes occasionally, whether in your sexual life or in your diet; yet a reasonable suggestion is that you teach yourself to enjoy the rewards available from natural situations in everyday life. Have time for a smile and enjoy other people smiling at you. Notice the beauty of nature as you pass by on your way to work. And if you are sufficiently hungry, your packed lunch will taste good, even if the bread is dry and the cheese has vanished.

The art of living is to tune in to positive sensations without resorting to spectacular stimuli.

The Default State of Good Mood

I have saved probably the most important point concerning Darwinian happiness for the last section of this chapter. Before I go on, let me recapitulate the main idea. In the definition of Darwinian happiness, I distinguish between "avoiding stress" and "obtaining rewards," but there is no definite line separating these two principles. Generally speaking, behavior that is in tune with your genes will be supported by your brain, and is thus pleasant. You feel good in the company of friends. The experience may not be thrilling, but it is natural and thus stress-reducing; and it is rewarding because socializing is something the brain encourages.

There is, however, another reason why we are advised to listen to our genes—a point that I have not touched on so far: I *believe evolution has preferred the basic, or default, state of mood to be agreeable.* The reason is simply because it is in the genes' interest to reside within a content carrier. Thus life can be good, even in the absence of particular stimuli, if we are able to find this state. And one way of finding it is to adjust our way of living to our innate nature.

Pain and negative moods are there for particular purposes. As long as the stimuli eliciting such feelings were avoided or dealt with, the "Stone Ager" was most likely happy—and the same could be true for us. Animals in the wild presumably experience a similar state of contentment as long as the situation is not disagreeable.

One piece of evidence supporting the idea of a **default good mood** lies in the eyes of children: As long as nothing is troubling them, their eyes sparkle with joy. If *they* have the propensity to enjoy life, why should not the genes favor the same state of mind in adults? Why does the glittering of the eyes tend to fade as we grow older?

We *are* potentially able to experience happiness. The drugs some of us take to achieve that state actually prove the point: Happiness is possible within the design of the adult mind. In fact, we appear to possess a psychological "immune system" that works to hasten recovery from emotionally negative events. Even serious misfortunes, such as the loss of both legs following an accident, typically leave the individual about equally happy once what can be healed has healed. Yet, too many people have a problem finding that state of mind. One interesting observation is that persons with Down syndrome appear to be better off than the average individual.[38]

Our positive inclinations are also reflected in the observation that people—at least those who have found contentment—tend to be optimistic. People typically believe they are more skilled than they really are, that bad things will never happen to them, and that they are likely to win in their next bet on horses—because a good mood, and to some extent a rose-colored view of the world, is to the genes' advantage. (Under normal conditions anyway, it may be added that the genes have not evolved a response to the invention of lotteries and gambling.)

I believe the concept of default good mood is the state of mind the gurus of India guide you toward, using techniques referred to as meditation or yoga. It is also related to the objective of various Western forms of mental therapy,[39] and to the concept of *flow*—the optimal experience—as described by the psychologist Mihaly Csikszentmihalyi.[40] To obtain the experience of "flow" you should try to engage yourself, to the extent that you may be totally absorbed, in tasks that, in my vocabulary, the mind is designed for. In short, default good mood is life as close to nirvana as your biology allows.

Your lifetime measure of Darwinian happiness can be charted on a diagram, where time is on the X-axis, and happiness on the Y-axis. (See Figure 3.) The curve will necessarily go up and down—the peaks reflecting periods of agreeable sensations, the deep valleys misery and pain, while the in-between plateau reflects the more common state of mind. All lives yield a varied landscape; some look more alpine, while others tend to reside on a plateau. The principle of seeking positive sensations implies that you let the diagram be dominated by peaks rather than troughs. Finding the default good mood, however, means lifting the whole curve—including peaks, valleys, and plateaus—upwards on the happiness axis. It is like a major land upheaval.

Although money does not correlate very well with happiness, psychologists have found four parameters that do correlate rather consistently: The first one is that extroverts are happier. This should come as no sur-

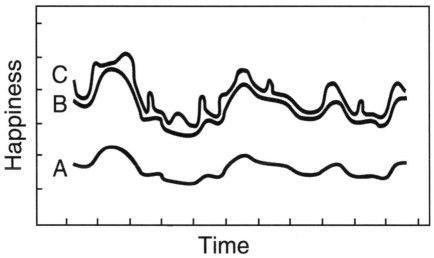

Figure 3. Your mood, and thus your score of happiness, varies with time as suggested in these diagrams without scale. The average person of today's society presumably has a suboptimal score (curve A). However, if you have learned how to find the default good mood, your score improves (curve B); and if, in addition, you are able to tune in to the potentially positive sensations from a variety of experiences, a series of small peaks will add further to your score (curve C).

prise when considering the importance of social life. The other three indicators of joy are optimism, a feeling of personal control over life, and liking oneself.[41] I believe these last three personality traits are mainly a question of being able to retain the default "good mood" setting of the brain.

Unfortunately, as pointed out at the beginning of Chapter 1, something appears to be wrong in the so-called civilized societies: Too many of our citizens have lost their joy of life. It is actually possible that our average score on Darwinian happiness is lower than that of our Stone Age ancestors. What went wrong?

Blame evolution for negligence. Our genes are lagging behind and have not yet reached the civilized state. The default good mood, I believe, is one of the first victims of Discord conditions. The glittering joy disappears long before you can observe more overt symptoms of misbehaving and psychological distress. Only those who are less burdened by the Discord situation can maintain the full capacity for default good mood—either because their way of living is closer to human EEA, or because they have acquired techniques for coping, or because they have an innate personality that is less sensitive to Discords. People with Down syndrome may represent a particular example of the latter.

We cannot expect evolution to come to our rescue and change the genes; the process is not necessarily heading in the right direction; and anyway it is much too sluggish. Thus, there is only one option left if we wish to do something about the Discord between genes and environment: We need to improve the environment.

Life on Earth was never paradise. Our remote ancestors were spared certain undesirable consequences of cities, but there were plenty of other adverse factors: They suffered from diseases, predators, and lack of food. It is important to study our evolutionary history, not because we should reinstate every aspect of our previous existence, but because it helps us understand how our genes influence us. Our way of life is necessarily different from life in Stone Age tribes, and it is not possible to have both the blessings of a modern society and optimal conditions perfectly suited to our genes at the same time. Yet an understanding of the behavioral biology of humans should help us improve society, because it is possible to decrease the problem of Discord. It is therefore feasible to create a society with a quality of life that surpasses both our tribal past and our present condition. If people are more content, and particularly if they are more content while consuming fewer resources, it will also be easier to save Planet Earth for future generations.

I believe the notion of Darwinian happiness can help us.

Summary—the Concept

The main purpose of this chapter has been to introduce the concept of *Darwinian Happiness*, which is based on twin principles: (1) to avoid stress, and (2) to utilize the rewarding sensations that the brain is designed to offer in a way that gives optimal long-term benefits. On the surface these principles may look straightforward, but as I have tried to explain, there are a series of concerns that should be considered when trying to translate them into practical advice. However, the remark that we should be careful when applying these principles does not mean that there is nothing to be gained. I hope the remainder of the book will convince you that it is possible to improve life by bearing in mind both what sort of conditions humans are designed for, and how to obtain pleasing sensations. What I advocate is the search for "default good mood"—the Holy Grail of Darwinian happiness—and to choose a way of living that optimizes positive sensations and contentment integrated over a lifetime.

As to the concept of Discord, I believe it is important to emphasize that we should think in terms of deviations from optimal conditions, rather than of mismatches from the human environment of evolutionary adaptation. I refer to the effect of Discord as "stress." Although this stress can result from both physical and mental Discord aspects of the environment, I choose to concentrate in this book on the aspects that more directly influence our psychological well-being—that is, on the behavioral and social environment, rather than on such factors as nutrition, temperature, or ergonomics. Please also keep in mind that Discords are not necessarily recognized, whether they are related to the physical environment—such as in connection with myopia—or related to the social environment, as exemplified by the number of strangers one encounters.

CHAPTER 4

Human Origins:
The Age of the Dangerous Hero

A place they once called Palestine.

Why We Should not Complain About Lumbago

Going back 200 million years, there was nothing to suggest that Earth would ever see anything resembling human life: The dinosaurs ruled on dry land. Mammals, it is true, were also present, and coexisted with the dinosaurs for at least one hundred million years, but only as small and insignificant creatures. Then, some 65 million years ago, an unforeseen catastrophe occurred—an asteroid hit the Gulf of Mexico. The impact must have shaken the earth with tremendous force; and the consequences, such as the accumulation of dust in the atmosphere and subsequent change of climate, lingered for years.

Large animals are presumably more vulnerable to changes and catastrophes than small ones, and typical dinosaurs were large, some of them even huge. It has been suggested that the asteroid was instrumental in their extinction, and thus offered the opportunity the mammals had been waiting for. Without it, we might still be hiding in treetops or under rocks, terrified of the mighty reptiles.

Actually a second event, some 10 million years after the asteroid impact, may have been the final nail in the dinosaurs' coffin. Seen from space, it was not as dramatic as the asteroid, but by judging certain fossil records, the second event caused an even greater stir. The earth let go of the biggest fart ever! More than a trillion tons of methane burst from the ocean floor. The release of this gas came during a period of general warming of the climate, and it dramatically intensified this trend. The average temperature of the globe may have gone up several degrees. The blowout, or rather the accompanying change in climate, possibly provided the cue our distant ancestors needed to take control of the stage.[42]

One of the new groups of animals to appear at this time were the omomyids.[43] They lived in Asia and were probably the ancestors of the first simians, a group including monkeys and apes. The simian lineage flourished and spread to North America, Europe, and Africa. Boosted by the demise of the dinosaurs and the increase in temperature, the simians had a ball. Those that found their way to Africa did particularly well; the

63

fossil remains prove that they diversified and thrived. Eventually they gave rise to the hero of our story. The first ape—that is to say, the common ancestor of gibbons, orangutans, gorillas, chimpanzees, and humans —appeared some 30 million years ago, probably in Asia. Our lineage, the **hominids,** diverged from what was to become modern chimpanzees only five million to six million years ago, while the gorilla lineage probably split off just before that.[44]

Let us imagine a biologist from another planet coming to study life on Earth: He may at first consider humans to be essentially different from all other species, our cultural characteristics clearly separating us from other animals. But as his knowledge improves, he would realize that humans are actually closely related to the chimpanzee and the gorilla; if he analyzed our genes he would find that they are approximately 98 percent similar to the genes of these species.[45]

At some point our ape ancestors apparently moved from Asia to Africa. Thus, although there are remains of hominids in Asia dating back almost two million years, the evolutionary drama that produced us was hosted by Africa. The presence of people on other continents, both now and in earlier times, reflects the results of migration.

Our distant primate ancestors lived in trees. They had excellent balance and well coordinated movements at their disposal; their legs were flexible and their feet were able to grasp branches, allowing for secure foothold in the trees. They also possessed first-rate vision, which was essential for moving around in the canopy. These properties provided the appropriate basis for some fascinating evolutionary events.

Mammalian evolution typically causes an increase in body size, for large individuals tend to oust their smaller cousins. The primates, however, had a problem: Tree-living monkeys move like squirrels, and animals that balance on thin branches and jump from tree to tree must keep their weight low. Evolution devised two strategies to elude this dilemma: In the Tarzan approach the animal moves around in trees by hanging from its arms and swinging from branch to branch. This type of locomotion allows for some gain in weight, but it also requires further improvement in the strength, flexibility, and sensitivity of the arms and hands. The apes, including our ancestors, evolved this technique.

Plate 5. Ten million years ago our ancestors presumably lived in trees of dense forests (top), but eventually they came to live on the ground in more open landscapes. Most of the present remains of early hominids are found in East Africa, along the Great Rift Valley (bottom), but today this region is more open and barren than it was during our evolutionary past.

The other obvious option is to climb down from the trees and find a niche on the ground, where even animals as large as rhinos and elephants can thrive. This option was chosen several times in the history of primates. The baboons climbed down, as did our ancestors some five million to ten million years ago, but that was only after they had evolved the Tarzan approach. Now, chimpanzees and gorillas spend most of their time on the ground; however, when moving in trees, they generally hang from their arms.

Besides a selection for increased size, there may be other reasons why our ancestors descended from the trees. As in the case of the baboons, we too probably moved from dense forest to a more open landscape. The climate may have changed, causing the jungle to dry up and wither away, or life in the savannas (or in a less luxurious forest) may have offered advantages such as reduced competition for food.

Baboons evolved from the branch-balancing type of monkey, which means that they never developed the ability to move around by hanging from their arms, a talent that gave our ancestors a unique chance. The strength and sensitivity of our arms and hands, combined with a more upright position, encouraged further development of manual dexterity. What happened was a piece of evolutionary ingenuity. The early human ancestors gradually became able to balance on their hind legs, which allowed them to take full advantage of their hands. As a consequence, they were able to develop tools and weapons. Selection pressure obviously pushed early humans into using their new abilities to the fullest, and this in turn selected for improvements in brain function.

Thus, walking on two feet was presumably instrumental in initiating the two most fundamental human capacities: The use of tools and intelligence. But with these capacities came the trade-off of with the problems connected with a spine not optimally designed for an upright position.

The Speed of Evolution

Skeletal remains of our hominid relatives, the *Australopithecus*, who lived from four million and maybe until one million years ago, suggest that they walked on two legs prior to the major increase in brain size, which is to be expected if the use of hands initiated the evolution of intellect. These hominids were able to utilize tools, but the repertoire was probably not much more impressive than what a chimpanzee can handle. Chimpanzees have, for example, been observed to strip a twig and use it to fish for termites by sticking it down the holes of termite colonies. They also crush leaves to create a kind of "sponge" and use it to obtain water from inaccessible places.[46]

Some two million to three million years ago a new stock of hominids appeared: They had a significantly larger brain, and are the first to be considered worthy of the name *Homo*, which means human. The evolution of the spectacular intellectual capacity associated with humans presumably occurred along with, or after, the emergence of *Homo*.

It is interesting to note that at the same time as our brains started to expand, we can also see changes in the bones making up the hands, indicating greater dexterity. The anatomical changes to the brain and hands suggest the invention of advanced tools, and, not surprisingly, the oldest preserved tools (made of stone) date back to this period.[47] From then on and up to the present, the artifacts recovered reveal a series of improvements in terms of tool design and workmanship. Other animals utilize the products of nature, birds for example use twigs to build nests. But we do something unique: We use tools to construct other tools.

The tools recovered from our distant past reflect, of course, the small subset of objects that were made of durable matter. The materials in question are primarily stone and to some extent bone; tools made of fiber and wood may be equally old, but their remains have decayed and rotted away. For example, humans may have used wooden spears more than two million years ago, yet the oldest spears we have unearthed are only 400,000 years old.[48]

Two million years may sound like a long time to us mortals, but in the evolutionary time scale it is like last year. You may agree that the creation of the giraffe's neck is a less astounding piece of evolutionary engineering than the human brain, yet it required a lot more time. So how did the process of evolution come up with a live computer in such a short period?

Studies of fossil remains have made it clear that evolution is not a linear process. Sometimes changes occur rapidly; in other cases a species may go on with the same old, boring routine for a hundred million years or more. The way we breed animals, such as dogs and cats, is an example of high-speed evolution.

Another example of presumed fast evolution involves certain British moths. The argument goes something like this: Two hundred years ago the moths were mostly light-colored with some dark specks. This gave excellent camouflage when they rested on trees that at the time were whitish due to the overall color of the trees and the luxuriant growth of lichens. Then soot and other pollutants from factories, ushering in the industrial revolution, changed the color of the trees. The trees were covered with soot, the lichen killed, and the white moths became an easy target for hungry birds. However, thanks to the magic of evolution, darker moths saved the species.[49]

The Galápagos finches, which helped Darwin form the theory of evolution, offer another well studied example of how evolution acts. Some 2.5 million years ago one species managed to move to the Galápagos from South America, and today there are 15 species that have evolved to occupy different niches in the ecology of the islands. Peter Grant and Rosemary Grant have studied these finches for almost thirty years, and have demonstrated the power of the Darwinian evolutionary process in action.[50]

Two conditions are required for evolution to act quickly: The genes must have the option to improve by small increments in the desired direction, and there must be a strong selection for improvement. The British moths already had genes that produced dark pigments. The required evolution thus involved the selection of the darker moths of the existing population, and, presumably, small changes in genes governing the production and the distribution of the pigments in order to create even darker individuals. Furthermore, as the moths with the whitest wings were rapidly eaten, the second requirement was also fulfilled.

Evolution can also be speeded up by moving a species into a new territory, or habitat, which was the case with the Galápagos finches. The islands offered ample opportunity for procreation, but also a need for finches to adapt to particular niches, or ways of living, in order to survive in the competition with other finches.

Our ancestors two million years ago were unable to understand the theory of relativity, but the structure of their brains was such that gradual changes could yield dramatic results. We certainly would expect the more intelligent individuals to have had a tremendous advantage, and maybe our ancestors were still struggling to adjust to a new habitat—life on the ground—and were under heavy selective pressure. Thus, we had the conditions required for rapid evolution of brainpower, such that now two million years later some readers may understand the theory of relativity.

I shall try to paint a more detailed picture of this particular evolutionary event, and thereby suggest the main fitness-increasing factors that propelled the transformation to a higher intellect. The resulting picture also portrays central features of the human environment of evolutionary adaptation; that is, the conditions that were instrumental in shaping present humans.

Was Language a Bonus for Hitting a Target?

It is easy for the nervous system of a vertebrate to control muscles; arms and legs are equipped with sensors that continuously send messages to the brain about what they are doing. Even a lizard has perfect coordination of its four legs.

The use of tools, however, is more difficult: Nerves simply do not extend into a hammer, which is why hitting the finger rather than the nail is a common problem. Your brain knows exactly where your hand is, even without looking at it, but not exactly where the head of the hammer is. Hitting the nail with your fist is therefore easier, but unfortunately less effective and a lot more painful. Throwing a spear or a stone at a target is an even more formidable task. In addition to assessing the movement of something you are holding on to, the brain has to make a very complicated calculation about the force and direction with which the weapon should leave your hand. Our ability to handle tools was a driving force in the evolution of intelligence, and this ability may also have been a prerequisite for the evolution of language.

In order to substantiate the connection between tool use and language, I should begin by pointing out that the tool repertoire of the chimpanzee is restricted to objects whose operation does not require accuracy; they do occasionally throw things, but typically with the precision of your three-year-old daughter having a fit. Moreover, chimps are able to produce roughly three-dozen different sounds, each presumably corresponding to a particular intent. They may repeat the sound, or increase the volume, in order to emphasize its meaning, but they do not combine sounds like we do.[51] Neither are they able to make sounds as distinct as ours. Yet the big stride forward was probably not so much a question of clarity of sound as the ability to make sequential patterns of sounds. In human language, the individual sounds have generally lost their meaning, but by connecting them we form words and sentences. We can therefore generate an enormous variety of messages. Chimps are actually able to learn simple strings of meaningful sounds, as long as the content can be gathered from the sum of the components. The proficient chimpanzee can pick up messages such as "banana under box," but only humans learn to understand and construct complex sentences. This capacity is programmed into the genes and appears as part of the normal development in two- to six-year-old children.

An intriguing observation is that language apparently employs the part of the brain involved in the control of tools and weapons. A possible explanation is that the two tasks use, or at least are derived from, the same nerve circuitry, inasmuch as they do share one important feature: Both involve the analysis of a complex sequence of events. In one case the sequence is a string of sounds; in the other it is the movement of a spear starting with the arm and ending at the target.[52]

Some scientists believe that an advanced use of gestures predated oral language. As with spoken language, human gestures can be combined in sequences: If, while out hunting, you point at yourself, then at your friend standing some distance away, and then to a nearby hill, your friend will understand that he should follow you to the hill. Gestures also have the advantage of being silent; if you yelled to your friend that you had observed an antelope on the other side of the hill, you could not expect the antelope to be there by the time you arrived.[53]

Evolution requires scaffolding on which to construct novel abilities. The nerve circuitry developed for the analysis of throwing a weapon was presumably a useful scaffold for evolving language capacity. That is to say, the first step took place when our ancestors evolved the ability to handle tools and to throw weapons. The next step may have been to put gestures together in a sequence, which involved the same brain structure developed to take care of sequential movement. In the third and final step, the capacity for language developed with the help of brain structures acquired for the former purposes, and changes in the vocal apparatus.

Success Is Not What It Used To Be

Diet is another factor that probably pushed us toward higher intelligence. We are an omnivorous species, which means we eat all sorts of things: fruit, roots, leaves, insects, and meat. A variety of information is needed to successfully extract such a mixed diet from the environment, and the processing of this information requires brainpower.[54]

Proteins, moreover, were presumably a limiting factor in our ancestors' menu. Game was the main source of proteins, so successful hunting improved survival. But humans never had the speed and natural killing capabilities of the big cats; in order to snatch our share of the proteins of the forest or savanna, we had to devise strategies, construct weapons, and collaborate with fellow humans. All these tasks encouraged the evolution of intelligence.

The socializing part, however, probably had the most far-reaching consequences. A variety of animals have chosen to live in groups, the most common benefit probably being defense against predators, but for humans it also became a question of hunting in groups. In the early stages, human alliances probably involved primarily close relatives, but eventually the advantages of tribal life made kinship less of a requirement for participation: We were able to derive sufficient benefit from each other to cause affiliations to make evolutionary sense, not just of close kin, but even of individuals outside of kin groups. The human tribe finally turned into a well-organized, intimate, and complex social unit.

The evolution of social life must have encouraged the development of both language and intelligence; to master social relations demands a lot of brainpower. Perhaps equally important, the combination of intellect, language, and gregariousness opened the way for culture, the final element in the countdown toward the appearance of our dangerous hero.

Culture involves the non-genetic transmission of factors relevant for the survival of a species. Even birds have some claim to culture. A well-published example is the way some birds learned that they could obtain milk by pecking holes into the caps of bottles placed outside British homes; the lesson in foraging spread rapidly, not only among adults, but also from parents to progeny. Chimpanzees have been observed teaching their children intentionally, but only in humans has cultural transmission drastically affected both life style and the biological success of the species.[55]

So how did evolution manage to create a super-intelligent animal? The answer to this question may be summed up in the following five points: the use of hands to manipulate objects, the development of language, the consequences of the human diet, social life, and cultural transmission. I believe these conditions explain the evolution of the most spectacular characteristics of human beings; moreover, I believe the resulting brain is the most spectacular feature of life on earth.

After having suggested how we obtained our impressive intelligence, it may be pertinent to mention that human behavior is not always that clever. Most people are presumably aware of the problem, having observed the whims and opinions of others. It may be more difficult, however, to accept that your own thoughts and actions are to a large extent shaped by relatively unintelligent innate tendencies—tendencies fully capable of brushing away reason and logic. But they are. We cannot escape our genes, and on many occasions they will overrule the intellect we are so proud of.

Since the development of the brain began to speed up two million years ago, the story of hominids has been one of accomplishment. Starting at that time, we find fossils as far apart as southern Africa and eastern Asia, demonstrating the expansion of populations; yet the tremendous success of our species, biologically speaking, is more recent.

Looking at the present world, most people may find the word "success" misleading. Not only would you hesitate to call all human behavior intelligent, but living conditions for the average person are not all that wonderful, and our tendency to co-operate has obviously not been developed to perfection.

The Mitochondrial Eve

Your body is the product of the engineering feat of sticking together some 10^{14} cells. Each cell contains two copies of the 23 different human **chromosomes**, which are long strands of DNA. The chromosomes carry most of the 40,000 or so genes required to create a human being.[56] A few genes, however, are not on the chromosomes, but inside cellular components called the *mitochondria*. Mitochondria are the remnants of bacteria engulfed by the primordial cells of higher organisms a billion years ago.[57] These mitochondrial genes are useful to the student of human evolution for two reasons: They are more variable than the chromosomal genes, and, more importantly, they are inherited solely from the mother, since sperm delivers only chromosomal genes.

By analyzing variations in the genetic material of modern humans, particularly that of the mitochondrial genes, it is possible to infer something about our evolutionary history. For example, we believe that all people alive today are the descendants of one particular woman, dubbed, of course, Eve, who lived some 150,000 years ago. She was part of a rather small population, consisting probably of fewer than 10,000 individuals— a group so small that we humans living today would have put it on the endangered species list.[58] These people presumably roamed around somewhere in Africa.

At the same time a more numerous subspecies of humans, called the Neanderthals, lived in Europe and the Near East. The molecular biologists Svante Pääbo and co-workers have managed to analyze the mitochondrial genes of a Neanderthal who died 50,000 years ago. The analysis substantiates that they are not our ancestors.[59]

Eve and her people made tools and had a knowledge of fire, and they had language and culture. For all practical purposes they were fully evolved from ape-like ancestors to the present stage of humanity. So, we call them modern humans to underline this fact. If one of them were to be born in New York tomorrow, nobody would probably raise an eyebrow.

Genetic analyses can also be used to trace the relationships among peoples living today: Certain tribal populations in the southern part of Africa, including the Kung bushmen and the Mbuti pygmy, appear to be the humans that are the least related to other populations of our species.

Their ancestors presumably departed from the main lineage some 100,000 years ago.[60]

About that time the lineage of modern humans probably started to skyrocket. The populations increased and consequently expanded to new areas. The tribes occupying the northeastern part of Africa moved toward Europe and Asia, and some people probably managed to get across to Australia 50,000 years ago. Somewhat later others discovered the North American continent, and it appears that 15,000 years ago they were settled as far away as the southern part of South America.[61]

At that time the sea level was much lower than it is today, because of the ice age; thus, the stretches of open ocean to be crossed were shorter. Yet the only way to get across to Australia would have been by boat. It is likely that the first people to move had devised a way to make a living from the ocean: Coastal waters harbor an enormous amount of high quality food for those who know how to harvest it. Once the technology, including means for transport across water, was there, the supply would lead to a drastic expansion of the population. Actually, many scientists believe the evolution of modern humans included a long-term relationship with water, an association that explains features such as the lack of fur, fat deposits under the skin, and our capacity for swimming and diving.[62]

As the shoreline in those days was below present-day sea levels, it is difficult to find remnants of coastal cultures. A few sites have been discovered, some underneath the sea, but most of the remains from the period belong to tribes that lived further inland. While much of the early immigration probably followed the coast, traces of people found in countries east of the Mediterranean suggest that another exodus went overland to Europe some 50,000 years ago.[63]

It is important to recognize that in genetic terms we are a very homogeneous species. If you analyze rats, crows, or even chimpanzees, you will find much more genetic variety, which is because the last common ancestor for each of these species dates back a lot further than to the time of Eve.[64] But it is also true that the anatomical differences we tend to focus on, such as skin color or the shape of noses, do reflect genetic differences brought about by recent evolution. Inuits, for example, live in the coldest

Plate 6. Many scientists believe that humans spent part of the evolutionary past in close association with water. The capacity to exploit the oceans for food and transport may have been instrumental in the colonization of almost every corner of the world that occurred some 70,000 to 20,000 years ago.

regions of the world and have evolved small noses and short fingers because these features help to conserve body heat.

It is easy to make the assumption that the common chimpanzee is a more homogeneous species than humans, a mistake that is due to two factors: One, recent evolution of humans happened to involve features that are easily visible; and two, we tend to overlook variation in whatever is less familiar. For example, for a European person, the Chinese look pretty much the same, and all chimps look alike. To the mothers, however, identical twins can be very different.

Most of the known human genetic variants are present around the globe, and when comparing populations, the differences we observe are usually a matter of frequencies of these variants. For example, blood type A is common in Europe, while blood type B is more prevalent in Asia.[65] I assume that there are differences between populations in the average genetic dispositions associated with emotional life, behavioral patterns, and the ability to perform various tasks; however, these differences are most likely small compared to the variation within each population. One of the most discussed, and best documented, differences is that some black populations seem to have an inherent advantage in certain sports.[66]

Some people like to think of present tribal peoples as more "primitive," in the sense that they are closer to early humans. There is no evidence to suggest this to be true. Living in Africa, the first modern humans probably had dark skin; however, other "primitive traits," which in biological terms mean traits that have been retained in some lineages but not in others, are likely to be present equally in white Caucasians and in African pygmies. For example, Caucasians have apparently retained more of the "primitive" eyebrow ridge.[67]

Although we are genetically similar, culturally we are not. Rats and crows are genetically more variable, but much more uniform in their behavior. The inherent flexibility of the human brain, combined with the fact that culture is able to change a lot faster than genes, explains why present humans live in such a variety of ways.

The Branches That Withered

Why did the Neanderthals disappear, and why did the sons and daughters of Eve inherit the Earth?

In order to describe the relationships between human populations, past or present, we have to draw an evolutionary tree. (See Figure 4.) It looks somewhat like the family trees you find hanging in the hallways of people who take a certain pride in their ancestors—some branches are short, while others become main stems. As to the hominid family tree, you should note two features: First, only one of the branches reaches all the way up to the present; and, second, in historical times this single branch has increased in size at a rate never witnessed before.

Since we split from our ape cousins five million years ago, the human evolutionary tree has sprouted a number of branches. Many of the branches represent hominids that were sufficiently different from us to be considered separate species. *Australopithecus* died out about one million years ago, after having shared the earth with *Homo* for a couple of million years. *Homo erectus*, which spread all the way to China and Java between one and two million years ago, may still have been present in those regions when modern humans arrived. The Neanderthals dominated Europe for up to half a million years. They eventually started to use tools similar to those of modern humans, suggesting that they did interact with our ancestors. Then they suddenly vanished 30,000 years back. Shoots are disappearing even today: The last Tasmanian died in 1876.

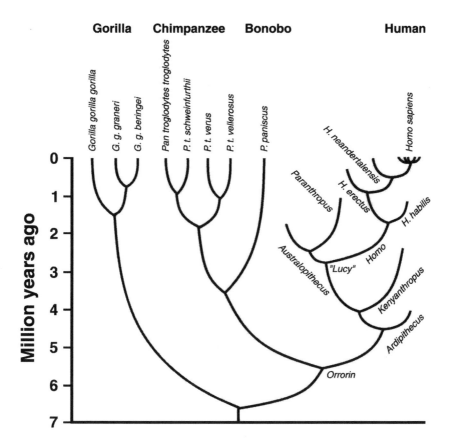

Figure 4. Our family tree, including some close relatives. It should be emphasized that the tree is highly speculative. The Latin names are written in *italics*; genus names begin with a capital letter and the names of species and subspecies follow in lowercase. Where the same name is used repeatedly, it is abbreviated to the first letter. While there are hardly any fossil remnants of gorillas and chimpanzees, there are lots of human remains. This striking difference reflects to some extent a preference for looking for human bones, and a concomitant preference for labeling whatever is found as human. However, ancestors of the other species probably lived in environments where fossils are less likely to be found, such as dense forest, and they may have been relatively scarce. Actually some of the fossils, such as the *Ardipithecus*, could be an ancestor of apes rather than humans. The most famous of our ancestors, "Lucy," was an *Australopithecus* who lived in Ethiopia.

All of these hominid populations were presumably highly intelligent, at least in comparison to apes and other animals. *Homo erectus* not only made stone tools but most likely also mastered the use of fire.[68] The ability to make fire may have been a required capacity for their exodus from Africa into colder climates. Yet, they still disappeared.

Genetic analysis suggests that the branch leading to us was indeed very thin during most of the last two million years: Our evolutionary history can be compared to walking through a long and slender bottleneck that suddenly opens up into a vast container. The implications are disturbing. Up until the last 50,000 years or so, other human lineages were presumably more successful than our ancestors.[69]

In the case of the Tasmanians we know what happened: They were killed or replaced by Europeans. A few genes were passed on, mostly through sexual exploitation of native women. This process has been repeated several times in recent centuries: New populations with a superior level of technology—or who are simply more aggressive—arrive on the scene and take over. They also bring along an assortment of germs for which the native people lack immunity. There are territorial disputes. You do not need to be a historian to guess at the results. A similar story may explain the disappearance of the Neanderthal, and possibly also the demise of earlier hominid branches.

So the evidence is disquieting. It appears that the worst enemy of mankind has always been mankind himself—humans have probably fought each other for a very long time. The winners were presumably distinguished by two characteristics: They were more intelligent, and they were more offensive, meaning that aggressive behavior has been selected for. Even today the "nastier" shoots of the evolutionary tree are more likely to expand and dominate.

Expulsion from the Garden of Eden

The most significant development in the more recent history of mankind was a revolution that started some 10,000 years ago: the Agricultural Revolution.

When the last ice age ended roughly 14,000 years ago, Europe and Northern Africa experienced a wet period—so wet that even the Sahara was a forest. The warm, wet climate with ample game animals suited humans and made it easy for populations to move between the central part of Africa and the Middle East. The Mediterranean probably experienced a considerable increase in population. But then a drier period followed.[70]

An intriguing observation is that the revolution started independently, and at about the same time, in three different regions—the Middle East, China, and Central America. In all three regions, naturally occurring plants suitable for cultivation were to be found: Barley and wheat, rice, and maize, respectively. What happened was that people started to sow seeds, rather than just harvest wild plants. They developed farming. The first animals to be domesticated for the purpose of being eaten— goats, sheep, cattle, and pigs—were probably attracted by the cultivated fields, and thus came to associate with the inhabitants.[71] Today we think highly of our farms. People do not seem to realize that farming was the first step on a very dangerous journey because, with this innovation, a battle with the natural world began that has had some devastating consequences, such as deforestation, soil degradation, and pollution. Furthermore, it is highly probable that agriculture was not a glorious invention, but rather a desperate act of survival. Life as a *hunter-gatherer*—that is, people who do not cultivate food but instead live by gathering edibles and fishing or hunting for animals—has obvious advantages. This life style is believed not only to require less effort than early farming, but also to yield a richer and healthier diet.[72]

So why did they farm? I believe there are two reasons: For one, global changes in climate may have caused the Garden of Eden of the hunter-gatherer to dry out. We know that the three regions involved became more barren, and the fact that farming started in three areas more or less simultaneously suggests a common cause. Second, it is also likely that the human population had expanded to the point where it was no longer easy to find new territories for an increasing number of individuals. The hunter-gatherer way of life requires a sparse population and a rich environment. Such cultures had to rely on the availability of food throughout the year, since the technology needed for long-term storage of provisions was presumably not readily available prior to farming. Moreover, an increase in dietary breadth (that is, the variety of edible items exploited) apparently predated farming—a change that suggests an increase in population density compared to the carrying capacity of the environment.[73]

The biblical book of Genesis describes how Adam and Eve were expelled from the Garden of Eden and relegated to a life of toil. This seems to be a fairly accurate description. The leisurely free roaming life of the hunter-gatherer (in a rich and sparsely populated environment) was exchanged for a life of endless days bent over a piece of soil. The fossil evidence even suggests that, before the invention of agriculture, our ancestors were taller and had larger brains than the average human today.[74] Thus, I believe we were expelled from the Garden of Eden by a combination of climate change and congestion.

What farming did allow for was the congregation of a large number of people, since even early agriculture could sustain a more than a 100-fold increase in population density. This paved the way for two very important features: the creation of states and the division of labor.

The success of agrarian communities is easy to explain: A large society is obviously more powerful than a small tribe, and a technologically advanced population will fare better than a primitive tribe. Farmers will thus tend to subdue non-farmers, which is exactly what happened. The vast majority of the earth's current population has presumably descended from the people who took up farming.

It should be mentioned that the shift to farming was not all that sudden. Over a period lasting thousands of years people gradually became more and more reliant on agriculture as opposed to hunting and gathering. There is also evidence that in some places people formed large communities while still relying pretty much on hunting and gathering.[75] The important point is that, once started, the agricultural revolution could not be stopped; the densely populated states eventually came to rely on farming for survival. Today we are trapped: The path back to the Garden of Eden is closed; Earth is too heavily populated for a return to be feasible.

There are obvious favorable effects of agriculture and the ensuing industrial revolution: These cultural transformations have brought mankind enormous success, particularly if you choose biomass to measure accomplishment. Moreover, some people have been able to obtain very comfortable lives. However, the changes have also brought us to a Discord society. It is important to remember that our genes are adapted to a hunter-gatherer way of life; 10,000 years is a too short period for having much of an impact on our genes.

It is also relevant to recognize that the people we presently label as "primitive" or "back-to-nature" do not live in the environment human genes are adapted to. Today's tribal cultures are either forced into very marginal land, or the population density is too high. The pastoral cultures of Africa, or the mixture of small-scale agriculture and gathering typical of much of the Third World, may be less of a Discord than the cultures of London or New York, but they are not truly back-to-nature. And they lack many of the advantages of modern technology.

Consequently I am not suggesting that you should pack a loincloth and move to the mountains of New Guinea. We can create something better.

How We Know What to Believe

In order to extract advice from human behavioral biology, we need to paint a picture of how our genes influence behavior. To get a clear view of that picture, it is important to understand the sort of information that was used to create it. The evolutionary scenario that was instrumental in shaping our genes is highly relevant in this connection, but a lot of other information is also pertinent. There is no space in the later chapters for a complete listing of applicable data, so I shall use the remaining three sections of this chapter to focus on the sort of facts that are available. The question I shall address is: What information and facts do we have to back up claims regarding innate tendencies?

Traditionally, the study of human behavior has belonged to the social sciences such as psychology, anthropology, and sociology. An increasing number of social scientists believe that the evolutionary approach offers a valuable supplement to these disciplines. The famous biologist Theodosius Dobzhansky once wrote, "Nothing in biology makes sense except in the light of evolution." More recently, the psychologist Henry Plotkin offered his version: "In psychology nothing makes *complete* sense except in the light of evolution."

We are all products of both nature and nurture; the effect of nurture, however, is something added onto our innate tendencies. Biology can therefore offer a framework that covers all aspects of our behavior—a framework that may be used to organize knowledge gathered from various disciplines. It remains in the power of the social sciences to gather bits and pieces of information to fill in the open spaces. The point is that these bits and pieces, at least in my mind, are particularly illuminating if they can be added to the biological framework.

Such a framework will be more or less valuable depending on what aspects of human behavior you are interested in. The more the genes have to do with it, the more you will gain from an evolutionary perspective. The strength of biology lies in the insight it gives into the universal, innate features of mankind; the strength of the social sciences lies in describing individual and cultural variations. The relative importance of our genes in various types of behavior may vary from close to zero to almost one hundred percent. It is never at either extreme. For example, whether you use chopsticks or a fork and knife at the dinner table is primarily culturally determined. Yet, by designing your fingers, the genes set limits on the shapes eating utensils can take. When you sit at the table, the desire for something tasty to put into your mouth is a fundamental force universal to all fellow beings, but nurture can in rare cases overrule even this basic urge. The person sitting next to you, eating nothing, may have developed a condition called anorexia.

To think of the various characteristics of human behavior as being shaped by either biological or environmental forces is deceiving. We are not shaped by nature or nurture, but rather by the interaction *between* nature and nurture. The concept of Discord is a way of saying that the environment, which means nurture, matters. Knowledge about our genetic inheritance tells us something about why it matters, and what environmental qualities we should prefer.

The Faces of Science

In order to give an impression of what sort of information is available for painting the picture of how we are influenced by our genes, I shall first briefly mention key disciplines and lines of inquiry. The next, supplementary, section will include a more detailed discussion of an example. *Psychology* and *psychiatry* are the main sciences of the human mind. They teach us, among many other things, about the extreme variability possible within the frame of human nature. At the end of his great work, *On the Origin of Species*, Darwin predicted that psychology would be based on a new foundation. With the increasing acceptance of "Evolutionary Psychology" as a valid field, it seems as though Darwin's prediction is finally about to be fulfilled.[76]

Anthropology has chronicled the diversity of human cultures, and enlightened us about how to interpret the variation. Information gathered on various cultures vaguely defines the boundaries of what we can adjust to. Fortunately, field anthropologists have managed to gather invaluable information on several hundred tribal communities before Coca-Cola and McDonalds managed to permeate the most remote villages. This information is very important for cross-cultural comparisons. The number of independent societies sharing a particular behavioral trait is expected to correlate with the degree to which the genes contribute to that trait.[77]

An alternative approach to estimating the importance of the genes is to study people who are genetically related. Brothers and sisters share half their genes; *identical twins* share all of them. Particularly valuable information can be obtained from identical twins that have been reared apart—the differences observed in their personalities are due to environmental factors. By analyzing how closely they score on various psychological tests, in comparison to genetically unrelated children, we can estimate the extent to which the observed variation is due to nature or nurture. In cognitive skills and emotional characteristics we tend to find that nature and nurture contribute roughly equally; in the case of intelligence tests, the genes probably matter somewhat more, while they matter less in relation to emotional aspects of a personality.[78]

It is a popular misconception to assume that such estimates give us the total contribution of the genes. In the case of intelligence, for example, all healthy individuals are highly intelligent due to our common inheritance; the fifty-fifty split applies only to the variability in intelligence, the ripples on the surface of the ocean of human wisdom. In other words, to state that a trait has a heritability of 50 percent means that half of the *variation* is due to genetic differences. If you recall, in Chapter 1 I suggested that your personality, or mental characteristics, are derived from three units of shared innate tendencies, one unit of genetic factors specific for you, and one unit of environmental influence. A 50 percent heritability is saying the same as the allocation of one unit to each of the two latter parts.

Surprisingly, research suggests that a shared environment does not appreciably contribute to the similarity of siblings. Apparently the similarity is mainly due to their shared genes. Actually, the environment will often tend to amplify small differences in genetically determined talents. For example, a person born to be tall will typically be more interested in basketball and will eventually outperform the average kid to a greater extent than what his innate advantage should dictate. A similar reasoning holds for intelligence: With an innate propensity for handling brainteasers, you are likely to spend more time on the kind of challenges used in intelligence tests. Thus, some of the estimates of heritability are likely to be overestimates. The bottom line is that one should be careful about quantifying the importance of nature versus nurture; rather, try to recognize how both factors work together to shape the human brain.[79]

Genetics is an important topic because it describes the rules governing the process of evolution. As previously pointed out, analysis of present genes can tell us something about human evolution. It is also possible to examine genes that are actually involved in directing behavior.[80]

The fruit fly *Drosophila* is a favorite organism for scientists involved in genetics. These insects are sufficiently advanced to perform elaborate behavioral patterns, yet their nerve circuitry, and the number of genes involved in constructing it, is a lot simpler than in humans. One interesting piece of knowledge gained from the fly concerns a gene required for "etiquette." The male, like most males, is not very selective about which female he starts courting. A normal male, however, is able to take a hint: By interpreting odor signals released by the female, he can tell if the particular beauty is no longer a virgin. (If not a virgin, she is not worth further trouble because her eggs may already be fertilized.) In this case, the male interrupts his routine and buzzes around for a while in order to end up at a new spot with, hopefully, more "worthy" females. It is possible to create fruit flies that lack certain genes. If a particular gene involved in learning is knocked out, the male loses his ability to interpret the odor. Such flies continue their flirtation (as do certain men) regardless of the signals given by the female.[81]

Humans carry their own version of this fruit fly gene. It presumably has a function in connection with learning, but in our brains the effect of the gene is more obscure, because learning in humans is a more complex activity that involves a very large number of genes. We know of more than a hundred human mutations that impair learning or related cognitive functions.[82]

You may frequently read reports claiming that someone has found the gene for a specific type of behavior, such as aggression, homosexuality, intelligence, gambling, and so forth. The typical story behind the reports is that one version of a particular gene is found to be associated with certain forms of behavior. For example, people with one particularly rare mutation are more prone to violence. Such reports should be handled with care, although the gene in question presumably, as reported, influences aggressiveness; a variety of other genes are involved as well. Thus, the behavior depends on which combination of subtypes of several genes the individual is equipped with, as well as on nurture.[83]

Ethology is the study of animal behavior.[84] To the extent that there are parallels between the behavior of animals and man, ethology offers insight into human behavior as well. Animals that are closely related to us in evolutionary terms are the most informative. Apes, particularly the chimpanzee and the gorilla, have taught us a lot about ourselves. We currently recognize two species of chimpanzee—the common chimp (with three subspecies) and the bonobo, also known as the pigmy chimpanzee. There are three subspecies of gorilla, the mountain gorilla, the western, and the eastern lowland gorilla.

It is particularly interesting to compare the bonobos and common chimpanzees with humans. The two species of chimps share many behavioral patterns, and some of these patterns are also shared with humans, such as an outstretched open hand that signals begging, or a wish for contact. However, each species of chimpanzee also has a number of unique characteristics, and upon examining these features, some scientists consider the bonobo to be the species most similar to humans. They are, for example, quite adapt at walking on two legs, and they are apparently quicker than any other apes when it comes to learning new tasks. In other words, the bonobos may have retained more of the features associated with our shared ancestors.[85]

Ethology focuses on the study of wild animals in their natural environment. Experiments using animals under laboratory conditions also yield valuable information. For example, scientists have been able to demonstrate the evolution of behavior, as follows. In one experiment you start with an agreeable bunch of rats, then you pick the least and the most aggressive animals and breed them separately. By repeating this procedure you will eventually end up with two groups of animals: One group is comparatively peaceful; the other is one you would preferably not want to hang out with. The final difference will reflect the genetic variability present in the population at the start of the experiment. The experiment thus gives an indication of the extent to which the individual variation in aggressiveness observed in the original population was due to nature or nurture.[86] This type of experiment, as well as other types, typically conclude that 60 to 90 percent of the observed variation in the behavior of mammals is explained by genetic variation—compared to the common value of 50 percent in the case of humans.

We know in great detail how individual *nerve cells* function, how they interact, and how they form units of activity. There is, however, a gap between this knowledge and an understanding of the more complex functions of our nervous system, such as our ability to think and feel. Considering the complexity of our brains, the gap should come as no surprise. The human brain is an engineer's nightmare: It is an assembly of some 50 billion cells, many of them having thousands of connections to other cells. Yet the field of *affective neuroscience* is about to close this gap and tell us something about how the brain creates emotions.[87] (More on this topic in Chapters 5 and 7.)

We have learned a lot about behavior by studying *endocrinology*, the science of hormones. There are several examples of hormones with obvious effects on human behavior: When you are afraid, the adrenal gland produces epinephrine (also referred to as adrenaline), which is part of the fight-or-flight response. Changes in personality seen during puberty, which is initiated by sex hormones, is another example.

The above list is a nice mix of social and natural sciences. I believe an interaction between these disciplines is essential in order to fill in the details of the picture of human behavior.

Promiscuity

One notorious statement made by sociobiologists is that men are more promiscuous than women. For most people this is a statement of fact, but some disbelieve or resent the idea. I shall dwell on this statement because the underlying data illustrates the variety of information that is relevant for understanding how the genes influence us, and because the controversial aspect of the subject serves a purpose.

Promiscuity involves a desire for different sexual partners. Postulating that men are more promiscuous than women, however, does not necessarily imply that men have a stronger sexual drive; this may be the case, but promiscuity is more about desiring variety. I have listed below information supporting this claim:

Males and females are genetically distinct owing to the fact that females have two X chromosomes while males have an X and a Y. We know that anatomical and physiological differences between the mammalian sexes are genetically determined, and that sexual behavior is influenced by the genes. The differences are primarily due to the activity of gender-specific hormones.[88]

In biology a "male" is defined as the gender that invests less in offspring. In mammals the difference is very obvious; not only do females have long gestation periods, they also feed the baby after it is born. Evolution pushes genes toward optimal breeding. Because of the difference in investment, male genes gain an advantage by copulating with as many different females as possible; thus, males may opt for the "hit-and-run" strategy. Females, on the other hand, lack this option and should therefore be choosy. As a consequence, in most animals the male is more promiscuous.[89]

Among mammals, the difference in body size between males and females tends to correlate with the degree of promiscuity: The two sexes are typically about the same size in the more monogamous species, while in species where males compete continually for mates, they tend to be bigger. This is presumably because larger males will chase away the smaller ones, and because the females prefer larger mates. When comparing humans, men are generally taller than women.[90] Moreover, at least among apes, in the more promiscuous species the males tend to have larger reproductive organs (testes and erect penis). If you ever get the chance to take a closer look at male gorillas, which tend to form lasting bonds with one or a few females, you will realize that men are relatively well equipped.[91]

In animals characterized by male promiscuity the males have a larger reproductive potential, which means that the success of males varies widely. Some father a large number of children while others are left with none. In this situation it makes evolutionary sense to put more resources into the male child than into the female, since the females will be able to procreate anyway. It can be claimed that humans are designed to put more resources into boys: The average weight at birth is higher, and there is a tendency in many societies to take better care of sons than of daughters.[92]

Polygyny was apparently accepted in most cultures before Christianity started to dominate the world.[93] Cross-cultural studies reveal that polygyny (one man may have several wives) is still accepted in many cultures, while polyandry (one woman may have several husbands) is rare. True, there are rules limiting the practice of polygyny. Muslims set the upper limit at four (from then on it is concubines), and it is said that the king of Ashanti, an old West African state, had to do with 3,333 wives.[94] His genes must have rejoiced.

In the rare cases where polyandry occurs, it typically involves a woman marrying several brothers. The children will then have genes in common with all the males concerned. This tradition tends to have a specific purpose: For example in Buddhist areas of Northern Nepal, cultivable land is so scarce that it would be ruinous to disrupt a farm by dividing it among sons. Tradition dictates that the first and the third son share a wife, while the second enters a monastery. One of the rare examples of polyandry occurring in the animal kingdom, the Tasmanian hen, also proves to be a case of brothers sharing a wife.[95]

The primatologist Alison Jolly has made an interesting remark about polygyny: The constellation is traditionally referred to as a "harem" group, but she prefers to call it a "gigolo" group, since it is not obvious who is serving whom.[96]

The market for sex as a commodity shows a strong gender bias. The supply catering for the male consumer, whether in the form of pornography or prostitution, far exceeds the meager assortment offered women.

In most cultures males are the importunate sex: Males are responsible for (almost) all sexual abuse; men force sex upon women, but women are not inclined to follow suit. It should be stressed, however, that the fact that humans have the capacity, and occasionally the inclination, to violent and hurtful behavior is in no way an excuse for such behavior. It certainly is within our capacity to refrain from harming others.

If heterosexual relationships are typified by pushy males and restrictive females, what about homosexuals? One would expect male homosexuals to behave differently from their female counterparts; and indeed, we find that, while gay men tend to enter into casual sexual relationships, lesbians are more careful.[97]

Our fantasies are expected to reveal our true selves. Men typically fantasize about sex with total strangers, while this is rare in the case of women.[98]

All the information above is relevant to the question: Which sex is the more promiscuous? Yet, the data does not "prove" anything. A description of human behavioral biology is necessarily less scientifically rigorous than the description of a flower; the picture to be painted relies on information, but it also requires an interpretation based on proper judgment. A description of innate tendencies relies, to a large extent, on an intimate comprehension of both evolution and human biology. To my mind, the above evidence is more than sufficient to support the claim that men are by nature more promiscuous than women.

It should be mentioned, however, that there are several examples in biology where the females are highly promiscuous. One rationale for such behavior is described by Sarah Hrdy.[99] After observing how female langur monkeys in India aggressively seek copulation with multiple males, she concluded that the females gain an advantage by luring several males into assuming that the forthcoming child could be theirs. Having copulated with the female, the males were later more supportive to the mother and child, or at least less likely to kill the infant. There are other reasons for female promiscuity as well—and I shall return to two of them, the bonobo and the seahorse, in Chapter 8.

In biology, important phenomena are usually given a name. The contention that men are more promiscuous has been called the *Coolidge effect*—a name that I assume will keep the memory of that American president alive, unless the former President Clinton can convince biologists that the effect should rather be named after him. The honor is due to an episode when President Coolidge and his wife were given a guided tour of a farm. The farm boy first accompanied the wife. Impressed by the single rooster caring for all the hens, the First Lady asked the boy to point out to the President that this rooster certainly had a busy schedule. When the president was informed of the rooster's ability to copulate several times a day, he asked, "Always with the same female?" The boy replied, "No, sir." And Coolidge went on, "Well, tell that to my wife."

When you measure behavioral traits in humans, you find that the

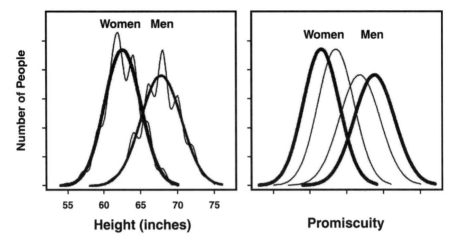

Figure 5. At left, the distribution of height in women and men, respectively. The thin lines represent the actual measurements of some 58,000 women and 52,000 men taken by the National Health Survey in the United States, from 1960 to 1962, while the thick lines are the theoretical (Gaussian) approximations in the form of bell-shaped curves. At right are hypothetical distributions of promiscuity in women and men. The thick lines are meant to indicate the innate tendency toward promiscuity, while the thin lines suggest how the environment might change the distributions.

distribution of properties typically follows a bell-shaped curve. (See Figure 5.) When a biologist states that men are more promiscuous, he means that the average for men is higher than the average for women. The two curves may very well overlap; thus, the observation that some women are highly promiscuous does not disprove the rule. But, it can probably be generalized that most women have genes that suggest a lower promiscuity score. Since the trait is strongly influenced by nurture, the curves may still overlap when the behavior of adults is assessed. We could create a society where women are on the average more promiscuous than men—a community of hard-working prostitutes would serve that purpose. The biologist, however, is interested in how genes influence the average human, and will declare that men are (by nature) more promiscuous than women, even if an individual, or a particular community, apparently contradicts this statement. Based on my experience in discussing the question of promiscuity with various people, I realize that I should also add that the statement is certainly not meant as a directive. As far as the science of human behavior is concerned, each person is free to take any number of partners he or she wants.

It is interesting to note that the above reservations would be unnecessary if the original statement had been that men are taller than women. The audience would intuitively understand that I was talking about the average man and the average woman; and although it is possible to create a society where women are taller, because stature is influenced by nutrition, such a community would not disprove the assertion. Moreover, the statement on differences in height would, I assume, not be considered an attempt to recommend that men should be tall or women short. Neither should this be considered an attempt to stigmatize or discriminate against those who end up at either end of the bell curve.

In order to understand human behavioral biology, it is important not to be provoked by any statement on innate tendencies, but rather to ask to what extent a claim seems to be substantiated. A subsequent question is whether it happens to apply to you as a person, and whether it has a bearing on your strategy to improve your share of Darwinian happiness.

Summary: How We Got Here

The purpose of this chapter has been to provide background information relevant for later chapters. Two topics are covered: the evolutionary scenario leading up to present humans, and the various sources of information that help us understand our innate tendencies. Both topics are aimed at giving the reader a background for making independent—and critical—judgments about issues to be discussed later.

The scenario is relevant not just because it helps us understand how the genes are influencing us, but also because it is a necessary exercise in identifying the theoretical Environment of Evolutionary Adaptation, or EEA. As for sources of information, it is important to recall that both the natural sciences and the social sciences make valuable contributions to our understanding of mankind, and that the various features of the human mind are not shaped by either nature or nurture, but by the interaction between the two. It is also essential to keep in mind that biologically based statements on human behavior relate to the innate tendencies of the average human, and may, or may not, apply to the individual.

CHAPTER 5

The Brain:
Your Personal Necktop Computer

In these wooden figures from the Congo, the woman is equipped with an extra head for wisdom and supernatural powers.

How Do You Feel?

The brain is of paramount importance in any question regarding Darwinian happiness: It delivers agreeable and punishing sensations, and the quality of sensations delivered depends on the extent to which it has been "bruised" by a Discord life. In order to recruit the brain to serve your well-being, you ought to know a bit about how this unique organ works. Be prepared for some slightly complicated sections that deal with a fascinating topic.

This chapter and the next one deal primarily with discovering how to find the pleasing sensations the brain offers, which is the first principle of Darwinian happiness. Chapter 7 will deal with the question of consciousness, and how the brain can be bruised—the second principle of Darwinian happiness. All three chapters lean heavily on a novel field of science referred to as "affective neuroscience," which tries to understand which parts of the brain and what brain chemicals are involved in the creation of feelings. I recommend the book *Affective Neuroscience,* by the psychobiologist Jaak Panksepp, for a scholarly review of the field.[100]

Much of what we know about this subject has been learned from research on animals, particularly rats. However, the processes we understand best are much the same in all mammals, including humans, and reflect ancient forces laid down in our brain to create particular feelings or emotions. You cannot totally escape these forces, but that does not mean you have no influence on the kind of feelings aroused. The point of this book is to show that you can make a difference about how well you feel, but in order to do so, you ought to know what you are up against.

All the main features of the human brain are present in other vertebrates as well, which means that our brain anatomy resembles that of experimental animals such as rats and monkeys. The outer layer, known as the cortex, is the part of the brain where the main expansion of functions took place in the evolution of apes; it expanded even more dramatically in the hominid lineage. Cognition and conscious functions presumably rely heavily on the cortex; yet other structures hidden further inside are primarily responsible for the initiation of emotions. The answer to the question—"How do you feel?"—depends on what sensations these ancient subcortical structures initiate, and on how the higher, more cognitive functions of the cortex modulate the sensations evoked.[101]

The emotional organization of the subcortical brain is rather similar in humans and animals, but it is the cognitive modulations exerted by the cortex that add "the human touch." The cortex gives us the chance to express our free will, but it cannot turn off the underlying push of the subcortical emotional functions.

The basic unit of the brain is the nerve cell, and interactions between the individual nerve cells are responsible for the creation of both conscious and unconscious mental functions. You may consider the brain as an assemblage of nerve cell activity designed by evolution. Theoretically, if you knew the nature and relevance of each interaction, you would know what was going on; however, since there are some 50 billion cells, each connected with up to several thousand other cells, this approach would most likely just leave you miserably confused. Still, it is worthwhile to understand the "language" of nerve-cell communication.

As we shall see, the language used by the cells consists primarily of two types of systems: electrical and chemical transmission. Both systems can be hijacked in an attempt to improve Darwinian happiness, but the question remains whether this direct approach is better than the alternatives I will discuss in the next chapter.

The Language of the Brain

Before discussing the processes that take place in the brain, I shall briefly introduce the anatomy of this organ. The only thing more complex than the structure of the brain appears to be the vocabulary describing it. Not only are the names difficult to learn, but there can be several names for the same, or overlapping, features.

The most important distinction is between the cortex (the two hemispheres of convoluted tissue that dominate the human brain) and the subcortex (the inner and older structures). In some cases I do mention the names of subcomponents, and although it is not essential to be able to place these on the map, I offer the following simplified figure for those who are interested. In this figure the brain is cut along the middle and we are viewing the right half of the brain as seen from the inside. (See Figure 6, below.)

The typical nerve cell has long "arms" that stretch out to the other cells with which it interacts or, to put it more bluntly, "talks." Some arms, known as the dendrites, receive signals and send them to the main cell body, while other arms, known as axons, pass the signals on to the next cell. The transfer of signals along the arms is based on electrical principles; but in order to get the message across to a new cell, chemical messengers, called **neurotransmitters**, are required. They are discharged by the "talking" cell, and bind to the "ears" in the form of specific receptor molecules on the surface of the receiving cell.

Cortex

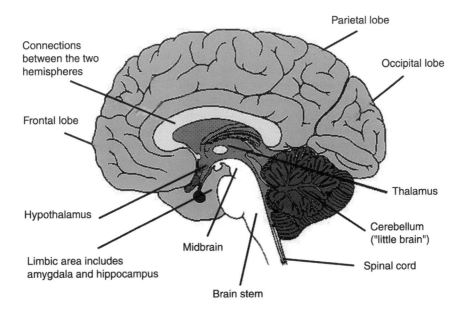

Subcortex

Figure 6. The right half of the human brain as seen when cut in the middle from the nose (left) to the back of the head. Only select parts are named.

The mechanism for electrical transmission of signals is pretty much the same in all nerve cells, including those of invertebrate animals. On the other hand there are many types of neurotransmitters, and an even greater variety of receptors and other molecules that modulate their activity; the latter are referred to as *modulators*. Thus, the defining part of neural activity is not the actual electrical signaling itself, but rather a question of which nerve cells interact, as well as the chemical characteristics of these interactions. Some neurotransmitter-receptor pairs seem to be allocated to particular functions, while others are more general-purpose.

As a gross approximation, neurotransmitters and modulators can be classified as either small molecules or peptides. Most of the small neurotransmitters, such as *glutamate, GABA, acetylcholine, dopamine, serotonin*, and *norepinephrine* appeared early in the evolution of nerve systems. They tend to be general-purpose transmitters that are active in many parts of the brain; they are still, as we shall see, important for the creation of sensations. Then, as evolution required a more fine-tuned nervous system with a larger variety of specific functions, part of the answer was presumably to design *neuropeptides*.[102]

Peptides are fragments of proteins. While it is somewhat difficult for evolution to design novel small neurotransmitters, it is easy to construct an enormous assortment of peptides. Those used by the nervous system tend to regulate particular functions, and there are at least a couple of hundred different ones active in the brain. *Endorphins*, for instance, are part of the *opioid system* and create a pleasurable sensation. Heroin, and the closely related morphine, hijack this system by binding to receptors reserved for endorphins.

The neuropeptides can serve both as neurotransmitters and as modulators. They can act locally or be transported around inside the brain. Some of them actually work both in the brain and in other organs, typically for the purpose of coordinating particular functions. Angiotensin is a characteristic example: It promotes thirst in the brain and water retention in the kidneys.

The Adaptable Processor

The genes carry a blueprint for the initial wiring of the brain—meaning the nerve cell connections that we are born with—and included in this blueprint is the design of the brain chemistry, such as neurotransmitters and receptors. This blueprint, however, allows for extensive modifications in the form of development and adaptation, which explains our ability to learn, and our capacity to be molded by the environment. Very few new nerve cells are formed after birth; thus, the alterations are provided by the death of specific cells, by changes in the connections between nerve cells or their level of activity (including an initial overproduction of connections and the subsequent removal of those that are not active), and by changes in neurochemistry. These types of alterations allow us to gather experience and wisdom. *The important point to recall is that the brain is not born in its final form, but rather designed to mature by means of interaction with the environment.*

The brain keeps up an ongoing dialogue with all parts of your body. There are two types of communication going on: One is by means of delegate nerve cells that infiltrate the various organs; the other is by means of hormones, typically in the form of peptides, transported in the blood. The intestines, for example, produce peptides that help the brain regulate our intake of food. These two forms of communication are somewhat analogous to e-mail and normal mail, respectively. The first message is fast and uses "electrical wires"; the second requires blood as a postal carrier.

To my mind, the most fascinating communication between the brain and life outside the brain involves the immune system. This communication is primarily achieved by means of peptides and proteins, and it works both ways: The brain influences the immune system, and the immune system affects the brain. As pointed out by Esther M. Sternberg in her book *The Balance Within*,[103] our understanding of this interaction goes a long way in terms of explaining why stress and emotional problems increase the likelihood of disease, and why being ill has such a dramatic effect on mental well-being—we can all recall the feeling of malaise associated with having to stay in bed with a fever. Her message is that, for both mental and physical comfort, it is advisable to adjust to our inner nature and thus retain the balance within.

It may be disheartening to be told that our thoughts, all our joys and delights, our love and hate, are no more than electro-chemical processes in the brain. Many people prefer to believe in something less subject to the vagaries of the material world: They prefer something more spiritual than a soup of chemicals. Sure, the idea of a soul makes sense. It feels good. But in the real world, the significance of the concept of a soul is just that you activate a particular subset of cells and chemicals.

We are admittedly unable to describe the exact molecular or neurological correlate for each emotion or cognitive function; yet nothing in the realm of human life is incompatible with our understanding of how the brain works. Moreover, we have actually come a long way in dissecting emotions at a molecular level. To be more specific, we know a lot about the chemicals and nerve circuitry involved in conducting various basic feelings such as joy, hunger, anger, and fear.

How Wire-Heads Exploit the Wiring of the Brain

Many scientists like to look at the brain as a toolbox in which each unit, or module, evolved to fulfill a particular function in humanity's Stone Age existence. The units operate semi-autonomously, and they presumably correspond to either distinct areas of the brain, to a more scattered but defined subset of nerve cells, or to the use of a particular "mix" in terms of neurochemistry.

The best way of describing the brain modules, which I sometimes refer to as nerve circuits, is to consider the various functions the brain has to perform. The simplified picture is somewhat like a deluxe version of the Swiss army knife—the one with five thousand pull-out functions. One unit would control the thumb of the right hand; another would process visual inputs; still another would deal with falling in love; and so on. Randolph Nesse has discussed various ways of describing brain modules.[104]

We have a detailed map of the brain that pinpoints a variety of functions. We owe this map primarily to two types of experiments: One mode of mapping is to stimulate particular regions of the brain with tiny electrodes, and to see what happens. The other mode consists of various types of computerized "scans" of the brain, in which the more active regions light up on the computer screen.

We also know a lot about the chemical workings of different brain modules. This knowledge has been obtained by experiments with chemicals that act on the neurotransmitter systems. They generally act either as *agonists*, which stimulate particular systems, or as *antagonists*, which are inhibitory.

What the brain map portrays is real, but necessarily a simplification. Rather than a Swiss army knife, we are dealing with an interacting community of modules: The screwdriver sometimes needs to cooperate with the pliers in order to complete a task; several parts are actually required to interact for anything to happen. Thus a car motor may be a more apt model than the knife; however, while each part of a car motor is designed by the manufacturer for a specific purpose, the modules of the brain evolved over millions of years. As a consequence, the brain has a much messier organization, and the design is not efficient and elegant. It looks more like an old house that has been repaired and redecorated over and over again to accommodate ever-changing styles of living. As a consequence, your brain contains elements that are obsolete. Some elements may even be maladaptive.

Goose bumps illustrate the point: They appear when you are cold or feeling threatened and are supposed to make body-hair stand erect. Their purpose is to improve the conservation of heat and to create the impression of a larger and more powerful body, respectively. It all makes good sense on an animal with fur, but human goose bumps are just funny; from a biological point of view, they look about as intelligent as a plucked chicken. Evolution apparently forgot to turn the process off when it decided to remove our fur.

In order to really appreciate what an extremely complex and powerful organ the brain is, one may think in terms of reverse engineering, as described by the psychologist Steven Pinker:[105] Reverse engineering is what you do when you take apart a gadget to try to understand how it works. The ensuing detailed knowledge on design and function is required for those who wish to construct their own gadget, or to make one with superior features. Thus, reverse engineering of the human mind is a required exercise if you wish to create a robot with human properties. You do not need to pursue this ambition very far, however, to realize that the task is immense. Any sane human being would soon give up. Even a reasonably simple assignment, such as coordinating two legs for the purpose of balance and locomotion, is almost impossible: Most robots require either three or more wheels, or four or more legs, in order to always touch the ground at three points. The more difficult assignments, such as designing a visual system that can extract all the information we so effortlessly obtain through our eyes, seem unattainable. No wonder it took our great constructor—the evolutionary process—some billion years to come up with our luxurious brain.

Then again, the product is not without flaws of design; as with the motor, each module of your brain is prone to breaking down or starting to malfunction. For example, damage to a certain area of the right side cortex can cause an inability to recognize faces (prosopagnosia); deafness can be due to impairment of the nearby auditory regions, and so on. Weaknesses in design sometimes manifest themselves as gross mental defects, such as schizophrenia and depression, that are not easily allocated to particular modules, while other types of malfunction, such as the inability to recognize faces, can be highly specific. The long list of problems and diseases involving the brain tells us a lot about which functions evolution stowed away inside our heads.

The idea that there is a weakness of design is substantiated by the fact that some people are genetically more prone to develop mental diseases than others. Those with the worst combination of genes are unlikely to avoid problems, whatever their conditions of living are; Discord conditions, however, cause people who are genetically less vulnerable to suffer as well. Presumably mental diseases occurred in the best of Stone Age communities, but because of our Discord way of living, more people suffer today.

For example, recent evidence suggests that one relevant Discord that may help explain the increase in schizophrenia is a lack of sunshine during pregnancy. Schizophrenics are born more often in the cities and more often in the early spring (in the Northern Hemisphere). Apparently too little ultraviolet (UV) radiation leads to a suboptimal concentration of vitamin D, a deficiency that may affect the developing brain of the fetus. As discussed in Chapter 2, UV-radiation promotes the formation of this vitamin. In other words, as people put on more clothes, and spent more time indoors, pregnant women did not get adequate amounts of sunshine.[106]

To the extent that the above theory is correct, it reflects a general principle that I believe is important: Here a Discord condition that most people would not perceive as troublesome, i.e., the fact that we tend to stay inside and wear more clothes during winter, has in rare cases drastic consequences. For most mothers the Discord doesn't matter. Maybe their machinery for making vitamin D is sufficiently effective to avoid any problems, or their particular fetus is less sensitive to vitamin D concentration. But when the Discord is combined with an infrequent blend of unfortunate factors (of either a genetic or an environmental sort), the situation gives rise to a lot of misery. Moreover, the problems do not arise while the Discord is taking place, but the fetus becomes predisposed for a severe mental disease that may break out many years later.

Another example involves anxiety. Apparently, if there is not sufficient activity of a particular serotonin nerve-cell receptor, at a particular stage in the early life of an infant, that child may later develop anxiety problems. (Medication that enhances the activity of serotonin is widely prescribed to treat anxiety.) At least this seems to be the case in mice. It is conceivable that the expression of the gene that codes for this receptor is sensitive to some unknown environmental stimuli. Thus, the present high rate of anxiety related disorders could be a result of unidentified Discord conditions that affect this particular receptor.[107]

I shall end this section with a more cheerful comment. The observation that functions tend to be located in particular parts of the brain led the science-fiction author, Larry Niven, to describe (in his novels) "wire-heads" as people with electrodes implanted in a reward center. Wire-heads are "hooked" (in both the direct and the indirect sense) on pleasurable stimuli that are supplied by attaching a battery to handy connection points on the top of the skull. The idea is not purely fictional; a rat with electrodes in the right spot readily learns how to press the switch to turn on the current. A simple electrical stimulation of an appropriate bundle of nerve cells is sufficient to send out a pulse of pleasure.

Instant Satisfaction

In the real world, it is impractical, at least for the time being, to implant electrodes into the human brain. Instead, people opt for the chemical approach. The use of *psychoactive* drugs, i.e., substances that exert particular effects on our minds by either inhibiting or increasing the activity of specific neurotransmitters, has a long history:[108]

Long before we learned how to brew beer and distil alcohol, we prized

Plate 7. Chemical stimulants do not appear to be a good long-term strategy for contentment.

plants that gave us a "kick." There are an estimated 10,000 species of plants and fungi that contain compounds with a known or presumed narcotic effect, some 150 of which have a record of use (or misuse, if you prefer). The list includes classics such as tobacco, coffee, cannabis, opium, coca, the peyote cactus, and the psilocybin mushroom. The more potent ones were traditionally consumed primarily in connection with religious or magical rites.

Many of these substances—such as heroin, which is derived from the opium poppy—delight laboratory animals as well. These drugs obviously deliver pleasure, so why not use them? In order to reach a personal stance on psychoactive drugs, it is useful to know something about how they function.

There are two main questions to be answered: Why does the brain bless you with agreeable sensations in the first place, and how do the drugs take charge of the relevant brain modules?

The "why" question is the easy one to answer: Pleasure indicates that something is biologically useful; it is nature's way of informing you that whatever is happening is (supposedly) to your advantage. As a gross approximation we can distinguish between two types of situations or stimuli that yield pleasure:

The first type occurs in situations that promote survival. This typically implies that you return any bodily imbalance toward an optimal level of functioning, such as nourishment when you are hungry, warmth when you are cold, and safety when you are in danger. In other words, stimuli that promote *homeostasis* (the tendency to maintain physiological parameters in the body, such as temperature) are experienced as pleasurable, while those that impair homeostasis are unpleasant. Obviously a particular stimulation can be interpreted as being either positive or negative; for instance, a cool room is pleasant or unpleasant depending on whether you are warmer or colder than the ideal temperature of 37°C (100°F). Which is why you sell air conditioners in Texas and saunas in Alaska, and not vice versa. Similarly, a delicious cream cake is just nauseating if you have diarrhea, because under those circumstances it is not good for your stomach. The second type concerns procreation; anything having to do with falling in love, sex, and caring for children is great.

You do not need to be a biologist to see the logic of why evolution gave us pleasure to stimulate behavior appropriate for survival and procreation.

The "how question" is more difficult to answer and we are only just beginning to understand it. It is, however, an important issue, because how the brain actually delivers all these delights has a bearing on how best to exploit the system. The more pronounced pleasant experiences are presumably the consequence of the activation of either of two loosely defined modules of the brain: The one module, referred to alternatively as *wanting*, seeking, or desiring, has to do with motivating us to go out and capture some of the "goodies" in our environment. The function of the module is to wet the appetite and to energize the mind and the body for the task ahead. The other module, which has been referred to as the *liking* or consummation-associated pleasure, makes the actual intake a gratifying experience.[109] Thus, whatever your genes may have in mind—a cupcake in order to improve energy balance or an orgasm as a ticket in the lottery of eternal existence—you are rewarded not only for the consumption, but also for the desire. Just try to recall how you felt when you first smelled the bakery around the corner.

Various programs in the brain have access to these rewards. The button for the "wanting" module can either be pushed by bodily needs, as in the case of thirst, or by environmental incentives, such as the sight of a ripe strawberry. The "liking" button is pushed when your genes get what they set you up to obtain.

One interesting and important point is that the two buttons are served by different chemical neurotransmitters, and that these can be pushed independently by particular drugs. "Wanting" primarily involves the neurotransmitter dopamine, active in a part of the subcortical brain referred to as the hypothalamus, which is located in the center of the head just between your ears. Amphetamine and cocaine push this button. Less is known about the "liking"-system. The final rewards for food, sex, and sunbathing may converge on a single structure, or may be delegated to different parts of the brain. We do know, however, that opioid neurotransmitters, such as endorphins, are involved in a variety of rewards: They presumably signal that your bodily needs are in the process of being satisfied. Injected opiates, such as heroin or morphine, emit the same signal.

Of all the surrogates designed to harvest pleasurable sensations, narcotics are the most spectacular. They make other stimuli seem as sophisticated, and potent, as rubber nipples. It is the extreme way of fooling your genes. By hitting hard on the reward buttons, cocaine and heroin make your brain assume that you are doing the right thing—that you are in for a huge benefit of fitness.

Okay, my genes may loath getting duped by some simple chemicals, but it is *my* brain, and *my* Darwinian happiness that is at stake, so why not? If the genes dislike it, they can go and crash somewhere else! Unfortunately, although narcotics can boost your immediate measure of delight, the long-term effect tends to be more negative. The snag can be ascribed to the Discord nature of taking drugs. For instance, psychoactive substances act, directly or indirectly, on a variety of nerve circuitry. Vital organs such as the heart and the lungs require nerve functions. The wrong dose, at the wrong time, may do such nasty tricks as stopping these organs, which will most certainly not boost your future prospects of Darwinian happiness.

Although lethal overdoses are reasonably rare incidents, narcotics can reduce your desire for important life-sustaining things, such as food and warmth. This may not matter much in the short run, but in the long run, it is not just your genes that are duped. If given the choice, mice hooked on cocaine take the drug rather than food—up to the point that they may starve to death.

There are other problems as well. Bear in mind that, unlike your car, the brain is designed to be molded by use. The "wanting" and "liking" buttons are neatly designed for natural doses of stimuli; if you push them too often or too hard, the underlying nerve circuitry will change. It will try to adapt. And one way of adapting is to stop reacting, which is why many addicts require increasing doses.

Moreover, in connection with homeostasis, there is a tendency for the brain to sense differences rather than absolute values. In the middle of the night a small flashlight offers sufficient illumination, while during the daytime, the flashlight would hardly be noticed. A similar situation seems to exist for joy and sorrow. In order to be really joyful, the feeling should follow a period of gloom, which is another reason why it is difficult to experience continuous euphoria even with the help of potent chemicals. The point is also relevant when it comes to understanding how happiness, or well being, is distributed in the population. When examining various subpopulations (based on age, sex, race, or financial status) in affluent societies, they tend to be, on the average, about equally happy, because we all circle around the same capacity for joy and sorrow. What may vary, however, is the amplitude of the shifts from happy to sad. For example, age tends to iron out the highs and the lows.[110]

It is also possible for parts of the nerve circuitry to become revved up. This appears to be the case when addicts develop a compulsive desire: The "wanting" and "liking" modules get "hooked on stimuli" and make you take more. Many addicts claim they no longer derive subjective pleasure from the drugs; yet they are nevertheless compelled to take them, which suggests that the brain can separate the craving from the positive sensations. And worse, if the drugs are no longer delivered, rather uncomfortable experiences, generally referred to as withdrawal symptoms, set in. In these cases the benefit to Darwinian happiness has long since vanished.

One of the main points I wish to make here is that there are many ways to push the buttons of pleasure; you do not require drugs to do the job. Besides, drugs hammer on the buttons. It is like using a sledgehammer on the keys of a piano; at first you create overwhelming sounds, but eventually the piano is ruined, and silent. Furthermore, the drugs may leave a mark, a scar in your nerve circuitry, making it difficult to appreciate natural agreeable stimuli.

Another important point is that the "wanting" and the "liking" systems are not alone in determining how you feel. You do not spend most of the day eating cupcakes or flirting with (wo)men. The conscious processes of the cortex, as well as all the other emotional modules in the subcortex, have a lot to say about your mood. For example, pleasant emotions appear to correlate with arousal of the left frontal lobe of the cortex, while arousal on the right side of the forehead correlates with gloom. Moreover, the default good mood probably does not reside in a particular part of the brain, but is rather a question of a "happiness tonus" involving several modules and several neurotransmitters.

Emotions such as anxiety and sadness certainly have the capacity to ruin your share of happiness. Valium, for instance, improves the quality of life for people suffering from anxiety by boosting the GABA neurotransmitter system. Likewise other medicines, such as Prozac, improve the mood of patients suffering from depression by increasing the activity of the neurotransmitter serotonin. To use psychoactive agents prescribed by a doctor is obviously safer than taking street narcotics, and designer drugs are generally safer than natural products. After all, plants typically manufacture psychoactive substances in order to poison or deter creatures tempted to eat them—not to boost the mood of emotionally disturbed humans.

Yet, all psychoactive substances have potential benefits as well as a host of more or less well-known pitfalls. Since the right dose at the right time may work wonders, it is difficult to argue against restricted use for the purpose of improving Darwinian happiness. I guess the main argument for abstinence (or caution) is that certain substances, such as heroin, have a rather bad track record, and the pleasure easily leads to misery. Even for many of the less risky narcotics and prescription drugs, it has proven rather difficult to restrain use to a level that guarantees a long-term net benefit.

Western societies have selected alcohol, nicotine, and caffeine as their legal favorites, and have banned most alternatives, except for those prescribed by doctors. The choice is not necessarily that brilliant. When considering the potential for inducing pleasant sensations, weighed against the negative effects of the substances, it is not obvious that these preferences should top the list of preferred psychoactive substances. For example, many people consider alcohol to be more toxic, and to have a less desirable effect, than marijuana.[111]

In order to predict the possible usefulness of psychoactive drugs—whether illegal, legal, or prescription—it may be practical to divide people into three groups: The first consists of those who are advised to take medication due to a clinical diagnosis of, for instance, phobia or depression. The second group is made up of reasonably healthy individuals who are unable to find the default good mood of the mind; they may generally benefit from drugs, but are vulnerable to the pitfalls. I would identify a third group as more or less able to retain the default good mood and therefore unlikely to benefit much from either cocaine, heroin, Valium, or Prozac. In other words, drugs may make apparently normal people feel "better than well"—because the average person in modern society starts out with a "less than well" mental state—but drugs are unlikely to surpass our natural propensity for happiness. If we can find the state of default good mood, and learn to enjoy natural stimuli, I believe drugs will have much less to offer us.

Adverse consequences of narcotics have become a major problem in many countries, and the statement in the previous sentence suggests that if people were more satisfied, the gain in delight experienced when taking drugs would be smaller. Thus, more content people should translate into fewer problems associated with the abuse of narcotics. I believe one step in this direction would be to create a society designed with reference to our genetic inheritance.

Most stimuli that push the "wanting" or "liking" reward buttons can, to a certain extent, act somewhat like narcotics. Overindulgence, for instance, in food and shopping, can lead to a consumption beyond what is healthy. What is more, it can lead to a compulsive desire partly uncoupled from rewarding sensations—in other words, to an addiction. In a natural setting it would simply be impossible to obtain the kind of doses you can gorge on today. As in the case of narcotics, the present availability of potent stimuli is a Discord situation. If you let your sexual desires, or your craving for money, or the wish for new clothes, get in charge of your mind, you become obsessed and won't stop sensing other pleasurable stimuli; and even the ones you really crave will not necessarily give you that much joy anymore. The long-term effects on the nerve circuitry are likely to be negative. You are therefore advised to be careful about how you feed your desires, and to avoid getting hooked on particular types of stimuli to the extent that fulfilling them becomes compulsive. Even television can be addictive.[112]

Hedonism had a heyday in ancient Greece, but it did not last. A society that pushes too hard for gratification may seem like paradise for a while, but sooner or later the most unexpected bills are bound to pop up. Yet hedonism seems to be on the move again. We are more or less poorly adapted, but we still have great expectations regarding life. We want pleasures, all sorts of them, and materialism and narcotics are the preferred "fast-food" types of solutions.[113]

Cosmetic Psychopharmacology

Pharmacological research continues. The billion-dollar question is still whether it will be possible to create an ideal psychoactive drug—a drug that just makes you happy, with no adverse consequences.

As we learn more about the chemical workings of the mind, we may be able to devise compounds that hit the targets more accurately. However, if you administer a substance that affects a certain neurotransmitter-receptor-modulator combination, it will affect all the nerve-cell connections that make use of that particular type of chemical communication, and therefore all functions that involve these connections. Thus, whether we can make drugs with specific actions depends on the extent to which the relevant brain modules are distinguished chemically, or distinguished by the wiring of the nerve cells. (Alternatively, we need to find a practical way of administrating drugs to particular nerve circuits.)

The psychoactive ingredient of cannabis, THC, illustrates the point. It is known for its ability to enhance certain feelings: Music becomes more melodious, food more tasty, and art more artistic, while pain is reduced. That is why cannabis has been prescribed to improve appetite and lessen the suffering in people with diseases such as AIDS and cancer.

THC can have a desirable effect on your mood, but it also affects attention and learning: You become unable to complete a string of thoughts. The effects on attention could be an indirect consequence of mood enhancement, but the problem would also appear if THC disturbs a single messenger-receptor pair that is involved in both functions. There is a third possibility: The attention effect could be a consequence of THC acting on more than one messenger-receptor pair (there are at least two different receptors that THC can bind to in the brain). Only to the extent that the latter option is correct, will it be possible to design modified versions of THC with more specific euphoric action.[114]

Some people see visions of a future where we are able to chemically interfere with any mental condition. All you need is the right pill. Any emotional module, anything from impulsive shopping to logical thinking or enjoying flowers, can be obliterated or stimulated; we will stop thinking in terms of sick or healthy minds, and instead ask what sort of personality or emotion we prefer for the day. Fine-tuned chemicals catering to reward mechanisms would be only one item on the menu. You may decide that it is the day for melancholy, or for being an extrovert; or you would choose to add some drops of chastity in order to convince your new boyfriend that you are still a virgin.

Right there, in the most visible part of the supermarket, near Coca-Cola and not too far from the potatoes, you will find the shelf for cosmetic psychopharmacology.[115] Is this scenario likely? And if so, is it desirable?

I believe it will prove difficult to create electrical or chemical stimulants that have the required specificity, simply because the human brain is probably not sufficiently organized into distinct units. Moreover, no two individuals are exactly alike; what helps one person may cause havoc to another. The use of drugs is necessarily a Discord: They cause habituation, some of them with rather drastic withdrawal effects, and it is hard to predict what they will do to you the next time, or what the long-term consequences may be. Thus, although we already have a variety of drugs that are of obvious benefit in particular situations, including pain relievers and sleeping pills, chemistry is unlikely to be the solution for implementing universal happiness.

Nowadays you offer your guests tea or coffee, or perhaps for the more frivolous, whisky or cognac. In future, will you set the table with pills and batteries? Cheap, clean, easy. It saves washing the dishes. Your guru is tempted, but, on second thought, the guru recommends a glass of water.

Summary

Basically, your measure of Darwinian happiness is related to the activity of a single organ—your brain. Whether you are concerned with the pain of a thorn in your toe, or the delight of a delicious meal, the feelings reflect processes going on inside your head. Moreover, it is important to note that much of what you experience can be graded on a scale from positive to negative. And how you feel—that is, where on the continuum from suicidal to ecstatic you spend your life—is of obvious importance for your quality of life.

In this chapter I have tried to explain some of our knowledge about how the brain operates in general, and the neurological correlates of pleasant and unpleasant feelings in particular. This information should be useful for later chapters, where I shall occasionally refer to what is known about neurotransmitters and brain anatomy in regard to various innate tendencies. However, the less technically inclined reader may appreciate that this information is not essential to an understanding of the text.

As I have tried to convey in the present chapter, neurology is highly relevant when reflecting on the various "shortcuts" that promise to move you up the scale toward positive sensations. Narcotics, for instance, may do so, but, as should be obvious, you are advised to exercise extreme care when dealing with such chemical strategies. There are a lot of other approaches that reach for the coveted sensations in ways that offer much better prospects for long-term happiness.

In the next chapter I shall discuss some of these options.

CHAPTER 6

Rewards:
Use Your Head—That's What It's There For

What is the head for?

Fun Taken Seriously

A recurrent topic in this book is how to get the most out of your brain—in other words, how to recruit it for the benefit of your measure of Darwinian happiness. If chemicals are not an advisable strategy, what else can we do? I shall use this chapter to deliberate on a couple of the many alternatives we have.

Playing is not for fun. In fact, it is dangerous (some 80 percent of deaths among juvenile fur seals occur because playing pups fail to spot predators), and it is expensive in terms of energy. (The additional cost has been calculated at two to three percent of energy consumption in typical animals while up to 15 percent in humans.) Evolution did not invent this form of behavior just to please you. It is fun to play because games and related diversions serve a function: The genes have connected playful behavior with rewards, because it is in their interest that you participate. The real purpose of games is development and bonding; they are meant to teach your mind and body tasks the genes assume are required for survival, including social skills. Play is a question of molding your unfinished brain. It is important for the genes that you improve your nerve circuitry, such as the circuitry required for muscle coordination; thus, relevant exercises are rewarded. And in a social species such as humans, play behavior is presumably meant not just to teach you how to behave socially, but to help create long lasting affiliations.[116]

As already noted, the brain is designed to be molded by experience: Play is a special form of experience invented by evolution. Moreover, play is candy for the brain, and you are advised to help yourself to the bag. The larger bag of candy is up for grabs by children. It has been shown that the developmental timing of play behavior in animals such as mice, cats, antelopes, and baboons coincides with the postnatal window in which most changes in the brain take place.[117] The brain also compensates adults with rewarding sensations, but children have more need to learn, and are hence rewarded with more intense pleasure.

Your son's eyes may not reflect this fact the fifth time you command him to do his homework: Lessons at a typical primary school are not what the genes envisioned when they tell children to go and play. Unfortunately, normal play behavior does not teach infants the particular (and biologically "bizarre") knowledge required in a modern society. It would be highly desirable, but rather difficult, to create a school that tutors in a way that utilizes the innate inclination of children to learn by playing. Actually, primary schools tend to involve a Discord, inasmuch as they obstruct natural play behavior; thus, we seem to be moving toward the "playless society." If schools managed to accommodate their way of teaching to our innate tendencies for play, not only would children learn more easily, but the negative consequences of the Discord would diminish.

Plate 8. Typical play is social, and the desire to play is designed to yield a fun version of skills required for adult life.

Genes do have a variety of opinions about what they prefer you to spend your time practicing. For instance, girls and boys tend to play different games: While the average girl prefers role play, amusing herself with dolls, the typical boy desires more physical action. For a biologist this comes as no surprise; after all, girls are (on average) expected to be more tuned to caring for babies and boys more into hunting as well as to a hierarchy based on physical power.[118]

Play seems to be pretty much a mammalian invention. As with humans, the playful behavior of animals reflects skills required by adult members of the species: Kittens enjoy catching moving objects because one day they will rely on this skill to obtain food. The foal delights in running. To eat grass does not require vigorous practice, but to escape predators demands speed and a steady foot. Female lion cubs are at least as keen on mock fighting as their brothers, because for lions hunting is primarily the female's job.

Mock fighting, or rough-and-tumble play, is actually one of the most important forms of play in many species. It is also the kind of play we understand best, since it can easily be studied in laboratory animals. One important function of mock fighting is probably of a social nature; the "fights" not only teach the individual how to interact with others, but they also help weave individuals into the social fabric. In species such as rats and humans, the bonds that are formed tend to indicate a subtle hierarchy: Of two individuals playing, one will end up on top most of the time. However, successful play requires the stronger one to occasionally take the role of the underdog: The desired outcome is not a variation of the "master-servant" theme, but rather that of almost equal comrades. This sort of amusement also educates the individual in dealing with emotions, and it reveals an intimate knowledge of the personality of those one is expected to depend upon in adult life.

Simple touching or tickling may actually be the key to unlocking the nerve circuitry of play in animals as far apart as rats and humans; both have specialized ticklish zones in the neck and the upper part of the torso.[119] Touching these areas on another individual is part of a behavioral routine: The response is laughter and further physical play, and the underlying intention is to develop attachment—particularly in the case of infants and their parents. Chimpanzees are not that different from us. Chimp play starts with mother-infant interactions: The mother tickles the infant with her hands or her mouth. Their play-face is characteristic and easily understood, even by a human observer. In fact, too little tickling may be a Discord. The caretakers of a group of abandoned orangutan infants in Indonesia say they make sure to tickle the animals ten minutes each day. Maybe some human children could do with a bit more tickling, too.

You cannot tickle yourself, simply because the system is designed for interaction with others. This is partially achieved by the fact that you are unable to fool your brain into not knowing what your hands are up to; therefore, however ticklish you may be, your own fingers cannot do the trick because your brain is aware that it is not somebody else touching you. On the other hand, just to expect to be the victim of a tickle-attack may be sufficient to trigger a response. It is possible to initiate laughter just by putting on a play-face and moving your hands slowly toward the ticklish zones of another person.

The pleasure of play is at least partly due to the release of opioids inside your brain. Neurotransmitters that activate the brain, such as glutamate, can intensify play behavior, while the more inhibitory transmitters, such as serotonin and GABA, tend to reduce willingness to play.[120] Furthermore, play requires the right environment for full expression: Feelings such as fear and hunger will drastically reduce playful behavior and, of course, restrict the harvesting of relevant rewards.

I assume that most parents prefer their kids to enter a mock fight rather than to take a shot of heroin. Unfortunately, parents and kindergarten teachers often seem to treat both options with about the same aversion: Boys are not supposed to fight. Nevertheless, rough-and-tumble play is an important innate behavioral tendency, and to suppress this activity is Discord, and can have unwarranted consequences.

Jaak Panksepp has suggested that Attention Deficit Hyperactivity Disorder (ADHD) may be due to an over-activity in play behavior circuits.[121] This child disorder is characterized by an inability to sit still and concentrate on a given matter (e.g., lessons in a classroom). It is interesting to note that rats deprived of rough-and-tumble play become extra playful when given the chance; their need for this activity seems to build up. The same phenomenon may explain ADHD. To sit still in a classroom is not exactly what a child is designed for in the first place, and to be deprived of physical play makes the situation even more unfortunate. Amphetamine, which is used to treat the condition, reduces playfulness in animals and in children. I believe that time off for relevant play behavior, perhaps before school starts, may be a better option than to prescribe amphetamine.

It is tempting to rephrase Shakespeare and state, "To play or not to play—that is the question."

Why Smile and Laugh?

The most overt signs of children playing are smiles and laughter. It makes sense to display anger; a good manifestation of anger scares away enemies, and helps you climb the social ladder. Your genes may even appreciate your display of suffering, as a distressed individual stands a better chance of obtaining help. But why on earth should we laugh?

Growling, crying, and whining are expressions that we share with many other animals, but correlates to laughter are less obvious. If everything is fine, you might think the best you can do for your genes is to keep quiet, and hope that nothing happens to change the situation. Loud vocalization is to ask for something to happen. What if a hungry lion happens to be listening?

The phrase "I laughed so hard I cried" may point to a possible explanation for the evolution of laughter. Laughter and crying are not as different as you may think. Both reactions include an open mouth with the corners pulled back, a tendency to sweat, and a vocalization that constrains breathing. And, as the phrase indicates, laughter may even bring tears to your eyes. The difference, which makes it possible to distinguish between the two, is that in the lustrous form we pull the corners of the mouth upward. The use of these muscles, which are the same as those used for smiling, combined with minor adjustments of other parts of the response, transform the misery signal into something joyous.

As parents know very well, we begin this life as expert criers; smiles and laughter appear later, and in that order. So when does a child laugh? Laughter is typically brought out when the stimuli include a combination of pleasure and fright, such as when the mother suddenly hides her face and then reappears saying "peek-a-boo." This is a mixture of one stimulus (the disappearance of the mother) that calls for crying, and another signal (her reappearance) that calls for a smile. The sum of these two is laughter.

According to the zoologist Desmond Morris, who is one of the pioneers in understanding human behavior from a biological perspective, laughter evolved for a particular function.[122] It used the smile and the cry as an evolutionary scaffold. Smiling was already an important socializing signal; when combined with crying it became a signal for interactive play, a type of behavior meant to further strengthen social ties. Laughter possibly first evolved to strengthen the ties between children and parents, but was subsequently adopted to serve a similar function amongst children as well as amongst adults.

Most social mammals have play signals. In species such as rats and chimpanzees, we actually see vocalization and facial signals reminiscent of our laughter. According to Jaak Panksepp, even rats do "laugh" when they are tickled, but at a frequency we are unable to hear.[123] The situations that bring out laughter can be described as containing an element of danger in a safe and social context—for example, when a father throws his child in the air in order to (hopefully) catch it, or when riding a roller coaster. Tickling is a comforting touch with an apparent sting: It includes elements of both grooming and an attack on a vulnerable spot, and is a mixture of danger and positive socializing—as mentioned above.

Although human laughter may be a uniquely human feature, related play signals have a long evolutionary history. The idea that laughter evolved from the combination of smiling and crying signals (the latter often referred to as separation calls) is further substantiated by the observation that all three are associated with closely related parts of the brain. In fact, there is a rare disease referred to as "pathological laughter and crying," where the patients are subject to a defect in an element that controls both laughter and crying.[124] Moreover, bonobos and chimpanzees present similar faces when scared as when happy, presumably because fearful situations often call for appeasement and the happy face promotes positive relations.[125] The observation further strengthens the idea that fear signals (such as crying in humans) and socializing signals (such as smiles and laughter) are related.

The first smiles of a baby are directed at the face of the mother, or anything remotely similar, such as a mouth and eyes drawn on cardboard. In babies the smile is a reflex; they know nothing about what a smile is or how it functions, but eventually learn what good can come to a person who grins. We also learn that we can choose to smile. Actually, some rare neurological conditions indicate that different parts of the brain are involved in spontaneous smiles as opposed to forced smiles. The capacity for spontaneous smiles is lost in patients with particular subcortical lesions, while patients with certain cortical lesions have problems with smiling on demand.[126]

It is interesting to note that great acting talent is required to make a convincing smile (it is particularly difficult to force the eyes into a grin), while it is relatively easy to appear angry. Both the capacity to form facial displays, and the capacity to read faces, are laid down in our genes. When you see an angry expression, it means you should be careful, regardless whether it is for real or is just a person trying to bluff you. Outside the theater there is not much reason to act angry when anger is not called for. On the other hand, if you mistake a false smile for a real one, you may get tricked into some serious trouble. Evolution therefore presumably put more effort into teaching us to distinguish between real and fake grins.

Smiles and laughter are undoubtedly among the more happy solutions devised by evolution; they are normally accompanied by ample rewards from the brain. It should, however, be mentioned that certain epilepsy patients smile and laugh spontaneously—without feeling any obvious joy. Thus, the modules that direct the overt signals can be activated without eliciting distinct pleasure. In fact, electrical stimuli to the relevant brain centers will even cause smiles and laughter that may, or may not, include pleasure.[127] Fortunately for most people, smiles and laughter are excellent sources of Darwinian happiness. And, fortunately, neither module is restricted to infants: The smile is the most important welcome signal in our species. It works equally well in Zanzibar as in Katmandu or Bergen.

Laughter is less suitable as a welcome signal, since it is also related to fear and crying. A meeting with a stranger is associated with a touch of uncertainty, and it is therefore important to have a signal that will not be misinterpreted in a negative direction. The smile does the job because it is our original disarmament signal. Laughter is for signaling play and thus for improving relationships among people who already know each other.

To laugh together with others is reassuring. Laughing *at* somebody, however, has a negative content: To giggle not only suggests that the person in question is strange, but also that he has a low status and is of no potential danger. He is not even worth trying to scare with a grim face. Professional clowns bring out our companionship by making us laugh together at their expense.

We rarely smile or laugh much when alone, since these functions are there for social purposes. In order to harvest a full dose of accompanying rewards, we need company, which is why TV comedies are typically filmed in front of a live audience, or, at least, pretend to be. The viewer can join in with the laughter on the sound track.

The importance of social connections in humans implies that evolution at one point had to boost the glue designed to strengthen genial relations. Smiles and laughter are part of that glue. Surveys show that we are ten times more likely to be seen sharing a moment of laughter than any other form of emotion.[128] Scientists who take laughter seriously, such as the neurobiologist Robert Provine, have found that we giggle at almost anything when in the right social setting. Provine points out that the average "joke" has the qualities of an awkward TV soap opera scripted by an extremely untalented writer. Barely humorous banter incites most of our laughter, which makes sense, when realizing that the purpose is not primarily to prove intellectual brilliance, but simply to form social ties.[129] Thus, neither children nor grown-ups need fancy toys or clever comedians; we can all extract the joy of smiles and laughter from minuscule clues—as long as the social setting is right. And so we should, as this is an excellent source of Darwinian happiness.

An Adult Diversion

We are childish creatures: Humans spend some 20 percent of their lifetime as adolescents, compared to five percent in most mammals.

When most of us do eventually grow up, we may lose our capacity to delight in mock fighting, and it takes a little bit more to elicit smiles and laughter, but we have other ways to harvest rewards. I shall briefly comment on one of the many options—namely learning, since it is related to play behavior.

Learning is related to what students of animal behavior call exploratory behavior. Play behavior and exploratory behavior are presumably independent but related modules of mammalian brains.[130] They are both about gaining skills and knowledge; that is, putting more "goodies" into the brain circuitry. The former of these two is tuned to the needs of children, the latter gains in importance as we mature; thus, the more purposeful effort of studying is typical for adults.

Certain animals are specialists. Cows and anteaters exemplify the specialist's strategy: They concentrate on a limited range of sensory impressions, such as those relevant for evaluating the quality of grass, or for finding ants. Humans are quite the opposite: We are opportunists and specialists in the field of non-specializing. For an opportunist, any information is potentially relevant, at least the genes are inclined to assume so. We are therefore stimulus-hungry and ready to extract all sorts of data from our surroundings. As a consequence, we may delight in mastering anything from Hebrew to human behavioral biology. We also enjoy exploring new places, from the fashion shops of London to the ice-shelf of Greenland. We delight in finding a new restaurant (even when not hungry) and a quiet place in the park (even when we have no time to sit around and relax).

Most people are at some point compelled to take part in training and education. If you are able to tune into the pleasure that should accompany this activity, you will not only do better, but you will also add to your harvest of Darwinian delight. Even if education and exploration are not just for fun, they certainly can be fun: The guru advises you to exercise your brain. The rewards offered adults may be less obvious than the joys associated with the play of children, but you are nevertheless advised to seek them out and to nurture them.

The delight adults take in learning, I do believe, is related to both exploration and to a desire that, to the dismay of parents, is even less typical for the infant: Adults take pleasure in doing something "useful." We gather food or other practical items, knit sweaters, rework our home, and cook dinners. The motivating forces behind many adult activities include a combination of utility, real or imagined, and the development of skills. Exactly which activities are considered useful obviously depend a lot on cultural factors, but most people are able to think of some relevant alternatives.[131] The optimal experience, according to Csikszentmihalyi, is to find activities that you really get involved in, whether you consider them work or leisure, as opposed to activities that tend to inactivate your mind and body.[132] As with most reward mechanisms, it is possible to fool the genes. You may enjoy fishing, even if your family refuses to eat fish; and your girlfriend will happily complete the sweater she is knitting, even if you are about to move to Tahiti. We certainly have an inclination to hoard food and tools, but people also collect buttons and butterflies, even though they are as nutritious as mud, and as useful as sandals on the

North Pole. And why not? If it increases your measure of Darwinian happiness, just do it.

An Option for the Modern Person

Mock fighting has been described as a joyful social exchange with a competitive edge; a highly popular modern version is called sports. For children this is the most adult form of play; for adults it is the most playful diversion. Although the more spontaneous play activity probably serves children best, sports present grown-ups with an excellent opportunity for joy. As we shall see, participation offers a variety of rewards, and I am not even thinking about medals and prize money.

In your mind you may think in terms of muscles and stamina when you practice in order to excel at sports. Actually, the brain is the principal target for many forms of exercise. The power of your muscles may improve, but that is typically of limited value unless your brain learns how to control them. Most great athletes are distinguished not so much by their brawn as by their dexterity, the fine-tuned control of arms and legs: It is the brain, not the legs or arms, that requires the most practice to perform a triple somersault or to deliver a golf ball to the correct spot.[133]

A typical problem for the athlete is that precision tends to decrease rapidly as you approach the maximum force the muscles can exert: The "noise" associated with nerve-cell communication increases as the brain sends stronger signals to ensure a more powerful movement. It is therefore difficult to utilize both brute force and exact coordination at the same time. Tasks that require muscle power combined with precision, such as gymnastics or pole vaulting, need extensive practice to overcome this problem. Again this is primarily a question of improving your brain.

What I am trying to say is that one of the many rewards available for the athlete is related to learning. The genes encourage you to exercise inasmuch as they assume it will improve your fitness to rehearse any trick you are capable of performing. There were no snowboards in the Stone Age, yet the genes want you to learn to run the slopes because coordination and balance are considered useful skills that are worth an investment of time and energy for the purpose of improvement.

Although most forms of exercise can be rewarding, it is useful to look at what sort of physical activity our genes are presumably prepared for: Life in the Stone Age involved more activity than most people get today. A typical day for a hunter-gatherer might have included a long trek, the picking of edible plants, bursts of rapid running, and occasionally throwing a spear at a potential meal.

The most vigorous actions were presumably associated with hunting. Most sports include elements related to the hunt, such as moving fast, hitting a target, or fighting; thus, sports may serve either as pretended practice for the hunt, or as a surrogate.[134] The presumed importance of wild game for Stone Age subsistence suggests that a reasonable reward should be forthcoming in either case. This is what the genes expect, and it is quite different from the monotonous hard labor of the farmer, or the six hours of intense daily practice by the Olympic champion.

Of course, for most people sport is just another way of fooling their genes. The best way to catch food is to slowly walk down the aisles of a supermarket; and the only thing that is hit is your wallet. But who cares, your genes do not know what a supermarket is. You may still enjoy improving your competence as a hunter by participating in throwing the javelin or running the hurdles.

To occasionally move faster and farther than just from the refrigerator to the dining table should improve your Darwinian happiness. Practicing to become the world champion in a sprint, however, tends to involve a Discord, as it requires larger doses, and more specialized forms, of exercise than your body was originally designed for. But then again, to participate competitively in sports offers rewards that may compensate for the element of Discord, such as the pleasures of achievement and success.

Our delight in competition, and particularly in winning, also has a lot to do with status: The genes reward you for any attempt to move up the social ladder. Actually, both the play behavior of children and the sports of adults are ways of socializing that typically include a competitive edge. There are obvious rewards to be extracted from both the status-seeking part and the social part.

It is worth noting that at least some of the rewards from sport are a result of the release of natural opioids such as endorphins.[135] The boost in endorphins explains the "high" of the long distance runner, but it is possible to measure an elevated level even after a short burst of physical activity. The endorphin reward is presumably not designed to induce you to practice; the effect is more likely related to the adrenaline kick I have described earlier. Your brain assumes that you will only run fast if this is important for survival. In such situations it is essential to be motivated enough to squeeze the last ounce of effort out of your body—to give it, so to speak, your best shot—and at the same time to remain in an optimistic mood. I believe this to be one function of endorphins: to induce a cheerful optimism, and at the same time to quell the pain signals coming from a body that protests against extreme toil.

The number of people involved in competitions testifies to the potential of sports in eliciting positive sensations. For the average office worker and television slave, on the other hand, the main motivation for exertion is probably not the pleasure of using the body, but rather the status and the joy associated with better health and improved looks. Unfortunately, the delights of exercising your body are less obvious than the delights of eating an ice-cream cone. Those who rarely train just do not see, or feel, the point. For the enthusiast, however, the satisfaction is familiar, and research has shown that exercise indeed makes you more content.[136]

In a gym I saw a sign stating that exercise can benefit your self-esteem, reduce stress and blood pressure, enrich your sex life, improve your relationships at work, and make you a better person. That should cover most desires. But then farther inside the gym there was another sign: "No pain, no gain." The main gain in health is actually obtained with modest doses of training. Enough exercise to speed up your pulse and make you sweat, repeated a few times a week, will probably do. There is no reason to refrain from the benefits of improved health and looks, but if you keep exercising, you may eventually come to appreciate the pleasure of physical activity, not just the pain. In that case all the other benefits are pure bonus.

The Ultimate Surrogate

One of the nice things about your genes is that they are so easily fooled. If there is nothing you wish to learn, no games to play, and you really dislike the idea of sweating, it is still possible to harvest Darwinian happiness while leaning back in a comfortable chair with your eyes closed.

The first surrogate devised by mankind may still be the most precious we have: It has the advantage of being freely available in unlimited quantities, and it neither disturbs the environment, nor is likely to destroy your brain. Although misuse may occur, it is as safe as any stimuli will ever be. Your fantasy, that is to say your capacity for daydreaming, is a true source of Darwinian delight.

You may enjoy daydreaming about being a hero and earning the admiration of others, or you might pretend to be the queen of the dance, or you may conjure up sexual fantasies that may bring you untold sexual delights. The brain willingly hands out rewards. Children appear to be the experts in this field, but the power is not lost in adults—although present Western culture may not be optimal for supporting this possibly unique, human capacity.[137]

Daydreams do not require you to spend any money, but that does not mean there is no profit to be made from them. Books and films are a major industry, and they are based on the fabulous capacity of our brains to move into a virtual reality. Although these products may feed your fantasies, they will (I hope) not make your fantasies dependent on external stimuli.

People everywhere demand more money and more things to buy. This is unfortunate because the consequences of satisfying the material desires of six billion humans will necessarily hurt the environment. The message that should go out is that much of the pleasures the brain offers can be accessed without opening your purse. Exercise and fantasies are just two out of the many options that satisfy this criterion.

Fantasies, nonetheless, can turn into an addiction and serve you poorly. If love and sex were fueled solely by internal stimuli, you might avoid certain bad experiences, and a few bugs, but you would also miss out on a lot. Yet I believe your internal guru agrees with what the gurus of India claimed thousands of years ago: Happiness can be achieved by promoting what is already inside you—by seeking the default good mood, and by hitting the reward buttons with "the power of the mind."

Summary

The main point I try to make in this chapter is that by exercising your faculties, which means using your head (and sometimes your body as well), you should improve your quality of life. The snappy version of the advice reads: Use your head for what it is designed for. In the long run this strategy ought to beat any drug use. Some of the more obvious options for harvesting rewards—such as sex, love, and social life—are covered in later chapters. Here I have restricted myself to the discussion of a particular set of opportunities, which can be roughly categorized as play, learning, sport, and (last but not least) daydreaming. These options have been chosen because they are illustrative, and because they point toward a way of thinking, namely to use the faculties already installed in your head. In this book I do not pretend to cover all the alternatives nature has so sweetly bestowed upon humans. In fact, one of the most important options—food—is hardly mentioned, and I would refer you to cookbooks and Michelin guides for the joys of cuisine.

In the next chapter I shall try to give you a deeper understanding of the possible damaging consequences of Discords between your genes and the environment. The chapter begins with a discussion of consciousness and "free will," since these concepts are important for the topics to be covered, and also highly relevant as a background for judging to what extent one ought to listen to the "whispering of the genes."

CHAPTER 7

Consciousness and Emotions:
On Burns and Blossoms

A road that may lead to the ocean.

A Peculiar Feature

The various modules of the brain can be divided into the following three main categories: Those that control muscles, those that process sensory input, and those that create feelings for the purpose of directing our behavior. The latter are obviously the most important for Darwinian happiness.

It is easy to subdivide muscles and senses into distinct units and to find corresponding centers in the brain. But how should we categorize feelings, which manifest themselves primarily inside the brain? Compared to other organs, the brain is still pretty much terra incognito. Sure, we all know what love is; yet, in contrast to ears and biceps, it is a rather imprecise entity.

Well, we actually do know quite a bit about the neurological correlates of some emotions, such as fear and anger. But before I take a more detailed look at emotional modules, I wish to discuss what might be considered a fourth type of module: The processes that regulate our changing states of awareness and arousal.

Consciousness is a term commonly used for the normal state of awareness.[138] Life, however, is not solely a question of being conscious or not. For example, during the normal off position, which is sleep, there are two very different stages: Rapid eye movement (REM) sleep, where the brain is active but the rest of the body is "cut off" from its control; and slow wave sleep, where apparently both brain and body are at rest. Furthermore, in the awake stage, we can be more or less aroused. The state of mind changes swiftly if you are drowsing on the sofa and then suddenly hear the sound of an ambulance or police siren outside. At other times it feels as if the whole frame of consciousness shifts, as when drugged. I shall, however, simplify the matter by considering consciousness as a single "on"-stage of awareness for the present discussion.[139]

We know a bit about the nerve circuitry controlling sleep, and we know something about how typical anaesthetic agents act. (Barbiturates, for example, potentiate the effect of the neurotransmitter GABA, which has a general inhibitory effect on nerve action.) Subcortical centers, possibly in the thalamus and midbrain, are probably the more important ones to freeze in order to turn off consciousness.[140] This may come as a surprise, as our thoughts and cognitive functions are assumed to be primarily the work of the cortex. Yet, it seems as if the deeper structures are the ones that decide whether or not to make you aware of what your cortex is up to.

With the exception of the strange phenomenon of REM sleep, most of the brain is slowed down when consciousness is "off." REM sleep proves, however, that turning it off is not just a question of slowing things down; the various stages of sleep are more distinct than that.

Consciousness is a peculiar feature that gives us an awareness of a part of what the brain is up to. While in the "on"-position, we have this curious perception of a *subset* of all the processes going on in our heads. An understanding of the wonders of consciousness is highly relevant for the question of how to recruit the brain for the benefit of Darwinian happiness. In the next four sections I shall deliberate on the phenomenon of consciousness. With that as background, I shall then take a closer look in the remainder of the chapter at the ups and downs of the various feelings that are a part of the brain's design.

What Is Consciousness?

All the three main categories of brain modules share the fact that they are partially controlled by the conscious brain and partially by the unconscious brain. The decision to move your legs stems from the conscious part. The same is true for deciphering the visual signals required to read this text. On the other hand, control of the intestinal muscles, and the sensory input telling the brain about the extension of the biceps, belong to the realm of the unconscious. And even though you can decide to move your legs, the execution of that decision requires help from the unconscious part of the brain. Emotions, such as anger, are typically initiated by the unconscious, but reach the conscious and are molded there.

Your brain is continuously active, day and night, but only selected activities reach the conscious level. There are, for example, many sounds you never notice; but if the unconscious part of the brain recognizes a noise as being potentially threatening, it makes sure that the signal is passed on to the appropriate conscious center.

Much the same is true for emotions. The feelings we are aware of have surfaced at the conscious level, but precursors roam the unconscious part of the brain. Not all of them surface: Your mood may actually improve due to external or internal stimuli without your knowing why, which means that the brain may shape your frame of mind without your realizing what is really going on.

There is actually no distinct line separating the conscious from the unconscious, and certain functions are on the borderline. These functions can be addressed by the conscious, but this typically requires training. For instance, it is possible to learn to regulate your heartbeat, and if you are good at concentration, you can tell the unconscious part of your brain to "please do not disturb" while you're reading this text.

Another example further illustrates how it is possible to invade the unconscious: Many people have a fairly accurate internal alarm clock; they can "set" themselves to wake up at 5 a.m. the next morning. Not only do they get up at the chosen time, it is also possible to demonstrate that hormonal changes related to the wake-up process occur prior to that. Thus you can give the conscious part of your brain an order, in advance, to start up a process belonging to the unconscious mind.[141]

The brain employs a rather different strategy from that of a computer. If it had been like a computer, you would expect only the module(s) required for a particular task to be busy; instead, many nerve cells chat with each other constantly. The incessant activity is an underlying force that influences all brain functions. Thus the brain is not just an input-output machine. There is a strong tendency for both conscious and unconscious factors to continuously manipulate activity, and the various modules often interfere with each other's business.

A computer is set to do certain tasks, and to do them in an orderly fashion; the brain, on the other hand, is more dynamic. Here, tasks evolve rather than being switched on or off. Life is more like the sum of commotion, rather than the sequential messages on a computer screen.

The brain is also wired to "feel" before it "thinks." If you flash a picture of a smiling face in front of a person, the smile will induce a positive frame of mind, even if it is flashed too fast for the face to be consciously recognized. If you flashed a picture of a smiling Hitler, the initial gut reaction would be positive; it might become negative if you let the picture linger, because then cognitive awareness of whose smile it is would kick in.

The snap decision to like or dislike, to advance or to retreat, exemplifies our primeval responses. Our conscious capacity for thinking evolved on top of that platform, but still, what the brain feels in the first few thousandths of a second influences subsequent thoughts. As people in advertising can tell you, a beautiful, scantily clad girl sitting on the hood of a car can boost sales. It creates a manipulative association between the car and the module controlling desire, at least in men, so that the unconscious brain envisions mating when the car is bought. If a man wants to buy that precise model anyway, he might consider it a bonus; otherwise he should probably feel cheated, since the car is unlikely to satisfy his sexual desires.

Who Has What It Takes?

A parrot does not know or care much about who he is, so then why did evolution tell *us* who we are?

The basic answer is pretty straightforward: Evolution followed the path toward consciousness because of the advantages of being able to respond flexibly to the demands of the environment. We have been given the highest level of versatility in any organism. When decisions are brought to our attention, behavior can be fine-tuned to each particular situation.

For example, instead of responding instinctively to the characteristic shape of the mouth in a smiling face, we use all our past experiences to evaluate whether the person can be trusted or not. The experiment using the picture of a smiling Hitler illustrates the point: The first reaction is instinctive, but the sight is subsequently brought before the scrutiny of the conscious mind, where previously knowledge about the person helps us form an appropriate response.

If self-awareness is such a smart thing, are we the only ones who have it? There is no clear answer available to this question. Even animals that are unable to recognize who they are may still demonstrate a flexibility of response resembling what we consider to be conscious decisions. On the other hand, animals that apparently know who they are may lack attributes associated with human self-awareness. It ends up as a semantic question: Human ears are different from those of a dog, yet we use the same word to describe them. You may choose to reserve "consciousness" for the human version, or to let the term include versions present in select animals.

Still, human consciousness is unique. For example, to the extent that animals do have consciousness, it is presumably more restricted to the present; they do not think (or worry) about the future like we do.

Consciousness and self-awareness are often used for pretty much the same thing; however, the latter term seems to fit better in regard to one important experiment we can undertake to examine the phenomenon in animals—the mirror test.[142] Animals that clearly demonstrate that they recognize their reflection pass the test. They may, for example, try to remove a speck on the face that would be impossible to detect without a mirror. Those who treat their own image as a new neighbor flunk.

This test has been tried on a range of animals; apes, particularly chimpanzees and gorillas, pass for sure, and dolphins may have evolved this capacity as well.[143] Birds, on the other hand, just feel less lonely in the company of a mirror. Children start to show evidence of mirror self-recognition at an age of 18 months, and at 24 months most of them pass the test. At the same age they begin to use the words "I," "you," and "me"; and *they begin to infer the mental state of others*. Prior to an age of 18 months, a child who sees another baby crying is likely to join in; after 18 months, that child will try to comfort the one in distress, or to recruit help from an adult. Apparently, self-awareness, and the concomitant awareness that other children are just like you, paves the way for empathy and sympathy.[144]

The primatologist Daniel Povinelli offers an intriguing suggestion as to how self-awareness evolved: The common ancestor of apes and humans lived in trees and moved around by swinging from branch to branch. Observing the surviving champions of this technique, the orangutan and the gibbon, he found that they often need to make a branch or trunk sway by moving their bodies before launching themselves off to the next branch. The exercise resembles the way a child generates momentum to begin to swing. The swaying, of course, brings them within reach of the next branch. In order to generate this sort of movement, you need to use the weight of your own body. It is tempting to propose that this task requires, or generates, some degree of self-awareness. In other words, the experience that moving your body influences the swaying of the tree tells you that *you* are that body. Thus it is possible that human consciousness, on which our free will depends, is a by-product of the Tarzan approach to locomotion![145]

It is fair to argue that the mirror test only reflects one quality of consciousness; those who flunk are certainly not hopeless cases. Both awareness and the experience of emotions evolved gradually in vertebrates, thus it is a question of types—or degrees—of consciousness. However, the evolution of these features probably made a jump from amphibians to reptiles, another jump to mammals, a third hop to apes, and a fourth major leap between chimpanzees and humans.

The general direction of evolution was one of "opening up" nerve modules, which means letting the mind gain access to the activity of the modules, and giving it the option of modifying the response. The job was pretty much handed to the expanding cortex.

Why Is It Sometimes Devastating?

The unconscious mind can preside over voluntary muscles as well: You run without thinking about how to move your legs, and without being consciously aware of minor details on the ground that your feet need to adjust to. Consciousness actually just gets in the way sometimes. A tennis player may find that he or she performs best by letting instincts guide the arm; forcing the conscious mind to retain complete control of the racket just makes for a clumsy hit. They say the inner eye has sharper vision.

This brings us to the wonder of intuition: Intuition has been defined as non-verbal, non-conscious thinking. According to Laura Spinney, it is rooted in mechanisms that enable the brain to soak up and ruminate on information.[146] The brain looks for subtle patterns and connections "behind your back." Intuition has access both to your conscious memory and to a body of knowledge you are unaware of ever having acquired, and which you cannot express in words. In fact, some people believe that the rare superhuman mental skills of certain autistic people (referred to as savants, and popularized by the film *Rain Man*) are related to an ability to cut off higher mental processing and let the unconscious take care of business.[147]

The type of incident where the answer to a question you were pondering suddenly pops up the next morning is related to the experience of the tennis player. They both are concerned with the division of labor between the conscious and unconscious parts of the brain. The conscious mind is designed to help you with particular problems, but elements outside conscious control can help your performance in many situations by utilizing brain resources that you are unaware of. Your overpriced conscious mind is simply not that good when it comes to fine-tuning muscle activity, or when accessing all the information that at one point entered your brain. Intuition is your guiding angel.

There are several examples of tasks where the unconscious side, or intuition if you prefer, does the better job. For example, when it comes to evaluating the size of objects, your conscious brain is easily deceived, which can be demonstrated in experiments where misleading visual clues are added on purpose. In one experiment, two identical chips are made to appear different in size by surrounding them by either small or large chips. Your mind is fooled. When asked, you claim that one is bigger. However, if you are requested to pick up the chips, your fingers open to the correct size in both cases. They are not conned because they are directed by the unconscious.[148]

A related example is that of an ape jumping from tree to tree; it is important for the ape to judge the distance accurately, as well as the size of the branch the hand is about to grasp. There never was any reason for having the conscious brain interfering with such a task. The conscious mind initiates the movement, meaning that the ape decides to jump to the next tree, but once the decision has been made, the fine tuning of the muscles is best cared for by intuition.

The important point is that the conscious and unconscious functions of the brain have their particular strengths and weaknesses. The conscious mind, on the one hand, is easily led astray, because occasionally what you experience does not at all reflect what is going on. The point is most vividly demonstrated by the way another person can manipulate you, such as in hypnosis, but the same principle applies when you begin to believe in your daydreams. Truth is stored in the unconscious, while the conscious is full of fabrication. The situation enables you to tell "lies" without any telltale signs of deceit, as you actually believe in the lies yourself. This particular division of labor is presumably there to serve your genes, but it may also serve your Darwinian happiness: Lies that are not recognized are typically to your advantage. Moreover, you retain optimism and a high self-esteem even when every sign points toward failure. As pointed out by Alison Motluk, self-deception is marvelous while memory can be bad for you.[149]

Furthermore, the conscious mind often misinterprets signals in situations where the unconscious mind gets things right. Conscious perception is actually slow and inaccurate. In other words, awareness was introduced in order to develop a more versatile behavior, but should only be activated in situations where it is useful. If the eyes spot a leopard, it makes sense to consider whether it is best to sit tight or to make a run for it—but not to spend time pondering on the fine-tuning of muscle movements once an action has been decided on.

Of the two aspects of brain activity, one is straightforward and dull, while the other is a very interesting and odd phenomenon. The unconscious is the dull part. We just fancy it to be mysterious and interesting because we do not know much about it. Basically it is just like the control unit of any odd animal—from a fly to a mouse. The unconscious is the caretaker of your body. It is continually active. It takes note of life's experiences, interprets them, and reacts accordingly. However, the more interesting aspects of brain function, our passions and thought constructs, may have a root in the unconscious mind, but they are not that fascinating before reaching the stage of awareness. Our cognitive capacity makes them exciting by introducing variety and complexity.

From the genes' point of view, an awareness of who you are, and the accompanying free will, is not an obvious advantage. Rather, it is a disturbing factor. Free will makes it difficult for the genes to rule you. Most organisms do fine without it, and even human genes are not necessarily better off with it. As suggested above, some tasks are best cared for without your deliberate interference, and many of the stunts initiated by your knowing brain are obviously of limited value for either genes or the quality of life.

I believe self-awareness is one of the boldest experiments ever undertaken by evolution—possibly exceeded only by a topic I shall return to in the next chapter: sexual procreation.

There are several functions, such as the control of heart and bowel muscles, that evolution never took the chance of handing over to your attention, because the risk of having your free will mess it up would have been too great. Consider a person who in a moment of despair decided to stop his heart. What would happen to his genes?

Suicide is supposed to be difficult, and in the absence of modern tools, it is. Suicide also reflects the extreme infringement of free will, but there are many less drastic ways of misusing the conscious mind. Many people try to grab control of services that are primarily the responsibility of the unconscious and that they would be well advised not to hijack.

Sleep is one illustration. Sleep disturbances are among the epidemics roaming our Discord society. Feeling sleepy is an obvious message from your internal guru; when the cue is given, you are supposed to relinquish control to an autopilot who then guides you through the process of sleeping. But for many people it is hard to give up control. Instead of closing their eyes and letting go, they believe the decision to fall asleep ought to be their own. The problem is that the more they insist on controlling this decision, and to be in charge of the process, the more difficult it actually becomes. The obvious solution is indifference. You should make an effort not to be in command. Now, the anxiety that typically troubles modern humans does not improve the situation: If you are afraid of not falling asleep, you are in real trouble, because the reaction accompanying fear makes sure your body is aroused. It is like telling the unconscious that you insist on going to sleep right now, and at the same time demand to be wide-awake to supervise the process.

Breathing is another example. The process is normally dealt with by the unconscious, but the genes allow you to grab command. A typical result is sub-optimal breathing. We hyperventilate, or we do not use the full capacity of our lungs. In most situations respiration is best left to the instincts—skin diving or having to breathe in a sand storm being typical exceptions.[150]

Our mistrust of the unconscious might be included in the list of diseases of civilization. It seems to be related to the popular assumption that our biological inheritance has no impact on behavior, and that each human should take a rational command over all actions. The guru, on the other hand, advises you not to let your conscious self try to hijack your unconscious self. By allowing the autopilots of the brain to take command, you should be able to sleep better, hit the tennis ball harder and more accurately, improve your golf handicap, and lessen the burden of anxiety.

Then again, in certain situations, the opposite advice is more appropriate. There are some rather mad pilots lurking in your head. Giving in to your cravings involves handing them the controls, and refusing to let thoughts of consequences stop you. This is true of the drug addict, and of the middle-aged man who sexually makes a fool of himself. When too many signals stimulate the reward system, it is hard to resist. Thus, in a stimulus-soaked society you must be prepared occasionally to tell the autopilots that they are heading in the wrong direction.

Psychologists operate with a phenomenon referred to as the "mere exposure" effect: Animals will develop a preference for stimuli they are exposed to, as long as the stimuli are not aversive, and particularly if the stimuli are paired with some positive experience.[151] It seems to be a question of caution toward the unfamiliar, and a desire for anything that served you well in the past. In humans the effect is exemplified by how people tend to prefer certain types of food or places to go to on vacation. Sometimes these preferences can go as far as to take on compulsive or "narcotic" qualities. The "mere exposure" effect helps explain why, in a stimulus-soaked society, it is so difficult to navigate without getting stranded on particular stimuli.

The Freedom of a Free Will

Our genes have created a luxury version of a brain that includes consciousness, intelligent reasoning, and decision-making as standard equipment. In stark contrast are the genes of an earthworm, which do not allow for flexibility in behavior; earthworms eat their way through the soil with no thought about whether the earth in Hawaii would be any better than the soil they are presently munching. Human genes, on the other hand, found it useful to give us a reasonable measure of independence. Yet humans have pretty much the same instinctual systems as other mammals; it is just that in adult humans these systems are difficult to observe because they are no longer expressed directly as behavior, but instead filtered and modified by cognitive activity. Most human instincts manifest themselves only as subtle psychological tendencies (such as subjective feeling states) that provide guidance for behavior.

There have been a lot of discussions through the ages about whether humans have free will or not. The biological perspective on human behavior has been accused of determinism, in that it steals our free will by claiming we are under the power of the genes. So, do we really have such a thing as a free will?[152]

The simple answer is that if the information contained in this chapter is compatible with your concept of "free will," then you should use the term. Yes, we can do pretty much what we want within the limits of human competence. *But our free will is restricted to the conscious mind.* It may occasionally penetrate the upper layers of the unconscious, but it has limited power there. Furthermore, although we do have choices, the average human tends to take the hints laid down by the genes—that is, we are inclined to follow instinctual feelings. The actions that feelings are supposed to elicit can be controlled, but the feelings tend to push their way through conscious barriers: We may choose not to eat, but it is very difficult to choose not to be hungry. The question of free will thus boils down to the semantic question of how free a will should be in order to be called free.

The biological perspective does not steal your free will. On the contrary, free will is something the genes have bestowed on us, and represents a strategy we should approve of. Without this property we would presumably not have acquired the intense pleasures provided by the brain; without it we would not have experienced many of the joys and sorrows of life. We would have been more like the earthworm. For those who feel that the sorrows outweigh the pleasures, the human condition may not sound like an improvement. It is, however, possible to harness our capacity for pleasure and joy. Thanks to our measure of free will, we do have a potential for happiness that was never offered the rose.

Sensations, Feelings, and Emotions

The limitations of our free will should be obvious. If, as some people seem to claim, we are in total charge of our mind and body, we could simply decide to be happy. Unfortunately, it is not that easy. It may help to put on a reggae T-shirt saying "Don't worry, be happy," but it is unlikely to solve all your problems. While you sense feelings with your conscious mind, what you actually feel is strongly influenced by processes occurring in the dark corners of the unconscious mind.

We cannot escape our feelings, but we do have the power to influence what sort of feelings are allowed to roam inside our heads. In other words, we can do something about our measure of Darwinian happiness. Unfortunately, the choices that tend to pop up out of our free will do not always serve us that well, which is why most governments try to direct us, for instance, by restricting our access to narcotics. A deeper understanding of what our mental life is all about is a useful platform for the erection of a more sensible free will—a free will that guides us in the direction of positive feelings. The remainder of this section is about the modules of the brain concerned with generating the human repertoire of feelings.

Sensations are the compass of the brain. (I use the word "sensations" in terms of a category somewhat broader than feelings.) They not only include the processed input from our sensory organs, but also the conscious experience of the internal state of mind; thus, sensations are a part of every conscious mental process.

Feelings are the more affective, or more overt, form of sensations. The evolutionary process shaped our propensity for various feelings in the same manner as it shaped anatomical and physiological features. They were designed to serve particular purposes relevant to our Stone Age existence, and they typically have an agreeable or non-agreeable flavor, which is what I refer to as rewards or punishment.[153]

There have been a number of attempts to categorize feelings. The exercise can be quite useful as long as one realizes that any categorization necessarily has to be a gross simplification of the continuum of the mind. Psychologists, for instance, distinguish between two main types of feelings: *motivations* and *emotions*.[154] Motivations include hunger, thirst and sleepiness; they are typically activated from within, in that they are elicited by specific bodily needs, and their purpose is to retain a certain homeostasis in your body. Moreover, they are reasonably easy to categorize: The main types correspond to the basic needs of a human being, such as food, drink, and temperature regulation. The pain of crushing your finger and the sweet sensation of chocolate are similarly included under this heading. Emotions, on the other hand, are normally triggered by external stimuli; they are designed to deal with the threats and possibilities of an environment. Their main function is to create various forms of action readiness. Yet it is important to bear in mind that the external stimuli do not "create" emotions; they just trigger pre-designed circuits. (A third group of feelings might be associated with reproduction, such as sexual arousal and caring for children, involving both intrinsic needs and external stimuli.)

Motivations and emotions both evoke positive and negative sensations, and the experience varies in intensity depending on how powerful the instigation is meant to be. It is possible that all the various feelings potentially can push the buttons for the two main reward modules: the "wanting" and the "liking." But then again, how well you feel is only partly a question of activation of these circuits, since the pleasantness of your state of mind depends on the quality of the sum of sensations.

Although the modules for motivations and emotions are based primarily in the old, subcortical part of the brain, they interact extensively with the cognitive functions of the cortex. In humans there may be thoughts that are free of affect, but many thoughts certainly do evoke emotions. On the other hand, there is probably no emotional state that is free of cognitive ramifications; the emotional modules seem to have a fair amount of power over cognition. For instance, if your neighbor annoys you, the way you judge his personality tends to be influenced by your anger.

In sum, this means that our conscious thoughts are influenced by feelings initiated by unconscious, emotional processes, while it is (unfortunately) difficult for the conscious to decide how to feel. It might be added, parenthetically, that the power of the cortex (our cognitive conscious mind) increases as we mature.

Psychologists have tried to categorize emotions by distinguishing between primary and more complex emotions. The former presumably corresponds to separate modules in the brain, while the latter may involve either activation of two or more modules simultaneously, or a more extensive interaction with cognitive functions.

The list of primary emotions typically include joy, fear, anger, separation distress (loneliness), and surprise (arousal). Some experts extend the list to include others, such as disgust, sorrow (grief), trust, lust, play, dominance, anticipation, and love and affection; but these emotions may also be listed as composite or complex.

Most of the items on these lists make immediate evolutionary sense. As in the case of motivations, they serve functions with reasonably obvious survival value, and we actually know quite a bit about the involved brain structures and neurochemicals. The authenticity of the more basic emotions is proved by the fact that they can be initiated from specific brain centers by electrical stimuli, and modulated by particular chemical interference, in animals as distantly related as reptiles and humans. It has proven more difficult, however, to find neurological correlates to the more complex emotions, but that does not mean that such correlates do not exist. In the future we may have a menu of neuropeptides that deal more or less specifically with many of our emotions and motivations.

Emotions are usually displayed as facial expressions, and sometimes the display includes sounds and behavioral patterns as well. The reason why they are expressed is because emotions are social in nature; in other words, it is important to be able to communicate them to other people. Although they can be sensed in solitude, their relevance is related mainly to our need for communicating states of mind. Their occurrence, or at least the intensity involved, typically depends on the presence of fellow humans; however, the company of another human being does not necessarily need to be physical. Sometimes it just helps to have someone on your mind.

Motivations such as thirst and hunger are not displayed. This makes sense since they are concerned with internal homeostasis and thus do not need to involve others.

The social nature of emotions has consequences for the question of Darwinian happiness: It adds something to be able to share agreeable experiences. If your friends cannot come along on your vacation to Greece, or be next to you on top of Mount Kilimanjaro, they can at least join you in looking at the pictures. One important thing in the way of general advice is that keeping your emotions to yourself is Discord. In the company of comrades, positive feelings give more pleasure, and the negative ones are more easily relieved.

We are not only equipped with the capacity to display emotions; there are also particular modules of the brain (apparently located in the right cortical hemisphere) to interpret emotions in others. Again this makes sense. Wrath is of no use unless it is correctly understood. People with Huntington's disease have problems recognizing one particular emotion—disgust[155]—an observation that suggests there are separate modules set up to read each type of emotion.

The core set of emotions, and the corresponding displays, are universal. A picture of an angry face will be interpreted correctly, regardless of culture. It is even possible to measure the contractions of various facial muscles and to prove that a certain pattern of contractions corresponds to the same emotion around the globe. Their universality underlines their biological significance.[156]

Randolph Nesse has pointed out that there are more feelings with a negative connotation than with a positive one.[157] The imbalance presumably reflects our encounters with a larger variety of threats than opportunities. The "wanting" and the "liking" motivate us to take advantage of the opportunities; threats, however, come in several shapes, such as predators, diseases, starvation, quarrels, exclusion from a group, and loss of a mate—meaning that a larger variety of responses exists to deal with them. Furthermore, missing one particular opportunity rarely has a fatal effect on survival, while not heeding a threat can instantly kill you. As a consequence, the negative feelings are typically more powerful—but do not despair at this apparently depressing information, for when it comes to Darwinian happiness, it is less obvious what is negative and what is positive.

If you are able to deal with the emotions labeled as negative in a natural way, then the sensations involved need not hurt you that much. A dangerous situation evokes fear, but as long as you believe yourself to be in reasonable control, the sensation accompanying the uplift that stress hormones give you can actually be quite pleasing—the previously mentioned "adrenaline kick." For example: Imagine yourself stumbling upon a snake. By slowly retreating, you know that you could most surely avoid being attacked. Granted, the episode would be frightening and exciting, but not necessarily annoying on the whole. On the other hand, if you had never seen a snake before, and would have no idea of what to do, the sensation would be highly unpleasant because you would be less in control and less able to come up with the correct response.

As pointed out in Chapter 3, even sadness can feel good. Moreover, an attempt to suppress sadness in a context where it is an appropriate emotion is a Discord, and likely to be more destructive to your Darwinian happiness than the feeling of sadness itself. It is not in the genes' interest, however, to be in a person with a lasting depression. Thus, once the point is made, and preferably dealt with, we have a natural capacity to return to the default good mood.

You may be able to find some pleasure in sorrow, but few people enjoy the pain caused by hitting their thumb with a hammer. Why does pain have to be so painful? If you hold your finger in the flame of a burning candle, you will react swiftly and correctly by jerking your hand away; nevertheless, the pain still lingers for a long time. Would not a short burst of pain suffice?

For a biologist the answer is obvious: Pain must be sufficiently disagreeable to assure the correct action, not just in the present situation, but in future situations as well. You need to be taught a lesson, because your actions depend so much on bodily signals. Actually, the inability to feel pain is a rare, but severe disease; patients tend to die at an early age since they fail to protect their bodies against damage.[158] Evolution wisely enough never allowed our measure of free will to go as far as to let behavior depend solely on knowledge. To allow yourself to scream, however, may give some relief, and so may an understanding of what pain is for.

Nesse distinguishes between defenses and defects: Defenses are analogous to the low-oil-pressure light on the dashboard of a car; the glowing bulb itself is not the problem, since the light is a protective response to the problem of oil pressure. Defects, on the other hand, are analogous to a flat tire or a faulty transmission. In the case of your body, unpleasant feelings are defenses designed to protect the body against something harmful. The list includes pain, nausea, vomiting, coughing, diarrhea, fever, fatigue, and anxiety. Evolution has added these feelings to your repertoire because they help you avert dangers. For instance, if you eat a toxic mushroom, the natural response is to vomit. The action is designed to remove whatever remnants of toxins are still present in your stomach; the associated discomfort makes sure you will avoid that mushroom in the future. Technically, there is no reason why vomiting should be unpleasant; many animals regurgitate food as a way of feeding their infants. Physiologically this action is very similar to vomiting, yet it appears to be an agreeable activity. Thus, the conclusion is that the discomfort you associate with vomiting is there to teach you an important lesson.

Not all manifestations of disease are defenses; many result from serious bodily defects. Tumors, seizures, and arteriosclerosis merely reflect a deterioration of normal function. You do not sense a tumor until it has caused some form of havoc. Evolution saw no reason to make you aware of a tumor, because, during our evolutionary history, there was nothing you could do about it anyway. In other words, pain is elicited when, in an evolutionary sense, it serves a function.

Emotional suffering can be just as useful as physical discomfort—for instance, when you are annoyed because you fail in a task. Let us assume that your spear missed the buck that you thought you would bring down; then sadness tells you that something in your strategy went wrong, meaning you ought to try a different approach the next time you go hunting, or maybe you need some more practice at throwing. Similarly, the joy associated with a successful hunt tells you that you did well, and that you should try to repeat the performance next time. I have heard golf players compare a good hit with an orgasm.

Some of the less desirable emotions, such as embarrassment, guilt, shyness, and submissiveness, presumably help regulate one's place in a group hierarchy. If the chance of losing a conflict is high, the genes ought to induce emotions that restrain the individual from fighting. Most primates exhibit low-mood characteristics when their continued membership in a group demands that they submit to others. In other words, one function of sadness is to signal a low social profile.

The idea that sadness and withdrawal help people adjust to their social position is substantiated by the effect of Prozac—a drug that not only makes people less depressed, but also more outgoing and dominant. Similar effects have been demonstrated in monkeys; low status individuals move up the social ladder if that type of drug is administered.[159]

To conclude so far: We do have a measure of free will, and we do have a propensity for a complex bouquet of feelings. Happiness is all about how we feel. The main question is therefore how to use that bit of free will to send the state of mind as high up the scale of happiness as possible. The simple response of "Just decide to be happy" does not work all too well. We should instead try to adjust our way of living to match human nature. Furthermore, for the purpose of improving Darwinian happiness, joy may be more potent than pain and fear, but the trick is both to seek the more delightful feelings and to deal in an appropriate way with any sensation that may surface. Your feelings may serve you well if you give the auto-pilots of emotions an appropriate amount of freedom.

Vulnerable Systems

As with a car, certain parts are more likely to malfunction than others: The exhaust system is likely to break down, while the seats have a fair chance of lasting for the lifetime of the car. Similarly, evolution has not been able to give all the various parts of your body the same robustness of design. As we shall see, some of the emotional modules of the brain are more likely to cause you problems than your tongue or your eyebrows.

The burden of pain is presumably no worse for us today than it was for our Stone Age ancestors. Pain is actually less of a problem today: We have medicine that deals rather efficiently with that sort of suffering. On the other hand, emotional problems, such as anxiety and depression, are not just difficult to treat, but they are apparently more of a burden today than they were in our tribal past. I believe the reason why they are more of a burden is that our emotions are the big losers in a Discord setting. Part of the explanation may be that emotions are social, and the main Discord factors haunting present society concern the social fabric.

Before examining the above assumption more closely, let us consider two illustrative analogies. One involves our immune system and the other deals with rat whiskers.

The various functions necessary for survival can be graded in terms of complexity, and in how much external input is required in order to ensure satisfactory development. To lift a leg is fairly straightforward. No elaborate environmental stimuli are needed; a little bit of practice and you will be doing just fine. The kidneys take care of the rather difficult task of filtering your blood; nevertheless, you need not worry about their maturation because as long as you avoid infections and stay away from toxic substances, they will function the way they are designed to and serve you well.

Emotions and the system assigned to counteract infections, however, are different. Our immune system has two things in common with our emotional system: Both have highly complex assignments and both require environmental input for proper maturation. But this presents a problem, because intricate functions that depend on external stimuli for proper performance are particularly vulnerable to Discord conditions. I believe immune defense and emotions to be among our most vulnerable functions; abnormalities in the signals meant to guide their development easily lead to suboptimal performance, like sand in delicate machinery. Moreover, I believe the consequences can be observed in the form of emotional problems, such as anxieties, aggression, and depression; or in the form of immune problems such as asthma and allergies. All these conditions have reached epidemic proportions in industrialized societies.

The immune system evolved as a defense against microbes; it is a system that matures by constant interaction with germs and parasites. Evolution made this process appropriate to the life style of our Stone Age ancestors, but in modern society interactions between humans and germs are quite different. For example, our children are less likely to be exposed to the mostly harmless flora of microbes found in the soil, and they are given vaccines instead of letting them contract natural childhood infections. Thus, the stimuli are qualitatively and/or quantitatively different from what the system expects.

Can this situation explain the inappropriate immune response regarding asthma and allergies? Apparently immune cells with nothing else to keep them busy are prone to attack components of your own body. As a consequence, scientists are constructing "vaccines" (containing bacteria) for the purpose of fighting autoimmune diseases, hoping that feeding the immune system with enough harmless germs will prevent the system from attacking the self.[160] In fact, the suggestion that the surge in adverse immunological conditions, such as asthma and allergies, may be partly related to excessive cleanliness has gone from detested speculation to mainstream science over the last few years. There is now evidence in support of the hypothesis, and detailed models help explain the putative connection. Science journals today carry articles with snappy titles like "Let them eat dirt" and "Give us today our daily germs."[161]

Our emotions, I do believe, are in a similar quagmire. They too depend on the environment for proper development, meaning the occurrence of social interactions; and they evolved to function in a particular setting—in our Discord society the conditions are less than optimal. We can suggest in some detail why a lack of dirt may lead to an increase in asthma and allergies; emotions, on the other hand, are less well understood at the molecular level than our immune system. Still, it is possible to indicate why a suboptimal environment may have dire consequences for emotional well being.

Let us look first at rat whiskers. The stiff hairs are important sense organs: When one of them touches something, signals are sent to a particular location in the brain. Eventually the brain develops the ability to assess in detail what caused the touch. Now, what happens if all but one of the whiskers are removed from the young rat? The part of the brain that receives signals from the remaining hair becomes larger than normal, while the centers connected with the removed hairs almost vanish.[162]

The example reflects a general principle alluded to above: The brain needs relevant input for proper development. Unused regions degenerate while overstimulated components may expand disproportionally, either by growing larger cells with more connections or by becoming more active and sending out more neurotransmitters and modulators.

The significance of this is apparent when considering what happens when an infant grows up without proper parental care. Several studies have examined the consequences of this particular Discord aspect of upbringing, including studies on the immunological, emotional and social problems of rhesus monkeys deprived as infants.[163] One particular line of investigation concerns the role of the master hormone of stress responses,

CRH (the corticotrophin-releasing hormone), in rats. The psychologist Michael Meaney has shown that if rat mothers lick their offspring often, the pups produce less CRH.[164] More importantly, the effect lasts; the amount of CRH-produced in the hypothalamus of the adult depends on the amount of licking received during the first 10 days of life. In the absence of maternal care the adult is more vulnerable to stress. Thus, early experiences set the sensitivity of an individual's stress response.

Other scientists interested in the development of children have looked at the withering of nerve cells in the rat brain. A certain number of cells are supposed to die during development as a normal pruning process, but it has been shown in orphaned pups that twice as many cells die in certain parts of the brain. The situation is worst in the hippocampus, which has a central function in learning and memory. Apparently a lack of tactile stimulation, i.e., the mother's licking, causes the additional cell death. The situation is similar to the case of removed rat whiskers.[165]

These types of studies may help explain the observation that maternal deprivation increases the risk of depression as well as retarded physical and mental development in human orphans (presumably because some parts of their brains are underdeveloped).

Growing up without proper parenting may be one of the worst forms of Discord, but certainly not the only one. I believe there is a vast array of aspects of modern life that are suboptimal, both for children and for adults. One example is that while your brain has evolved to deal with sudden dangers, and even disasters, it is presumably less well primed to deal with lasting dilemmas for which finding a suitable remedy seems impossible. Two members of a tribe may have a fight, but their close social ties imply that the quarrel will be resolved: Their relationship is generally strong enough for friendship to recover. On rare occasions one of them may be killed or expelled, but the case will nevertheless be resolved. A quarrel with your neighbor or your colleague at work, on the other hand, may smolder on for ages. Such unresolved conflicts are probably a main cause of stress.

Another problem is that we lack control of our lives, or more importantly, we lack the feeling of control: We require a job to earn a living, but have limited influence over such important matters as working hours, tasks, and job security. In the tribe of the hunter-gatherer, each adult was presumably more independent. All the adults collaborated, but they collaborated as close comrades and autonomous units.

Mood is there to "track the progress" toward the fulfillment of goals. When we continue to pursue goals that we cannot reach, the consequence can be to activate low-mood circuits to the extent that it results in depression. Unfortunately, the unobtainability of goals is another typical consequence of our present Discord society. In tribal society, for instance, each person could be the "world champion" in some task, because the known world contained only a handful of people; today your chances of really proving excellence is rather slim. Moreover, it seems as if we tend to look at the number of people ahead of us, rather than at the percentile rank. As a consequence, not only does the situation cause stress, but it becomes more difficult to harvest the rewards associated with success and status.

The main point in this section is that our emotional life is vulnerable to Discord conditions, and that this vulnerability can have dire consequences. In the next section I shall look at problems related to one particular basic emotion: Fear.

When Learning Is Bad For You

Let us take a closer look at fear—a state of mind that can drastically diminish your harvest of Darwinian delight. Fear is about "fight-or-flight," or, to put it more specifically: Freeze if the danger can be avoided by keeping still; run away when that is the best option; and fight with all you have when there is no other alternative. The system yields the feeling of sudden terror when strongly activated, and chronic anxiety in the case of sustained arousal. None of these states is to be desired.

We know which parts of the brain have been assigned to deal with fear and anxiety (the subcortical amygdala and a part of the midbrain), and we know some of the neurotransmitters that are at work there: Excitatory neurotransmitters, such as glutamate, are involved in the response, in addition to a bundle of known neuropeptides.[166]

Some fear signals need to be learned, while others are innate. The rat's reaction to the smell of a cat exemplifies the latter, and humans presumably react to height, snakes, spiders, and pain in a similar innate fashion. However, innate fears are no big problem, the problems arise primarily out of our capacity to learn fear.

Most emotions start off in the unconscious mind. From there they initiate a particular feeling, a facial expression, a physiological response, and a conscious appraisal of the situation. The roar of a lion is brought to your attention by the module of the brain that analyzes sounds. The gut reaction is initially fear, but then you start thinking about how far away the lion must be: If it is obvious that the lion is close, you really jump, whereas if it seems to be far away, you slowly relax.

In fact, the signals or information prompting an emotion sometimes never reach the conscious mind: We are able to feel afraid without knowing why, because the unconscious part of the brain can trigger the fear module without "informing us." Presumably there are many budding emotions that you never become aware of at all, and you may not even realize that the fear button has been gently pushed. Yet, even if the unconscious pre-emotions are not recognized, they can still leave an impact on your mind; normally just a slight increase in anxiety will nevertheless affect your mood.

The unconscious mind initiates emotions such as fear in order to protect you. The defense system is designed to be hyper-responsive instead of being too sluggish, the obvious reason being that an unnecessary defense is cheaper than failing to respond in a dangerous situation. A sting of fear is reasonable even if what you heard turned out to be one of your tribal-mates practicing singing, rather than a lion roaring.

In the current Discord situation, however, the ease with which fear and related feelings are elicited causes problems. You may try to shut off the fear, but once it reaches the conscious your influence is pretty much limited to what you become aware of. Moreover, it can be difficult to keep the door of the conscious mind closed when fear comes knocking.

Not only are the daily stimuli different from what your brain has been designed to receive, as previously exemplified by the number of strangers you encounter, but the problem is probably made worse by a Discord childhood. If the mind does not develop the qualities envisaged by the genes, we end up with a suboptimal mind that has to deal with suboptimal surroundings. The innate touchy finger on the defense trigger worsens the situation. We pay in the form of disabling anxiety disorders, panic disorders, loss of self-confidence, shyness, phobias, obsessions, compulsive disorders, aggression, depression, and psychoses. Added to the bill, as an extra "value added" tax, is less than optimal Darwinian happiness. The price is unduly high.

The molding of the brain can be referred to as learning; the human brain drives this process rather zealously. We learn the vocabulary of a foreign language, or how to perform a triple somersault, by repeating the task over and over again; when a particular type of stimulus is repeated, the nerve circuitry dealing with it is strengthened. Associations—that is to say, links to other bits of memory—further strengthen the nerve circuitry, and thus help you learn.

Phobias and excessive anxiety presumably develop in the unconscious mind by a mechanism similar to other forms of learning. The over-responsiveness of the defense system intensifies and strengthens them. Edward Hallowell, an expert on anxiety, says that worry can burn itself into the brain.[167] A pathway is formed linking particular stimuli with the worst form of nervousness. If you fear enclosed places, just the thought of an elevator can make you sick.

Let us assume your parents took you to the beach for the first time and you ended up nearly drowning. The association linking water with danger would become pretty strong; even if you later on learn to swim and tell yourself that water is fun, the associated water phobia nevertheless may drown you in punitive feelings every time you approach the sea.

The bottom line is that our talent for learning can have dire consequences, particularly when the circumstances are in Discord with the inherent design of humans.

Emotional Sensitivity

As previously pointed out, any of the modules that constitute our minds can malfunction. Anxiety presumably has to do with overheating of the fear module; depression seems to be related to problems with the module involved in care-eliciting behavior. Interestingly, anxiety and depression tend to go hand in hand; in other words, those who are prone to worry are also more likely to be victims of depression. Let us look more closely at these two states of mind in this section.[168]

To suppress the need for care, and to deny nurture in situations where it is appropriate, are both Discords, as is the lack of proper response to attempts at eliciting care from others. Do we get, and do we give, enough love and support? A lot of people are probably victims of Discord conditions when it comes to these aspects of interpersonal relations. As a consequence, I believe that depression, or just a generally low mood, is a major problem in our present society.

Women seem to be affected more than men. A possible evolutionary explanation is that women are more in need of care than men, inasmuch as they are more inclined to search for providers in the opposite sex. If the care-eliciting module in women is more active, you would also expect it to be more exposed to Discord conditions. Moreover, you might anticipate that after giving birth a woman's need for support and care is particularly strong; and that if the emotional module has been corrupted, the situation is likely to cause problems. This may explain the well-known phenomenon of postpartum depression. [169]

Some people are born more vulnerable than others. We know about one of the genes implicated in creating this variation; it is a gene involved in controlling the level of serotonin.[170] People with a low level worry more, and they are more likely to enter a low mood. They are more apprehensive, fearful, and tense. The trait is referred to as "harm avoidance" or *emotional sensitivity*.

When we are sick, our immune system signals the brain to take it easy, to keep a low profile. Too much signalling may translate into a depressed state. It is possible that those prone to depression have overactivity in the part of the immune defense responsible for those signals. Thus, an innate variation in how the immune defense is set up may further explain why some people are more vulnerable than others.[171]

The brains of emotionally sensitive people presumably have a particularly low threshold for sounding the alarm in threatening situations; in fact, the alarm does not even have to be tied to any event or situation; sometimes it is just a free-floating worry. In most people the cry of alarm is silenced as the brain realizes that it was, as usual, a false call for being alert, but the typical worrier is unable to turn it off. In the most destructive cases, anxiety has the power to take complete control of conscious activity. It can be one of the worst curses to scorch the brain.

It is hard to tell people to relax and listen to their internal guru when their brains are already maladjusted, or "scarred." Unfortunately, although anxiety is easy to acquire, once the associated brain circuits have been established, it is difficult or impossible to erase: Emotional memory can last a lifetime. As with other memory, it will, however, fade. Thus, most therapies act not by undoing the nerve circuitry responsible for the anxiety, but by "subduing" it and allowing patients to live without being disabled by it.[172]

Patients who go to see a doctor represent probably only the tip of the iceberg, as I believe excessive nervousness and low mood to be major devastators of Darwinian happiness, even for people who consider themselves healthy. As gurus, and suppliers of alcohol, have long suspected, happiness is linked to an absence of anxiety-inducing thoughts.

The psychiatrist can offer the sufferer both therapy and medication. There is already a long list of prescription drugs available, and many more on the way. Most of them work by increasing the activity of serotonin and/or dopamine neurotransmitters, but recent data suggest that agents modulating particular neuropeptides may serve the same purpose.[173] Modern medicine does indeed alleviate the problem for a lot of victims, but I believe that it is also possible to improve the situation without seeing a doctor:

One important piece of advice is to share your worries with others. This is the natural thing to do; we used to live in tribes where personal ties made it customary to share all concerns. The main rationale for talking to someone is not necessarily to obtain specific help; it may be more important to induce your mind to assume that the burden has been divided among members of the tribe. This can be sufficient to ease the load on your shoulders. A friend who listens and indicates that he or she cares can in a lot of cases be of more help than a therapist; moreover, the main function of the therapist may be just that—to act as a friend.

Another piece of advice is to head for the real gurus of India. They teach all sorts of techniques designed to alleviate anxiety and depression, and there are a number of schools, most of them with their own particular version of meditation, yoga, or related exercises. Their techniques typically aim at diverting the activity of your scarred mind, and bringing it back to the state described as "default good mood" in Chapter 3, which resembles the carefree state of mind of our animal ancestors.

Of course, the main advice, based on this book, is to make life less of a Discord. Your internal guru may prove to be better than any of the gurus of India.

Burns and Blossoms

The present Discord conditions are not the only explanation for immunological and emotional problems. There are numerous causes. *What the Discord does is to amplify problems associated with vulnerable points in the design of mankind.* Asthma and anxiety presumably troubled our hunter-gatherer ancestors as well, but because of our present lifestyle, as exemplified by excessive cleanliness and a lack of the tribal form of social life, they now trouble us more.

Anxiety and depression are related in that both presumably evolved partly for the purpose of making us keep a low profile. Anxiety may be more concerned with overt danger, while depression is part of the inherent response to social situations in which you are better off not to stick your neck out. They are there to help you avoid damaging confrontations. Related emotions are presumably present in other mammals as well, but they are more likely to cause problems for us. One reason is that the human consciousness offers the added disadvantage of becoming obsessed about these emotions, and such an obsession can reinforce the neurology: If you ruminate and fantasize about being inferior and having no future, the activity of the nerve circuitry involved in depression will tend to increase.

In addition to the problem of the escalating effect of mental rumination you may have the problem of Discord conditions: For example, it is common nowadays for us not to have the kind of lifelong relationships that exist in a tribe; rather, we are chronically and often inescapably exposed to hostile people. And it is not unusual that, when your children go off to school, they must mingle with individuals who are dominant, and who bring that dominance down upon them. In the Stone Age tribe it did not matter so much because the dominant ones were his or her mates, and would therefore treat subordinates nicely.

The brain thus comes with a propensity to be "burned" (or "scarred" if you prefer) by experience; the consequence of such burns is that reinforced nerve circuitry sends hurtful signals. Fortunately it is also possible to grow "flowers" in the form of circuitry that encourages pleasant signals: If you were in love the first time you heard a particular song, your heart will lighten up each time it is played on the radio. That too is a question of "emotional memory." Unfortunately, we are equipped with more negative than positive responses, and the negative responses tend to be more forceful and to have lower thresholds. Therefore, the emotional memories we carry around with us are more likely to be burns rather than flowers; moreover, a brain exposed to Discord conditions is less suitable for cultivating flowers than a well-adjusted brain is.

Emotional memory is presumably stored in a way that is different from the normal (also called "declarative") memory. The latter consists of the information and experiences present somewhere in the brain, ready for recall, at the convenience of your consciousness. Although your emotional memories do influence thoughts and feelings, you are generally not aware of them. They are not listed in the archives of the conscious mind.

It is relevant to note that the brain is able to form emotional memory before it has developed the potential for long-term storage of conscious memory. Thus traumas experienced in early life may affect mental and behavioral functions later in life, even though they were never filed in the archives of declarative memory. In other words, emotional memory left by an early traumatic experience can act through processes that remain inaccessible to the conscious.[174]

Blossoms and burns do not exist solely in the sphere of the unconscious mind; it is actually possible to do some gardening in the fields of the conscious brain. We can use our measure of free will to help reinforce positive feelings. For example, both good and bad moods tend to perpetuate themselves: A cheerful mood makes the world brighter and steers you in the direction of positive sensations. It also has a favorable effect on the mood of those around you, and this in turn can help you feel better. Laughter is contagious. Apparently even a forced smile can produce a pleasant sensation. Thus, if you want to activate some positive brain circuits, it may be sufficient to use your free will and choose to smile. Try it. Do not worry about looking stupid. Indeed, it has been suggested that you do not even need to think in terms of a smile, but that the activation of the smile muscles is sufficient to grant yourself good mood signals.

In an interesting experiment to support this idea, subjects were asked to rate cartoons in terms of being funny while at the same time holding a pen either between their teeth or in their lips. Holding the pen between your teeth (parallel to the lips) forces your face into a pose resembling a smile, while holding it with your lips creates more of a frown. The cartoons were rated as funnier when the pen was held between the teeth rather than with the lips.[175] Of course, walking around with a pen in your mouth is likely to elicit smiles from others as well.

The main notion in this chapter is that in order to improve your Darwinian happiness, *you should avoid burns and help the flowers to blossom.*

This advice covers both the long-term effects related to learning and the more immediate effects related to how your surroundings and you yourself respond to the signals you send out. If you escape the adversity of

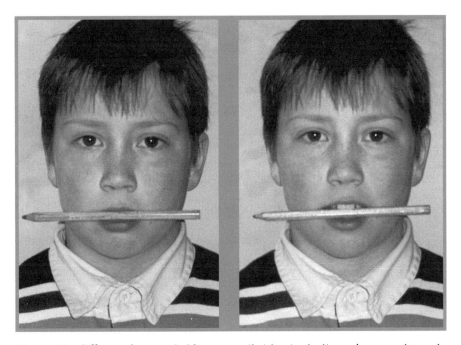

Plate 9. The difference between holding a pencil either in the lips or between the teeth.

Discords, you not only decrease the risk of burns, but also prepare the garden for the blooming of flowers. Unfortunately this is a bit more difficult than traditional gardening.

The Holy Grail

Your genes are not really concerned about the quality of your life. For them, happiness is relevant only to the extent that it improves fitness.

Genes are excellent managers. The moderation of the rewards for playful behavior as you grow up, and your propensity for indolence, both bear witness to their sense of economy. It is not in the interest of your genes that you spend time and energy on emotions and behavior that are not conducive to survival and propagation, so do not expect them always to promote joy. On the other hand, if everything is fine they prefer you to be cheerful and optimistic; thus, while it may be true that genes do not promote exuberance, they have nevertheless given us a default good mood. To find it, however, is difficult, even if you have been brought up in a suitable environment. If your brain has already been burned, it is even harder.

In Chapter 3 I called the default state of good mood the Holy Grail of Darwinian happiness. Our allocated measure of free will allows us to go out and seek it—it may be one of the most demanding treasures to recover, but also the one most worth going for.

Conscious choices are required for this enterprise, but I believe the Holy Grail lies hidden deep inside your brain, to a large extent beyond the reach of the conscious. Thus the default good mood requires the collaboration of a blooming unconscious mind. You need to have the affective modules well oiled and running smoothly, which is best achieved by avoiding Discords. If the modules are burned, you will need to try to soothe them.

Summary—Gardening Your Brain

We are bestowed with a measure of free will, and the important point here is that this freedom of choice can be used to improve our score of Darwinian happiness. Although human free will has a fair amount of influence on

Plate10. You should tend your brain as you would care for a garden.

conscious functions, it has precious little to say about affairs in the realm of the unconscious.

One important piece of advice is to let the autopilots of the unconscious care for the business they are designed to care for, with the exception of certain situations: Primarily, show restraint when the brain is bombarded with instigating stimuli. In short, give to the unconscious what belongs to the unconscious, and to the conscious what the conscious should dictate.

More advice: Utilize your free will to make the most of your brain's innate propensities for positive feelings. You may pursue pleasant sensations, but it is also possible to choose to avoid conditions that are in unnecessary Discord with our genetic design. The latter point is particularly relevant when considering the danger of creating a scarred psyche—in other words, a brain that has been molded in an unfortunate direction due to inappropriate stimuli. The social nature of emotions makes them particularly vulnerable to "bad learning," and possible consequences include anxiety disorders and depression. The guiding principle is to tend your brain like a much-loved garden: Cultivate flowers that are in the shape of positive conscious or unconscious memories, and avoid burns in the form of inappropriate and unfortunate influences. As anyone who has been responsible for creating and cultivating a garden can tell you, what you do in the first years has a disproportionately large impact on the quality of the more mature garden. Thus, it is particularly important to offer children optimal conditions from early on in their lives.

Another important point is that although joy may be more potent than pain and fear in improving our score of Darwinian happiness, the trick is not only to seek the more delightful feelings, but also to deal in an appropriate way with any sensation that surfaces.

One final point before I move on: Knowledge about human behavioral biology is a good first step when taking on the task of improving the quality of life; consequently more discussion in the following chapters will be allocated to describing our various innate tendencies.

CHAPTER 8

Sex:
The Most Important and Most Difficult Task

Sexuality is like walking in turbid waters—if you understand the biology of sex, at least you have a stick for guidance and support.

Potent Rewards

Evolution is at its prime when it comes to sexual behavior; it displays the highest degree of imagination and vitality when dealing with the need to copulate in order to reproduce. It is one of the paradoxes of biology that something technically so simple has evolved into a combination of exceedingly intricate and complex patterns of behavior. As a student of behavior, I marvel at the complexity and adopt it as a good enough excuse to take a keen interest. Moreover, the fact that sexual behavior troubles many of us makes it a worthwhile subject for this book. I believe most of us can obtain a higher score of Darwinian happiness by an improved sexual life.

You may find some comfort in the fact that sex is a most challenging matter not only for us humans, but for most mammals. Why is this the case?

Hitting a vagina with a penis at blank range requires neither precision, nor acrobatic skills, nor exhaustion. True, the act itself is not difficult, but in order to understand the problems involved, we need to look at the obstacles a sexually mature individual has to overcome in order to get there; that is, in order to get a chance to copulate.

Procreation requires the cooperation of a male and a female. There is a snag here, right at this point: The two individuals, or rather their genes, share a concern about sending genes off into the next generation, but they also have conflicting interests. Although the main question, biologically speaking, is whether or not to copulate, whom you choose to copulate with is rather important—and particularly so in pair-bonding species. Thus the genes push animals to engage in intercourse, but they also promote a concern for partner choice. They ask the individual—the female typically more so than the male—to be selective.

Selectivity is responsible for two types of conflicts: First of all, only one of two potential partners may wish to engage in sex with the other; and second, several individuals may desire the same partner. Moreover, selectivity requires displays, or other criteria that can be used to distinguish a "good" partner from a "not so good" one. These aspects of procreation have been instrumental in the evolution of the intricacies of sexual behavior.

Sexual behavior is directed or, in the case of humans, at least strongly influenced by innate tendencies. It is the combination of complexity and the distinct genetic input that makes it so fascinating for a biologist.

From the genes' point of view, it is worth all the trouble. After all, for them procreation is the main purpose of life. Whatever other appetites and desires you may have, they are basically just the means to sustain you until the next chance to copulate—or to help your children get there. As to your personal benefits, the genes have instructed the brain to offer generous rewards for your cooperation. Knowledge about how to best harvest these rewards is important for your measure of Darwinian happiness.

This chapter is about sex; the next one concerns love. I realize that separating these topics into two chapters introduces a bias, but it also makes the presentation easier to follow. If you feel that, in my description of sex, I forget the deeper commitment involved, please keep in mind that I shall explore that aspect in the next chapter.

Where Did All the Pleasure Go?

Procreation does not require a desire to have children; motivation to copulate is sufficient. In fact, it is not even important for the female to find this act all that enchanting, since the male drive toward orgasm is sufficient to make things happen. A certain amount of collaboration is, however, preferred; thus, there should be something in the copulation for her, too. It is relevant to note that in a few species, including humans, evolution has had particular reasons to offer females ample pleasures from sexual activity. I shall return to the "why" later.

The brain circuits involved in sexual desire are located in the subcortical region, which is to be expected in the case of such an ancient process. Either electrical stimulation, or an increase in the activity of the neurotransmitter acetylcholine, in a region known as the septal area, will cause arousal. As is the case with many other pleasures, sexual satisfaction also involves opioid circuits.[176]

For animals living under natural conditions, the behavioral mechanisms for sexuality generally function according to their intentions. This does not generally imply an absence of conflicts, since a bird may occasionally be left dead after fighting for a mate, but destructive actions are normally rare. In humans the activity seems to be fraught with all sorts of mental nuisances.[177]

As with other animals, humans need to deal with the two basic conflicts: (1) Men and women have different concerns, and (2) there is competition within the sexes. In addition to these conflicts, the combination of pair-bonding and group living carries with it particular problems: We are close to several persons of the opposite sex with whom we are not supposed to have sex. To top it off, we have this odd tendency to be shy and timid about sex.

The preference for doing "it" (the more descriptive words tend to be taboo) under the sheets—with the lights off, pajamas on, and nobody within hearing range—is probably a uniquely human attribute. Your dog would just laugh at this display of secrecy; after all, there is nothing more natural and biologically appropriate than adult intercourse.

I believe our shyness is not just a cultural bias, but is also in part an inherent consequence of the rare combination of group living and pair-bonding. In order to avoid conflicts, sex should preferably take place in privacy—as it probably did in the Stone Age. The point is obvious if you happen to be dealing with someone else's partner, but even with your own partner, it may be better not to tempt others by doing a live performance. A preference for secrecy easily translates into timidity and shyness.

When shyness is added to the complexity, the conflicts, and the social nature of the behavior, it should come as no surprise that sexual activity is highly vulnerable to Discord conditions. As previously pointed out, any brain module can malfunction, but those dealing with sex are particularly prone to cause trouble. Consequently, some people shy away from sex all together, or they end up with frustrations such as guilt and embarrassment, or with odd preferences. The problems may reduce the net yield of rewarding sensations to below zero.

Sex will never be easy. Moreover, it may be one of the more characteristic victims of Discord conditions, and can thus serve as an index for the soundness of a society. I believe that there is room for improvements in most present cultures, and that an understanding of the biological basis of sexual behavior is a good starting point.

Why Murder Is More Appropriate Than Intercourse

While we are relatively relaxed about the portrayal of violence, it seems odd that the naked body is highly taboo. On wide-screen films or on the TV screen, you can view in brutal detail bone-crunching displays, torture, and blood-letting or blood-spitting (and even children's cartoons are swamped with bullets and butchery); yet the most horrendous situation to be shown on television is two adults engaged in explicit sex. Slaughtering another human being can hardly be considered an ideal diversion, while sex, on the other hand, is roughly the most natural, the most joyful, and the most important activity to engage in. So why this strange priority?

The ban is not confined to Western society. It would seem as if most present societies work hard to suppress sexuality: Women are expected to cover up part, if not all, of their bodies in order to avoid stimulating men. In some parts of the world the clitoris is removed to stop women from engaging in sex for the sake of pleasure. On the other hand, men are taught that masturbation will empty their brains, or that appreciating pictures of nude women will cause heaven to cave in. Why all the secrecy and repression?

In my opinion, there are two factors that can help explain why violence is considered more appropriate than intercourse: One reason is to be found in our presumed inherent shyness. The other, more important one, is that sex is somehow more difficult to deal with than violence.

Aggression normally appears only when there is a specific cause for it. In other words, as long as the signals that give rise to fights are avoided, violence is pretty much under control. Sex, on the other hand, is backed by strong and continuously present desires. It is a more permeating mental force, and powerful emotions have a nasty habit of causing a mess, particularly when combined with Discord conditions and a potential for conflicts. The impulsive response of typical modern societies is, of course, to try to curb the urge.

The power of sex is exemplified by a recent study on mice: Normally, if an unfamiliar male mouse is brought into the cage of another male, the latter will be aggressive and try to chase it away; whereas, if you add a female the male will try to copulate. This choice of activity—attack or intercourse—depends on whether the smell of the intruder indicates that it is respectively a male or a female. Then what happens if the original inhabitant of the cage has had the gene that allows it to distinguish between these two types of smell removed? Catherine Dulac and coworkers found the answer to this question: The default behavioral pattern laid down in the mice is that if they do not know what the stranger is, then "make love not war."[178]

Another factor that has to be taken into account is that in a large society, as opposed to a traditional tribal society, more sexual temptations can be found: The presence of a vast number of women, live or in pictures, means that men are flooded with enticing stimuli, requiring a restraint that the genes have not quite adapted to. Female dress codes are an attempt at reducing those signals.

The main societal concerns are presumably that men will violently force sex upon women and that random or unwarranted sexual activity may cause the birth of children lacking proper parents. Moreover, many health authorities worry about the dissemination of sexually transmitted diseases.

The above concerns offer ample support for an effort to suppress our sexual desires. Or do they? The point is that, although the suppression at one time probably did make sense, the question remains: To what extent does it make sense today?

Nowadays we are in a position to avoid some of the negative consequences of liberal sex, such as unwanted pregnancies and infections. Furthermore, we can teach teenagers about sex. We can both help them understand the underlying mental mechanisms and inform them how to take precautions. In fact, it is likely that the attempt to repress such a potent mental drive just adds stress and frustrations that subsequently give rise to atrocious sexual behavior. The suppression is an obvious example of a Discord: While it may be somewhat appropriate in a modern society, the veil of secrecy should only be implemented to the extent that it truly serves a purpose. The more Discord the conditions are, the more likely it is that the underlying nerve circuits will develop in a wrong direction, resulting in more aberrant sexual behavior.

A Darwinian morality should accept natural sexuality and focus on kindness and consideration, rather than on avoidance and guilt. Sexual abuse is included in the list of civilization diseases, and I do not believe the present strategy in Western society to be optimal for lessening the burden. The principles of Darwinian happiness suggest that we should opt for more sex and less violence, on TV and in real life.

Why Not Do It Alone?

Why hassle with sex at all? Few people seriously contemplate total abstinence, but more have at some point asked themselves whether the pleasure is really worth the trouble.

Graffiti on toilet walls only rarely carries much intellectual depth, such as the point made in the following (slightly modified): "There is nothing as overrated as a bad sexual relation, and nothing as underestimated as a trip to the toilet." To empty one's bowels or bladder is an important physiological function, and the brain does indeed offer rewards to encourage us to do so. Unfortunately, the supply is limited, so the process cannot be repeated indefinitely; but on the positive side, going to the toilet does not require the collaboration of another person. True, sex is the key to more potent pleasures, but that does not do you much good if the psychological burden blocks the harvest.

Was it really worth it? The question occasionally pops up after an orgasm—forgotten again before the next attempt. The philosopher writing on the toilet wall remembered: The trip to the toilet was apparently the more memorable experience.

For the biologist, the question of whether it is worth it or not has a completely different answer. Mating is a biological paradox. Reproduction could be taken care of much more efficiently without the trouble of having to find a partner.[179] Aphids illustrate this point very well: Throughout the summer the females of these insects do fine without any males, and they produce progeny that are born pregnant. The whole process is asexual and extremely efficient. The aphid can concentrate on sucking sap from the leaves and still end up with thousands of offspring. But then, as

Plate 11. All important bodily functions, including peeing, are designed to involve pleasure.

fall arrives, they suddenly give up this leisurely life and seek a mate. Why bother?

The answer lies at the heart of the evolutionary process. A species that never cares to exchange genes between individuals can do great—for a while. Sooner or later, however, each line of descent will have accumulated so many bad mutations as to cause serious problems; or the species will be too genetically homogeneous to survive the attack of parasites or alterations in the environment. Many species have probably tried this strategy, and most of them are now extinct. Most of the surviving species have evolved some sort of mechanism for the distribution of genetic material among the lines of descendants. With such a system, the lucky ones that receive favorable genes get a chance to move on in the evolutionary race. Thus, even if the majority of descendants vanishes, the species survives.

Bacteria do not copulate, at least not in our sense of the word. It was originally assumed that they just replicate by fission. Upon closer scrutiny we have come to realize that most, if not all, microorganisms have actually evolved their own mechanisms for exchanging genes. They need genetic exchange for the same reason that we need it—to secure the survival of the species.

Sex is merely the name for the type of genetic exchange favored by mammals. For those who consider sex to be a burden, the biological rationale may not offer that much comfort. The important point is that sex should not be a burden. Sex has the potential for doing a lot more for Darwinian happiness than the bees can ever do for the flowers, or the aphids for each other. It should be a treasure chest well worth the effort.

Fortunately our brains are not that meticulous when it comes to handing out these rewards, meaning that it is easy to fool the genes. The use of preventives does not block the sensations; neither is it seriously in Discord. You may even take inspiration from the aphids, and harvest pleasures doing it alone.

Focal Attractions

In order to understand human sexuality from a biological point of view, we should try to paint a picture of how our innate tendencies influence men and women, respectively.[180] I should stress that the picture offered is that of the average man and woman; it is to be expected that not all the details apply to everybody.

In men the sexual urge is primarily directed at seduction and subsequent orgasm. The seduction (the term should be understood to include both "proper" and "improper" advances) part of the program is important, since it gives the woman a taste of what the man has to offer and thus a platform for evaluating whether or not there is a basis for a relationship. It also synchronizes the two to the possibility of mating, and even offers its own rewards.

This template applies to most mammals. In species that are not pair-bonding, the female tends to be less choosy; which makes sense because it is then solely the quality of the genes that matters, not the quality of infant care. In these species the seduction protocols need not be that elaborate; the whole procedure therefore takes less time.

To what extent the female is active in seeking mates varies greatly from species to species, and—particularly in our species—between individuals. Regardless of which sex started the process, the two must both get ready for copulation. Nature has devised a vast range of strategies in various animals aimed at this goal: anything from waving the ears to urinating in the face of the partner. The strategies may not all match your ideal of a romantic evening, but for the animal species in question, they obviously work.[181]

For human males a woman with visible signs of sexual maturity is sufficient to activate desire. Certain females, and certain types of clothing or display, tend to confer stronger stimuli. For example, youthfulness and an expression of virginity typically yield the more potent signal. The biological explanation for this observation is that the man's genes have a better chance of gaining a revenue from the investment if desire is directed at females that have a long fertile period ahead, and are as yet unlikely to carry semen from another male. In certain species of animals, including some of the baboons, the male apparently prefers the older, more experienced females. These species are typically not pair-bonding; the explanation therefore is presumably that an experienced female is a better bet in cases where the male does not intend to hang around and help.[182]

A preference for youth is definitely mainstream among human males, and the average woman adapts to this ideal; makeup, cosmetic surgery, and clothing tend to fit the description. The ideal female face has juvenile characteristics, such as soft skin, rounded cheeks and large eyes, in contrast to the male face, which should be more square, with distinct chin and cheeks. The breasts should appear untouched by babies, and a cross-cultural investigation concludes that the most desirable women have a waistline roughly 70 percent of the measure around breasts and thighs—a waistline more typical for those who have not yet given birth.[183]

The oldest known figures shaped by humans portray women that hardly match this ideal. Our forebears produced a lot of Venus figurines that typically have a massive belly, the first at least 30,000 years ago. My guess is that rather than being an early sign of a blooming porn industry, they were meant to venerate fertility. It should be pointed out, however, that a certain amount of fatty tissue is appreciated in several cultures as a sign of prosperity and health. Then again, it is difficult to carve stone

Plate 12. Are breasts just a human version of the peacock's tail? And did the people who lived near Willendorf in Austria 25,000 years ago make this Venus figure fat because they liked chubby women or because they venerated fertility? This 4 3/8 inches high limestone figure is in the Naturhistorisches Museum of Vienna.

without advanced tools, and it is possible that all the attempts at making sexier figures broke in the middle.

The sight of nude women, whether in stone, on paper, on the screen, imagined, or even live, is more than enough to elicit rewards in the male brain. Exploiting these rewards seems like a reasonable strategy to obtain pleasant sensations.

Some women appreciate the sight of a shapely male specimen, but as a sexual stimulant male anatomy tends to be less potent than that of the female. Situational, psychological, and social factors typically carry more weight for women, and it is useful to recall that it is the female strategy to be selective. For an individual who expects more from the partner than a set of genes, the criteria of selection should not be limited to simple anatomical features. The biological perspective, therefore, suggests that a female should look for a resourceful and healthy male that is likely to carry on the relationship and offer support. The shape of the penis, or other anatomical details, have only limited value for these criteria. Since the drive to initiate copulation is typically stronger in male than in female vertebrates, nature has apparently decided that it is more practical to allocate the drive primarily to the one sex. Consequently, a male needs sexually enticing stimuli more than females. Whereas females need signals appropriate for choice, a male needs signals designed to initiate sex.

This chapter concentrates on men's desire for women's anatomy simply because this force is more permeating than women's interest in male anatomy, which is why pictorial pornography for ladies never cashed in much, and why women buy stories about knights and doctors instead. I shall discuss the pros and cons of such surrogates at the end of the chapter.

Why Bulging is Beautiful

One feature of human female anatomy is particularly interesting: the breasts. They are there to feed babies, but they also serve another function. Other female mammals have nipples or udders designed primarily for the requirement of the infant: The nipples are long and easy to suck. In women, evolution has come up with a rather surprising design; instead of keeping the table set for babies, the nipples are flat and placed on top of a mountain of fatty tissue. The shape is awkward for both the baby and the mother; in fact the manufacturers of rubber nipples and nursing bottles know what shape the child prefers.

It is hard to imagine that evolution would come up with such a design without some sort of rational reason. In other words, women's breasts should offer an advantage—and so they do. They attract men. In evolutionary terms, it is obviously relevant to equip women with sexually attractive anatomical features; the strange thing is that this could be cared for without making life difficult for babies or for female joggers. So why breasts?

Women—and their babies—have as much reason to complain as peacocks do. Both glossy feathers and bulging fatty tissue are dubious designs, but, as pointed out before, evolution in general and sexual evolution in particular do not always work toward technically optimal solutions. I believe the evolution of breasts to be a consequence of bipedal walking.

In many Old World monkeys and apes, including presumably our distant ancestors, the buttocks serve as sexual stimulants.[184] They typically swell and turn pink when the female is in estrus. Since these species are four-legged, and the males mount from behind, the buttocks are as suitably located as the Times Square coke advertisement.

Bipedalism changed two things: The buttocks no longer stick out as much, and the concomitant movement of the vagina favors face-to-face penetration. Our female ancestors already had two small bulges in front, appropriately filled with milk glands. Evolution tends to go for the simple solutions: The bulges in front could easily be made larger by redistributing some of the naturally occurring fatty tissue that women are endowed with. Larger bulges served as mimics for buttocks, and males therefore preferred women with larger bulges. The rest is evolutionary history.

Breasts do not actually serve babies and men only; they are also erogenous zones designed to raise sexual pleasure in women. It is conceivable that this function contributed to the particular choice of position for the swelling to take place: As discussed in Chapter 6, the upper torso has "tickle skin" designed to be particularly sensitive to touch, and to promote play behavior and bonding. This part of the body is therefore fruitful territory in which to erect a structure designed to stimulate sexual relations and subsequent pair-bonding.

It is interesting to note that although the use of breasts as a mimic of buttocks is unique to humans, another species has acquired a related strategy. Females of the gelada baboon do not have breasts that will impress a human male, but what they do have up front is coloring and skin folds that have a remarkable resemblance to their genitals. These monkeys spend a lot of time sitting on the ground, which means that their genitals are less visible; thus, the extra skin folds presumably help to stimulate desire in males. (I might mention that males of the related mandrills have been equally "inventive"; their faces contain patterns that have been interpreted as mimicking male genitals.)[185]

Most male primates are attracted to female genitals: The rear view of a female presenting herself is stimulating. For a bipedal primate, however, the female genitals are less visible, whether viewed from the front or from the back. In order to preserve a signal with a certain power, humans retained pubic hair while most of the residual fur was lost. This ornamentation compensates for the hidden female genitals, and emphasizes the male organ as well.

The human female body contains several anatomical features designed to stimulate a sexual lust in men, yet men's desire is not exclusively concerned with these features (although some women may feel it to be that way). For most males, breasts and buttocks need to be attached to a face in order to be stimulating. The qualities of the face— including the personality it suggests—have a dramatic impact on the attraction of the body. Moreover, a long-term relationship, and the concomitant emotional attachment, should add qualities to the sexual life.

The importance of combining sexually stimulating anatomical features with a personality is evident from photos in men's magazines. It would have been a lot easier for the pornography industry to recruit models if it was sufficient to portray the parts below the chin, but the fact that most pictures include a face implies that pictures without it do not sell.

Lucky Women

Catholics have claimed that sex in the absence of intent to reproduce is bestial. It is an interesting claim, particularly since the truth appears to be close to the opposite.

Whereas human ovulation is concealed, not only for the man, but typically for the woman as well, most female mammals vigorously advertise their period of heat. Most non-human male animals are interested solely in these females, and as a consequence sexual life is highly concentrated in time. While a man may consider this an unnecessary restriction of possibilities, for a male baboon wasting energy on random females is absolute squander. Moreover, female animals tend to be rather indifferent to the sexual act. The average cow will not stop ruminating, or risk missing a good mouthful of grass, no matter what the bull is up to. Again, humans are an exception: Sexual activity can be surprisingly rewarding for women. Thus, human sexuality has a rather unique design: Not only are sexually stimulating signals continuously present, but both males and females delight in the act regardless of the period of fertility. Under those circumstances, sex with no intent, or chance, of procreation can hardly come as a surprise. And as to the Catholic opinion: Humans are bestial, while animals are. . . . well, human.

We ought to rejoice in the way evolution has shaped us. Although it may appear as though the design was made deliberately for the purpose of improving our Darwinian happiness, evolution unfortunately does not work that way. Our exaggerated sexual pleasures are there for a more practical reason.

In this regard, the zoologist John MacKinnon has made an intriguing observation in orangutans that indicates an alternative function of sex. To his surprise he found that orangutans living on the island of Sumatra have a merrier, or at least more active, sexual life than their cousins on the neighboring island of Borneo. The two islands differ in that Sumatra has more leopards, which eat orangutans, whereas on Borneo, the siamangs, a species belonging to the family of apes referred to as gibbons, competes with orangutans for food. The consequence of having these other two species is that on Sumatra the female orangutan and her infant depend on the presence of the larger and stronger male, which protects them and helps them obtain food. The amount of help obtained from the Sumatran males would probably not impress a human wife, but they do spend more time with the mother and infant compared to those on Borneo. It seems likely that the increased sexual activity stimulates the males to hang around.[186]

Our children depend a lot on the presence and services of the father. As in the case of the Sumatran orangutan, sexual activity is presumably an important ingredient in the glue designed by evolution to keep parents together; and the extensive sexual rewards evolved in part for this purpose. Moreover, the fact that males cannot zoom in on ovulating females implies that a single copulation is not worth that much. In order to obtain a fair chance of impregnating the woman, he has to stick around—at least for awhile—and then preferably long enough to provide support and to help raise the children. Actually, prolonged sexual activity not only increases the chance of impregnation, but recent research suggests that it also helps the immune system of the mother to accept the fetus. Apparently, if the immune system gets used to the foreign antigens associated with the semen of the father (some of these antigens will be present in the child as well), it is less likely to raise a destructive immune response against the fetus. The bad news is that the positive effect on the immune system is not achieved in the presence of a condom, while the good news is that the effect is obtained regardless of which bodily entrance the semen enters.[187]

In light of the above explanation for our extensive sexual appetite, other observations also make sense. For example, in most mammals the male has a bone inside the penis to facilitate penetration. Men do not. Instead they require a strong and continuous sexual arousal for the blood to keep the penis erect. As many men know, it is not always that easy. A penis bone would have been ruinous for the suppliers of Viagra.

Furthermore, we can complete an intercourse by entering either from the front or from the rear, but the most common, the so-called missionary position, is face to face. The reason may not be purely anatomical: The face-to-face position is presumably yet another element that contributes to bonding.

The dual function of procreation and pair-bonding does increase the mental complexity of our sexual life, and thereby the probability of dispute and frustration, but it also contributes to the amount of rewards available. Women have particular reasons to rejoice at this design, as it offers them pleasures that are unavailable to most female animals.

A Lucky Species

We have been described as the most sex-mad species on earth. Actually we are only a fair number two (not counting some individuals who try hard to regain the lead). One of our closest relatives, the bonobo (or pigmy chimpanzee), rightfully deserves the title.

Some people seem to take a special pride in the missionary position as a uniquely human—and, of course, venerable—way of doing it. The bonobos, however, were experts long before the missionaries voyaged to Africa to teach the natives how to do it properly. The bonobos actually know more positions and alternatives than you would ever dream of trying. Or how about penis fencing, where two males hang from a branch and dash their penises together till they come? Doing it like the bonobos is everyone doing it with everybody, everywhere and at any time. With that much activity you can hardly complain that the average stint only lasts 13 seconds. In other words, extreme promiscuity is not our style; it is a bonobo-specific trait. What they do have in common with us is that their sexual activity has taken on a dual function. They are not pair-bonding, which makes a lot of sense because fooling around with all the other members of the tribe would not do well in a pair-bonding species. So why do they waste so much time and energy on sex?

Instead of forming pair-bonds they form bands. The sharing of sexual rewards presumably binds the troop together—as it does for a man and a woman in our own species. The activity helps curb possible conflicts and boosts genial behavior. For example, when a band of bonobos come across a delicacy, instead of starting a fight, they have some fast-sex as a starter, and subsequently divide the main course as friends. Their instant sex serves much the same purpose our smiles do. Not a bad idea?

Bonobos are more affiliating, less hierarchical, less aggressive, and less male dominated than other primates, including the common chimpanzee. In fact, compared to most primates, they are exceptionally peaceful. As stated by the primatologist Frans de Waal: "The chimpanzee resolves sexual issues with power; the bonobo resolves power issues with sex." Thus, the bonobos really make sense of the slogan "Make love not war." Unfortunately, they belong to a different species.[188]

The Advantage of Homosexuality

For the sake of being social, it makes sense that bonobos enjoy sex with the same gender. Actually quite a few species have been observed to participate in apparent homosexual behavior, typically in the form of one male pretending to mount another male. This behavior, however, is usually interpreted as a way of confirming a social hierarchy, and, contrary to the bonobo activity, the act is not concluded by an orgasm.

Animals in captivity may try to mount any object, dead or alive, but that has more to do with Discord conditions than with their normal expression of sexual behavior. The key difference—that makes human homosexual behavior stand out as a paradox—is that in all the above examples regular heterosexual behavior is included in the animal's repertoire. Most gay people take little interest in the opposite sex! They typically become aware of their inclination as young adults, and do not change orientation later in life despite social pressure or even a personal desire to be straight.

According to the geneticist Dean Hamer, male homosexuality tends to correlate with a slightly different brain anatomy, as well as with certain genetic markers.[189] His conclusion, which is controversial, is that there are genes predisposing for this trait. Studies on twins support his idea; yet environmental factors are apparently more important than genes. For a biologist this is a relief: I would hate to see the beauty of Darwinian theory stranded on a few "misplaced" penises. In any event, it is a gross understatement to say that an exclusive interest in one's own gender is a dubious evolutionary strategy.

An evolutionary rationale for such behavior is very hard to conceive, but this does not mean that a biological perspective cannot help us to understand. One relevant piece of information is that you may be born with a personality feature without that feature being "inborn." Not only the sexual organs, but also the brain centers that direct sexual behavior, develop in the fetus in a process orchestrated by hormones. Thus, a person may be "born" a homosexual, even though there is nothing in his genes to suggest such an inclination, if part of the "orchestra" happened to play out of tune.

It is also relevant to note that the various physical and mental elements that define gender develop more or less independently of each other. The point is illustrated by experiments with rhesus monkeys. The young males of this species are distinguished from young females by two gender-specific behavioral elements: They engage in rough play, and they imitate copulation by mounting each other. If female fetuses are injected with male sex hormones, they too display these male types of behavior, displaying either one or both elements, depending on when the hormones are administrated, which thus demonstrates that the two types of behavior arise independently.[190]

Based on the above information, as well as on other aspects of human behavioral biology, I see several factors related to the design of our species that may contribute to an explanation for homosexual behavior: The importance of hormonal stimulation during fetal development is one clue. If the level of the main male sexual hormone—*testosterone*—is low during a critical period, a part of the brain is feminized. We know that stress reduces the level of testosterone, and stress during pregnancy may be sufficient to cause feminization of the fetus. In support of this theory, it has been claimed that there are more male homosexuals conceived during a war.[191]

Another factor is our strong, innate, human tendency to cooperate within genders. Among primates this is a rare feature. In most species there is more competition than collaboration within males or females. Moreover, in addition to appreciating the company of our own sex, we have a particularly strong sexual drive, and the combination of these two features should dispose toward sexual activity with individuals of the same sex. The bonobos use sex to improve cooperation; humans may have inherited a touch of the same. In fact, sexually implicit play among young human males seems to be surprisingly common, which may be a phenomena related to similar behavior in the bonobos. Moreover, even with animals that are a lot less concerned with sex than humans, it is typical to see odd (in the sense of biologically useless) sexual behavior when the conditions of living are in Discord. Thus, the Discord conditions of present societies may be another factor that boosts the frequency of homosexuality.

One aspect of our present condition may be particularly relevant: It has been postulated in psychological literature that "only the exotic becomes erotic."[192] While preschool girls and boys play with each other relatively indiscriminately, there is a tendency toward preferring the company of one's own sex in the years prior to puberty. This preference presumably leads to a gender identity and gender cooperation, but it also keeps the two sexes apart. Actually, most species, including humans, have an innate mechanism designed to avoid mating with close relatives. In our case this mechanism includes a preference for "exotic" mates, meaning someone we do not know that well. The preference for the company of one's own sex prior to puberty presumably causes youngsters of the opposite sex to become more exotic, and thus more suitable as partners. It is possible that the underlying mental mechanism is another victim of the present environment: Boys and girls typically attend the same classes at school; likewise, we meet with so many strangers of both sexes that no one becomes exotic. Thus, one of the mechanisms that should lead to a preference for the opposite sex may not function as intended.

In line with the suggestion of Dean Hamer, it is likely that some genes do predispose toward homosexuality. Genes that influence the production of hormones, or genes that are involved in directing cooperation within genders, would be expected to do so. However, whether it is in the genes or in the environment, the important point, as far as Darwinian happiness goes, is how to make the most out of the passion we have. Statistically speaking, male homosexuality is about as abnormal as having an IQ above 130. The guru recommends that we participate in sexual activity, but what sort of activity we choose is of secondary importance as long as all the participants involved are happy. Homosexual activity stimulates much the same reward mechanisms as heterosexual activity, and as far as the interest of your genes is concerned, it is no worse than normal intercourse with a condom. Homosexuals actually have the benefit of dealing with partners more similar to themselves. But then again, they are less likely to harvest the joys associated with raising children, and aberrant sexual behavior tends to be stigmatized by society.

If homosexual behavior still does not make sense, you should remember that evolution designs for survival, not for "optimality" or perfection. To illustrate this point, I shall describe an example of dubious evolutionary craft: Certain species of lizards are among the rare examples of animals that apparently get by without sex: Every individual is a "female." Since there are no males around, they have no reason even to contemplate copulation; yet, surprisingly, they do try to copulate with each other. These animals evolved from normal lizards where copulation encourages the production of hormones required for fertilization. Although the lizards changed to the strategy of virgin birth, their pseudo-male behavior still seems to increase fertility. Copulation is presumably enacted for the sake of stimulating the production of hormones that promote fertility, but fake sex is an unnecessary burden for an asexual species, and as such not something evolution should be proud of.[193]

The human species is doing a great job—that is, as far as reproduction goes—even if a fraction of the population does not contribute to propagation. Biologically speaking, I believe we are doing too well: Overpopulation is a major problem. If society was in need of raising more children, there would be a reason to discourage homosexuals, but in the present situation they should be praised.

Freakers' Ball

If you think human sexual behavior is odd, take a look at what other creatures are up to. There is enough freaky behavior among insects and other invertebrates to make the most perverted man look like a monk.[194] Here are a few examples:

Are you aware that the bedbug *Xylocaris maculopennis* rapes its fellow males? What happens is that the sperm of the attacker is brought to the sexual organ of the victim, so that when the victim later finds a female, there is a chance that he will impregnate her with another male's seeds.

How about hermaphroditic flat worms? In hermaphrodites each individual has both male and female sexual organs. These worms engage in a more serious form of penis fencing than the bonobos, the purpose of the fight being to penetrate the opponent's body with the penis and to inject its own semen under the other's skin. The loser has to take on a female role and produce eggs to be impregnated by the inserted semen, while the winner can then go on to fight other individuals.

Or how would you like to be a male spider? For some of them copulation can be particularly risky: The female is not only larger, but she is also hungry and cannibalistic by nature. To make life even more exciting for the male, her genital orifice is on the belly. Despite the hazards, the males are as horny as any man, and they willingly risk their lives, some of them ending it as an after-sex snack. No wonder that some male spiders are into bondage: They tie the female up in a silken web before they start.

Would you not agree the above examples are more bizarre than any human act could ever be? Not at all! These behaviors are not weird in so far as they all make perfect sense to an evolutionary biologist. If the male only contributes sperm, why should the female not eat her lover? It even makes sense from the male's point of view: His proteins serve a good cause, for they help the female produce offspring with his genes. Obviously it would not work the other way around.

It seems that humans are the real freaks. Much of the bizarre sexual behavior observed in our species does not contribute to anybody's genes. Yet, the important point when it comes to increasing the average Darwinian happiness of the population is not whether the behavior does your genes any good, but whether it hurts fellow humans. It can be claimed that forced sex is evolutionarily sensible; the male sexual urge does not depend on mutual attraction, not even on cooperation—and genetically speaking, why should it? Rape-like behavior has been observed in several animals, even in birds.[195] When social restraints are reduced in our own species, the number of rapes increases—as witnessed in times of war. Fortunately, humans have other "instincts"—our social inclination and empathy for others, for example—to restrain certain urges coming from the sexual modules of the brain.

Actually we are not the only species to have a problem with violent and unproductive sexual behavior, such as pedophilia: Male sea lions have a very strong sexual drive during the breeding season; in the frustration of not gaining access to an adult female, they may try to copulate with juveniles—the force exerted occasionally killing the pup. This behavior can be explained by the combination of sexual drive, stress, and the fact that females tend to retain juvenile features for the purpose of sexual attraction: Female sea lions are smaller and have a more rounded head compared to males.

Taking into consideration the particularly strong sexual drive in human males, it is not surprising to see a variety of brutal and inappropriate sexual activity; and the attraction of juvenile features places offspring at risk in both sea lions and humans.

You will not win any popularity contests by suggesting that rape and pedophilia are "natural" behaviors shared with animals. My point is that we stand a better chance at curbing the unfortunate manifestations of sexual desire if we seek to understand the driving forces, rather than denying their existence. Thus, please do not read the above discussion on aberrant sexual behavior in the light that I condone cruel or coercive conduct. I certainly do not.

I realize that some people might try to misuse the evolutionary perspective by statements such as: "We must accept that men rape women because it is in their genes." All sorts of nasty behavior can be claimed to be natural: The fact that we are born with a propensity to get angry at each other does not condone shooting your opponent. What is natural is not necessarily good. I believe the above type of excuse should be countered by pointing out that it is also within the power of the human mind to show restraint—rather than by denying the existence of sexual or violent urges. The fight against any form of aggressive or undesirable behavior should not be fought by sticking our heads in the sand, but rather by enlightening the public about human behavioral biology—and about the measure of free will that nature has bestowed upon us.

As a biologist, I am tempted to differentiate between genetically productive sex and evolutionary dead ends: Normal intercourse and rape end up in the first category, while homosexuality, pedophilia, and frigidity are the outcasts. In the context of Darwinian happiness, however, the question of biological sanity is not important. The important question is: How do those involved benefit? It is okay to be a freak as long as it is a ball for everyone in the party.

Even though rape and pedophilia can happen in the best of species, humans are probably the worst kids in the class. The final point I wish to make in this section on aberrant behavior is that it does not have to be that way. To understand the forces of human sexuality is only a starting point. One important cause of our problems is that the environment instrumental in shaping these modules in adolescent brains—more specifically, the attitudes of present societies—is in serious Discord. In other words, a more open-minded attitude might help ease the situation.

To my mind, the taboos and oppression raised against sexuality are not an optimal way for curbing the problems brought on by our intense sexual drive. Condemning, more or less, all sexual desire is not conducive to developing healthy sexual attitudes. The more Discord the setting, the more unwholesome behavior you are likely to get. For example, one controversial issue is whether children should be allowed to finger or play with sexual organs, either alone or with buddies. In many species, and in certain human cultures, this is common. I believe the sexual play of infants may help them develop a normal sexual life.

We teach our children lots of things with limited relevance. Sexuality, which is the type of behavior that will make one of the larger impacts on their Darwinian happiness . . . well, they more or less have to figure out what it is about by themselves. Unfortunately, they are more likely to be brought up with coercion and a distorted vision, rather than relevant information.

How to Deal with Surrogates

Any form of stimuli that hits the reward mechanism of the human brain can today be purchased as a "fast food" version. The most obvious example is the exploitation of male sexuality, which has advanced from that of a barter economy to the size of a large multinational corporation. The sales figures of the industry, to the extent that they are available, testify to the potency of the rewards involved. Furthermore, the turnover of the various products on sale testifies to how well each product fits male desires.

Even female chimps realize their potential. If a male possesses bananas, the female will approach and display her genitals—sort of as a reminder. Both chimp and human males are generous toward sexually interesting females.

Women are less likely to buy sex, but they do go for "social pornography." Catering to either male or female desires undoubtedly induces agreeable sensations. The question of whether we can get away with unlimited indulgence without dire consequences is relevant for both types of products.

We buy food rather than head out into Mother Nature to find it. Are there any reasons not to take advantage of commercial sex, or of love that is confined within the covers of a book? And, for the sake of Darwinian happiness, are not more stimuli better?

The market does not lie; the products do induce pleasure. Moreover, enjoying pornography is probably the safest sex there is, completely free of germs and unwelcome pregnancies. Yet there are pitfalls. The activity may mentally harm you because it is not a solely positive experience to take the pleasure out of its natural setting; in other words, commercial sex is more or less of a Discord. In addition, a habituation to the commercial version of sex and love may lead to an unrealistic picture of reality: Real women just do not look like the centerfolds of *Playboy*, and real men are not always noble heroes. Men and women who are tuned to the commercial versions may find it difficult to exploit real-life opportunities.

With regard to the sex industry, it should also be mentioned that participation is Discord for both consumer and supplier: To be a prostitute is typically a severe psychological burden. Although the burden may be partly a consequence of cultural attitudes, it is also partly biological, as it is in the female nature to be choosy about whom to engage with. The profession of prostitution, therefore, can be expected to generate Discord-associated stress.

Products catering to male and female desires do have the potential for augmenting Darwinian happiness, but they should be handled with care. The guru recommends moderation, and, if possible, to go for the real thing, which is live love, and sexual activity in its more natural settings. A live hand to hold is better than ten pages with knights, even if the owner of the hand has the usual collection of male weaknesses.

Summary—With an Apology

Sex is not only the most difficult human activity, psychologically speaking, and most important, biologically speaking, but it is probably also the one with the most intense rewards. The main purpose of this chapter is to help you tap that resource.

I believe an understanding of the innate sexual tendencies of men and women is an important foundation for improving sexual relations in society, and an open-minded and understanding attitude is a prerequisite toward that goal. For example, it is relevant to accept a male's attraction to a female's sexual characteristics, because an attempt to suppress this interest, or stamp it as tainted, is likely to cause stress. Men who are taught that their desire to see nude women is immoral are likely to develop unwholesome attitudes toward sex. At the same time it is important to emphasize that an innate urge is no excuse for hostile behavior, whether we are talking about sex or violence.

Female readers are probably able to guess that I am a male, just by reading this chapter. I believe my description of sexuality is reasonably impartial (but I realize that some people may disagree); however, the choice of subjects is likely to reflect my gender. I have focused more on male than female sexuality—for example, the section on homosexuality focuses on gays rather than lesbians. This bias is partly a consequence of what the science of sexual behavior has been most concerned with, but may also reflect a personal preconception. Moreover, I have focused on anatomy, rather than other aspects of a person that signal attraction. This latter bias will, I trust, be compensated for in the next chapter.

Sex is a touchy issue, and I would like to apologize for any prejudice or perceived distortion you may have observed in this chapter, and for any offense it may have caused.

CHAPTER 9

Mating Behavior:
What Has Love Got To Do with It?

Going separate ways in Rikuchu Kaigan.

Why Marriage?

In this chapter I shall look at the evolutionary history of love, and conclude that love is a lot more than mere romance. Questions to be discussed include: What brought love to our lineage, what is it about, what kind of mate do you want, and why are men and women different? But first, why do we bother to hang around with just this one and only partner?

Pair-bonding is a rare feature in mammals, but it is actually quite common in birds: Some 90 percent of all avian species form couples.[196] The bonds may last a lifetime, but is it really love? Do sparrows and crows feel as we do when spring comes and there are beautiful chicks around? Birds may very well have feelings that are reminiscent of certain aspects of human love, but there appears to be something special about human pair-bonding—something quite unique and highly valuable.

Biologically speaking, the need for pair-bonding arises proportionally to the difficulties of raising progeny as a single parent. Birds do not have kindergartens and a social welfare system. More importantly, birds do not have internal fetal development and milk glands. The eggs require brooding, and progeny that hatches from eggs typically does so at an earlier stage of development than mammalian newborns. On top of that, to fly requires more in the form of maturation and learning than walking does. Thus, in most birds, the offspring need a fair amount of support before they can care for themselves.

It is not necessarily an advantage to have a bond form between father and mother. In some mammals, such as bears and hamsters, males are violently chased away after copulation. To have the father hang around just means undesirable competition for food. In the case of the Syrian hamster, the male even risks getting killed if he does not disappear fast enough.[197] In order for the male to stick around, helping out should be a better option for all the genes concerned. The father's genes, for example, should not prefer him to spend his time chasing after other females; thus paternal care is an evolutionary sensible choice when the offspring is unlikely to survive in its absence. This implies that for an affiliation between parents to be of any value, the male must be capable of helping.

The case is obvious when it comes to most birds: Both parents are able to bring back food to the one who is brooding and to the offspring. On the other hand, there is not much a bull can do when it comes to feeding the calf; the calf either sucks the mother's teats or eats grass directly from the ground. The bottom line is that pair-bonding is useful for some species, but not generally for all species.

Humans give birth to children that, compared with other mammals, are quite helpless. This is partly due to the increase in brain size, for there is a limit as to how large the skull can be in order to pass through the female birth canal, and the female hip has already taken on a shape that puts extra stress on bipedal locomotion. As a consequence, more development has to occur after birth. All the complex tasks we need to learn contribute further to the exceptionally long time it takes to bring our children to independence.

Men are capable of offering a lot of assistance to the mother and child (even though it is not always apparent). I expect that, under the conditions that shaped human evolution, an alliance between the biological father and mother drastically increased the odds of successfully bringing up children. Fathers are of course less important in a society with reasonable social security, but bear in mind that our genes evolved long before the invention of a social welfare system.

There is actually another, rather unique, rationale for marriage in the case of humans: We evolved a requirement for adult men to cooperate, a trait that would be difficult to achieve if the alpha males demanded, and seized, the right to the reproductive potential of all available females. Matrimony offers the genes of subordinate males a fair chance of getting a return for their collaborative effort.

To summarize so far: Marriage does not start in church, since the genes have prepared the mind beforehand for the event. With birds this is relatively straightforward: They follow their genes with little self-destructive tendencies toward reflection and autonomous ideas. In humans, however, our measure of free will demands that the genes devise a more indirect way of influencing behavior. To have the generally selfish individual give up his or her independence and form a lasting coalition with the opposite sex, requires—and certainly deserves—generous rewards. The pleasure centers run high, which is why love is the most glorified emotion in the human repertoire—and an excellent source of Darwinian happiness.

On Moles, Voles, Men, and Witches

Studies of moles and small rodents have taught us something about how nature implements mammalian pair-bonding.[198] In moles, copulation stimulates the production of vasopressin, which acts both as a hormone and as a neuropeptide. In the monogamous, prairie-living species of mole, vasopressin contributes to the process of pair-bonding. It is possible to demonstrate this by injecting the hormone into the bloodstream: The animal that receives the injection will tend to join any member of the opposite sex in the vicinity, regardless of previous romance (normally a male and female will go through a "getting acquainted routine" before they form a couple and have sex). We are not the only species in which sex and love are meant to go together.

In the closely related mountain-living species of mole, however, the injection of vasopressin does not have such an effect. This makes sense inasmuch as this mountain mole species is not pair-bonding. The difference correlates with the presence of receptors for vasopressin in areas of the brain presumably allocated to the process of mating.

Two closely related neuropeptides appear to be the main players in this game—besides v*asopressin* there is *oxytocin*. The former is the more important in males, where it stimulates courtship and sexual persistence; oxytocin is more important in females, where it is considered the "nurture" hormone—stimulating the production of milk, amongst other things. A common denominator of the social effects of oxytocin is to say that it promotes social memory: The release of this hormone induces some sort of familiarity and affection with other individuals in the vicinity. Both substances are active in both sexes, and are assumed to play a major role in orchestrating the whole gamut from intercourse to infant care.[199]

Love and sexual attraction are probably orchestrated by a combination of hormones and neurotransmitters in humans as well, but our love life is more complex than that of animals. Thus, there is most likely a greater variety of substances and nerve circuitry involved in human mating, and, of course, our measure of free will means that we are more in a position to overrule the pressure exerted by these substances.

Moles are insectivores; mice and voles, on the other hand, are rodents. Rodents offer another lesson regarding pair-bonding: Certain species of voles are at least as monogamous as humans. The zoologists Sue Carter and Lowell Getz have shown that the bonding of females in the monogamous voles depends on oxytocin, but the signal that causes the release of oxytocin is the smell of a suitable male—she will not even ovulate in the absence of the right scent.[200]

Actually oxytocin is also active in males, which can be shown in mice. On the first date, a male mouse subjects the female to a getting-to-know-you sniffing routine. The routine becomes shorter with each subsequent encounter; but a male mouse that has been genetically altered to lack oxytocin goes through the full 40-second sniffing routine at every meeting; in other words, he acts as if he has never before seen the female he is courting.[201]

The use of smell as a form of communication in connection with mating is not restricted to rodents but is actually typical for most mammals. They employ *pheromones*, which are chemical substances that are secreted by one individual to be sensed (smelled) by another. Each individual has a specific odor, which allows you to know who is—or has been—around.

In humans the excellence of language has caused a decline in the use of odors, yet pheromones are not entirely obsolete. The cosmetic industry is definitely not dead, and according to their advertisements your odor can work miracles. I would not completely trust these advertisements, but we probably do respond more to smell than we are aware of. Apparently strange things happen in the part of the unconscious brain linked to your nose.

In one type of experiment, men and women wear T-shirts for a couple of days. The shirts are then collected and handed to another group who are asked to indicate preference by sniffing the shirts. There have been a number of versions of this experiment, with partly conflicting results, but some conclude that there is a preference for shirts worn by the more genetically dissimilar individuals. Anyway, most scientists seem to agree on one thing—that odors influence us in ways that we are not aware of. In a more recent experiment, women were given either a regular perfume, or the same perfume with a putative synthetic female pheromone added. The women did not know which of the two they were using, yet the ones with the pheromone reported significantly more sexual activity over the next weeks, presumably because the pheromone affected either their own behavior or the behavior of the men they happened to encounter.[202]

It is generally recognized that women have a better sense of smell than men. This may explain why they buy more cosmetics—but if women have the more sensitive noses, men should have the most to gain by putting on a fragrance. They might, for example, add some musk, a substance recommended by at least nine out of ten bucks (male deer). It is my impression that when men do leave enough of their own odor to recognize it themselves, such as after a week without washing, the typical fragrance is not the one most suitable to entice women.

Sex and love will never be unfashionable, and as long as we have a nose, the cosmetic industry will survive. In fact, the above discussion points toward another potential growth industry: Witchcraft. One day witches may be able to brew a real love potion; a few drops of pheromones or psychoactive chemicals in the morning coffee and your wife stays. Already there are some love potions that rely on more than just faith. Anecdotal evidence suggests that oxytocin helps if sprayed intranasally in women—and, according to the experiments on mice, the substance could counteract the indifference of some husbands as well.

Rumor has it that the aphrodisiac yohimbine (a norepinephrine antagonist extracted from the bark of certain trees) improves all aspects of your love life; but its putative effect on bonding could very well be an indirect consequence of an increased sexual appetite (which should not necessarily discourage its use). Alternatively, a synthetic copy of a naturally occurring neuropeptide called melanocyte-stimulating hormone (MSH) is to be marketed by Palatin Technologies as a nasal aphrodisiac that stimulates desire and sexual arousal in both sexes. It has also been suggested that certain components of chocolate (anandamide and the dopamine agonist phenethylamine), stimulate love. Thus, while waiting for a more potent brew, you could offer a box of chocolates to go along with the morning coffee. They even taste good.[203]

First Love

Messenger molecules in the form of pheromones, hormones, neuropeptides, and neurotransmitters are presumably the directors of all emotion. They are the main tools at the brain's disposal. The types of investigation referred to above have given us a vague understanding of love at a neurochemical level, but in order to appreciate and utilize this emotion, I believe it may be more important to understand love in an evolutionary perspective—that is, to learn about the evolution of affinity, or bonding, between individuals.

Any type of collaboration requires a force initiated by the genes, whether it is just hanging out together as in a herd of cattle, or in the form of a deep emotional relationship such as that between mother and child. In the absence of a genetic advantage favoring geniality, the expected behavior would be to look after one's own interest in solitude and to shy away from other individuals except for the purpose of mating. Love, in a broad sense, can be defined as the emotion that causes affiliation. The emotional force that keeps the cows together is presumably relatively weak and not identical to human emotions; yet, it may be referred to as "love."

In social insects the genes simply dictate cooperation, they are presumably not afforded the luxury of love. Mammalian behavior, however, is based on feelings. One important thing that happened on the evolutionary road leading to mammals was that the offspring evolved into something requiring extensive care from the mother; as a consequence, evolution appended a strong affiliation between mother and offspring. This, I assume, was the first love.

In the previous section I discussed how certain neuropeptides help orchestrate both sexual behavior and male-female bonding. We also know that the nerve circuits involved in maternal care are closely intermeshed with those that control sexuality, and that these are situated in the subcortical brain (the limbic area).[204] Our reptile ancestors practiced sex, but at least most present-day reptiles do not care that much for their newly hatched offspring. The mammalian type of infant care apparently evolved along with our peculiar strategy of breast feeding. It is logical that the required brain activity was recruited from the circuits involved in the behavior leading to the production of children; in other words, the "first love" presumably evolved from the reptilian circuits controlling sexual behavior and egg laying.

Love between a mother and her offspring is the strongest and most consistent tie in mammals. Mothers are typically willing to sacrifice almost anything for the sake of her young, certainly including her mate and maybe even themselves.

In several species of birds and fish, the father spends more time with the young than the mother does, but this "reversal of roles" is rather rare

Plate 13. The first love. A mother and child in the Simian Mountains of Ethiopia.

in mammals. In most mammals, the brain module for nurture, also referred to as the *care* circuits, is more developed in females. After all, in the
absence of human tools, only the mother is in a position to nurse the
infants. The titi monkey of South America is the odd exception: Not only
is the male the main provider, but the females seemingly care more for
their mates than for their infants.[205] However, in quite a few species of
mammals in which the females are the prime care-takers, including humans, the males do indeed develop a deep affection for their offspring.

No wonder that infants are labeled "sweet." They are sweet for much
the same reason that sugar is sweet: It is best for the genes that parents
get involved. Human parents want to be with and care for their children,
and in the eyes of a child, parents are equally sweet. Although we are all
responsive to babies, the reward pathways shift to a higher gear when we

obtain children of our own. The increase is reflected in the observation that parents typically enjoy other people's children more after they have had their own. The delight in infants makes evolutionary sense, and it is highly rewarding.

Various signals have been designed to strengthen the bond and elicit the satisfaction of being with children. As an illustration of the evolutionary, archaic nature of the affection, most of these signals are easily recognized in other species. Puppies and kittens are a lot sweeter than grown up specimens because they have rounded heads with a high brow

Plate 14. Lions are among the few animals that feed on humans, yet their cubs are as cute as any infant.

and flat nose; and their whines stir maternal instincts—not only in adult dogs or cats. The juvenile features disappear concomitant with the development of independence. Puberty involves the gain of reproductive potential and the loss of the protective response afforded the young.

Certain breeds of dogs, such as the Pekingese and Chihuahua, offer an interesting exception: They are bred to be childishly sweet even as adults. They remain small, with a short nose and rounded head, as these features elicit the pleasures of associating with children in their human masters.

Those who have raised children will acknowledge that using pets as surrogates does tend to avoid certain problems (your child can be more of a pest than a pet), but then again, teddy bears are even easier to handle. Unfortunately, neither of these surrogates will talk to you, smile at you, or present you with grandchildren.

The capacity of women to live beyond their reproductive age is an interesting feature; postmenopausal life is rare among mammals, possibly only shared with baboons and chimps. The phenomenon presumably evolved only in species where grandparents are likely to improve the fitness of their grandchildren.[206] Thus, the next time you are asked to babysit your grandchildren, recall that they are not only a fraction of your genes wrapped up for the future; they are the reason why you are still alive. In fact, they also happen to be another excellent source of Darwinian happiness.

Actually, parents—both animal and human—are not always that self-sacrificing. Occasionally, the infants are left to die. If you forget to feed your hamsters, they will kill their children and eat them. Cruel?

This observation makes sense when realizing that caring for infants is about herding your genes. Sensible genes tell a parent, just as your stockbroker would, that it is stupid to waste further resources on a bad investment. If the mother dies, or if there simply is not enough food to go around, the offspring die anyway. Killing them will concentrate the resources on the parents and increase the parents' chances of survival. When the conditions turn favorable again, they will have lived to be able to produce a new litter. Humans can be equally "inhuman" as the hamsters. Or, rephrased, our genes are equally "sensible."

The sociobiologist Richard Alexander has pointed out that in more than half of the 160 cultures for which there is relevant data, infanticide is permitted under certain circumstances. As with hamsters, the combination of many children and limited resources can be seen as typical circumstances leading to such behavior.[207]

Falling In Love—More of a Tumble Than Love?

Evolution is great at picking up a feature and remodeling it for a novel purpose. This is presumably what happened when the need arose for pair-bonding: The brain circuitry allowing mammals to enjoy taking care of their offspring was redesigned to induce males and females to care for each other.

We are not the only mammal to develop bonds, or love if you prefer, between genders. I have already mentioned moles and voles; among our ape relatives, siamangs and gorillas are the more romantic. The siamangs form stable couples, while the family groups of gorillas often include two or more females. However, I believe evolution went a step further in its design of human mating. As previously discussed, the evolution of free will presumably required the installation of stronger emotions and more potent rewards. Thus human love, whether it is for the child or the spouse, is possibly more intense. But I believe this was not enough. A particular dilemma associated with the human predicament demanded the invention of a novel feature: Not only did our ancestors have rudimentary consciousness and free will, but they formed groups that required collaboration between individuals of the same sex. On top of that, mating should preferably involve someone from another tribe in order to avoid inbreeding. To make the right thing happen, evolution needed a real love elixir.

For once the English language is poor in words. Some languages, including my native tongue, Norwegian, have separate terms for "falling in love" and the more lasting love that couples move into if the relationship is a success. The former is sometimes referred to as "compassionate love," as opposed to "companionate love" or just "old love." The distinction is important, because, as I see it, the former not only has a distinct evolutionary origin, but is quite different in nature from the latter. The ability to fall in love was the evolutionary response to the above problem.

We have actually started to get a clue at what is happening chemically when a person falls in love: The level of a protein that transports the neurotransmitter serotonin across the cell membrane (serotonin-transporter) is reduced. The interesting part is that the same occurs in people with obsessive-compulsive disorder—that is, people who are hooked on gambling, shop-lifting, or other behaviors they fail to control.[208]

The notion that love resembles an obsession or addiction is not new. Recently, however, even more evidence has accumulated to support the idea at a neurological level. A certain part of the ventral forebrain has been associated with drug addiction in both humans and animals. Interestingly, gene therapy in the monogamous vole, directed at increasing the level of vasopressin receptors in this part of the brain, did indeed make the male voles more faithful and friendly.[209] The voles may not "fall in love" like we do, but evolution could have used this part of the brain (which apparently contains both nerve circuits aimed at bonding between the sexes, and circuits related to addictive behavior) as a scaffold when the need for a "falling in love" routine arose.

The first strong emotional reaction is more uncontrolled than old love. It can snap into existence between total strangers—as part of the outbreeding strategy—and it is actually unlikely to happen between people who grew up together. Moreover, first love is "blind": You tend to overlook any dubious characteristics of the person you fall in love with. Falling in love is stupid and fantastic, to the delight of the couple—albeit sometimes to the dismay of potential parents-in-law. Falling in love is also a spectacular and weird phenomenon. If it was not for real, you would think a science fiction writer had invented it.

Old love is more objective, and as a consequence it comes in all sizes. In fact, in our modern Discord society, old love easily takes on negative values. It is possible that you would be better off marrying someone you know well, and whose company you enjoy even in the absence of passionate love, rather than someone who happens to pass by at a receptive moment. In other words, it is presumably easier to retain a positive value in the "old love" relationship if the partner has the qualities to fit in as a good friend. Unfortunately, the "falling in love" routine is not necessarily the optimal strategy for finding the right person. The routine was shaped in the Stone Age tribal setting to care for certain long-term biological needs in partner choice (that is, out-marriage as well as giving a head start to sex and pair-bonding). In the present situation, where you have an enormous variety of potential partners around, shaped by all sorts of subcultures that exaggerate individual differences, you are indeed lucky if you happen to fall in love with a person who matches your long-term demands of a good friend. But then again, for the first year or two, falling in love certainly beats old love in terms of brain rewards.

Cynical people claim that most of our mating appears to occur in the absence of *any* sort of love. Anthropologists have confirmed that in several cultures love, at least in the meaning of "falling in love," is not considered very relevant.[210] In some places women are looked upon as a commodity you are expected to pay for, freely convertible in exchange for cows or goats. In other places bringing a man and a woman together is more a question of creating liaisons between two clans, akin to the merger of two corporations. In these societies you could very well ask: What has love got to do with it?

With the "falling in love" routine, nature has devised a reasonably efficient and sincerely pleasurable way of bringing mates together. Why should a culture try to deprive people of the natural way?

True, the young person's choice of partner is often not optimal for long-term relationships, but I do not believe that this observation explains why parents in so many societies try to control mating. The phenomenon is more likely another consequence of civilization: The rise of agricultural communities led to private ownership of land and other resources, and it led to large communities with a dramatic increase in the number of potential mates. In this setting it became important to exert more control on the production of children within the family or clan. Resources should not be diluted by marriage with a poorer mate, and they should preferably follow the lineage. To ensure "proper couples," older generations needed to exercise some authority regarding their offspring's choice of mating partners. Furthermore, the presence of inheritable resources made it more advantageous to use marriage in order to form alliances.

The parents' interest in the mating of their children thus makes practical sense. Falling in love was not designed for these circumstances: It presumably evolved in a setting where the genetic quality and caring capacity of a potential mate mattered more than wealth and affiliations, and where the young did well to grasp the rare chance when a prospective mate came along. On the other hand, it is not easy to quell powerful emotions backed by hefty rewards. Even in cultures in which the elders control marriage, the young still fall in love. Love relationships may actually flourish; they are just less likely to coincide with marriage.

I would rate love, food, and sex as the three main dispensers of Darwinian happiness. Possibly even in that order. Sex only serves you in brief episodes, and although your meals can be extensive, there is at some point a trade-off with your health. Only love can permeate the day without ruining it, particularly if you have just fallen in love.

True enough, for the sake of procreation we do fine without love—but we need it for our quality of life. Unfortunately, love is not the easiest stimulant to handle; it sometimes seems as if men and women were not at all designed for each other.

What Kind of Mate Do You Want?

Whether you pick the only one available from the neighboring tribe, or choose among the two million participants on the internet dating games, certain preferences are common enough to deserve a biological comment.

There are generally recognized beauty factors that attract. Desmond Morris has summarized these in what he refers to as "biological beauty."[211] The key elements are: the basic gender signals (broad male shoulders, wide female hips, and the like); signs of youthfulness (smooth skin, vigor); signs of health (clean skin, lack of disease or abnormalities, physical fitness); and symmetrical features. Apparently even babies recognize these factors, in that they spend more time looking at people who possess the right qualities. Youthfulness appears to be more important for the male choice, while women tend to seek high-ranking males that are resourceful, courageous, and confident.

Interestingly, we do not try to find someone similar to ourselves: When testing spouses in psychological personality tests, there is little or no correlation. The preference for somebody different and unrelated, as suggested by the T-shirt experiment, is presumably derived from a biological need toward outbreeding. The easiest solution would be to choose a partner from your own tribe, but if everybody did that, the accumulation of detrimental mutations would eventually turn your tribe into some kind of creepy hillbillies. The preference for the exotic and novel is part of the eugenic program initiated by evolution—nature's way of improving the genetic makeup of a species.

Today, not only can we pick partners from across the globe, but the number of potential mates that we see, either in real life or on a picture, is stunning. This is a problem. It has been shown that looking at pictures of beautiful and handsome people decreases our self-esteem. If the number of people we compare with is sufficiently large, there will always be many that we rank higher than ourselves, or higher than our chosen mates. In other words, we are more likely to end up dissatisfied with both ourselves and our mates.

This problem actually involves many aspects of life: In the Stone Age tribe, everybody was one of the best at doing something, because there was only a handful of competitors and a sufficient number of arenas to compete in. Today you may end up competing with six billion people. The present situation reduces Darwinian happiness by putting an extra stress on relationships (there's always someone out there more attractive than your spouse), and by degrading your self-esteem (there's always someone out there better than you are at any given task). Luckily, evolution has come up with the design that there is an almost equal number of men and women, so most of us have a fair chance of finding a partner.

Fortunately, our more important preferences tend to be sensible: The evolutionary psychologist David Buss has done a cross-cultural study of mate choice. The most striking result from his study was that kindness and intelligence top the list of preferred qualities, and these attributes were actually preferred by both males and females. Surprisingly, traits such as physical appearance, wealth, and status appeared to be less important.[212]

Humans are not just smarter than other primates; we also seem to be kinder. In fact, we consider these attributes to be distinguishing features for our species—the above result helps explain why: The two traits have probably been selected for by mate choice, which means by sexual selection, for a very long time.

Another evolutionary psychologist, Geoffrey Miller, has suggested that sexual selection was in fact more important in shaping our intellect than natural selection. We appear to be kinder to each other than you might think evolution would prefer for the purpose of promoting genes, and more intelligent than what evolution requires for survival.[213] Understanding the theory of relativity, or multiplying five digit numbers, is unlikely to have contributed much to the survival of a Stone Age being; yet, it is in our power to do so, and we have a lot of other forms of intellectual acrobatics that may promote survival in the industrialized age, although these were unlikely to have helped our distant ancestors.

It is conceivable that once a certain level of intelligence and kindness had been incorporated in our brains, sexual selection kicked in and expanded these features. The story sounds almost like a fairy tale, but it may very well contain an element of truth. It implies that we are what we are today not so much because of the harsh forces of nature—the struggle for existence—but simply because multiple generations of men and women have preferred sympathetic and bright mates.

A Multi-Component Glue

It is time to summarize the main features of the human mating system designed by evolution: The logic of human procreation starts with the formation of two complementary sexes. Upon sexual maturity they fall in love, they copulate, and the female eventually becomes pregnant. Intercourse and the subsequently conceived baby strengthen the relationship, which gradually moves from the "falling in love" stage to a more lasting "old love" relationship. The affiliation is expected to last not only until the end of the reproductive period, but rather up to the point that all the children have grown to independence. In the tribal setting this would generally mean till death do them part.

The above scenario includes a need for a strong bond between parents in order to secure the upbringing of children. Whereas the bond to an infant can be turned on simply by the presence of a baby, the bond between two unrelated and alien adults (the parents) needs a variety of stimuli in order to form; in contrast to the mother and baby, the parents are not genetically related. Evolution designed a multi-component glue, the main constituents being falling in love, sex, and old love. The latter ingredient, however, is fuelled by a variety of elements, such as talking together, touching, sharing food and experiences, or simply being in each other's vicinity.

One component of the glue deserves particular mentioning: Dogs use their tongues liberally. Certain species of apes and monkeys smack their lips together, but only two species are known to really smear their lips and tongues tight together: we humans and, of course, the bonobos.

So why kiss? Especially when, from a biological point of view, it would make more sense if evolution had designed us to pee in each other's face. A number of diseases are transmitted by sputum (which contains loads of viruses and bacteria that rejoice at the practice of kissing), while urine normally is sterile. But please note that I am not saying we should pee on each other; humans are not designed like that. But the point remains, if evolution where to choose among one of these alternatives to help form bonds with a mate, the peeing alternative might be the more sensible due to the lesser infectious burden.

In several species of birds, and also in mammals such as wolves and wild dogs, it is common that the parents transfer food to their infants by mouth, typically by regurgitating partly digested foodstuff from further down the alimentary tract. Besides allowing the offspring to feed on a "cooked" stew, the behavior presumably helps to bind parents and infants together. The practice was probably prevalent among our ancestors, and it is supposedly still practiced by the Maori of New Zealand. It is tempting to suggest that mouth-to-mouth feeding is the template on which kissing evolved.[214]

Our lips and tongue are richly endowed with sensory nerves. A little bit of rewiring in the brain and the nerves could serve to boost love between man and woman, not just between parents and infant; and, as a byproduct, it would offer yet another source of Darwinian happiness. The rewards should make kissing worth the risk of infections. Actually some of the more typical diseases transmitted by kissing, such as the kissing disease (infectious mononucleosis), can result from excessive cleanliness during childhood. People who are acquainted with the responsible virus early in life do not become ill, regardless of exposure during kissing.

There is, however, another risk associated with kissing, because the sputum not only transfers microbes. When you engage in a deep kiss there is also a bit of chemical communication going on. A molecule called androstenone (related to androsterone) is a candidate messenger. In pigs androstenone is a pheromone released by the boar, which causes the sow to get ready for intercourse. Interestingly, the compound is found at a higher concentration in human male sputum than it is in female sputum. Apparently, whilst pigs do foreplay by airmail, humans do it mouth-to-mouth. Hence, for the woman kissing involves a risk of getting stuck on the glue.[215]

No wonder they say love makes the world go round. Poets and singers depend on it, but they are not the only ones who should salute love. All of us should rejoice at this choice of design; it is a prime source of Darwinian happiness.

Love, sex, and all the other components of the glue are meant to go together; yet it is possible to enjoy the components independently of each other. Just as sex can be enjoyed in the absence of love, love does not require sex. Thus, there is joy to be harvested even for those whose relationships do not function perfectly. And if nothing functions, you can always kiss your dog and listen to love songs—there's always a surrogate.

Yet it is fair to ask: Did evolution really display great craft in its design of the human mating system?

Dubious Design

To my knowledge there is only one species that has been brave enough to choose pair-bonding within groups consisting of sexually mature individuals of both genders who rely on extensive collaboration. If I had been an advisor for human evolution, I would probably have voiced my misgivings about this solution: It is highly risky. The potential for conflict is too great. Upon observing how evolution dealt with the problem, however, I might have decided that the warning was undue. There are conflicts, and we are certainly not world champions in pair-bonding. As previously mentioned, prior to Christianity a majority of cultures allowed for multiple wives, and even in Christian countries serial monogamy has a lot of disciples.

Birds apparently do better. At least they do not quarrel and fight until the affair ends with a divorce. However, if you look more closely, namely at the genetic composition of the offspring, you will find that a fair fraction of them have the "wrong" father.[216] Thus, even in animals that seem to be more into pair-bonding than we are, the sexual drive is not limited to the one chosen partner. In fact, I believe that the present problems of human love life are partly due to the Discord qualities of society. The number of potential partners we come across, and the lack of close ties to those who surround us, are examples of factors that may accentuate weaknesses in the design of the human mating system—and thereby cause more couples to quarrel and split up.

If I were called on to help direct the future evolution of mankind, I would be concerned about adjusting mental tendencies to modern civilization. As part of my program, I would certainly want to do something about the inconsistency of pair-bonding and a non-selective sexual drive. I would also look into the curious emotion we refer to as jealousy.

The evolutionary function of jealousy is presumably to initiate behavior that reduces the chance of losing a partner. The observation that this feeling rarely has much to offer in terms of Darwinian happiness can be attributed to the fact that evolution did not primarily design you to enjoy life. Jealousy, like other pains, is there to promote your genes; it is in the genes' interest that you avoid losing someone who can help pass on your genes.

One way of improving the situation would be to cut down on the emotional bonds between the sexes, and thus allow for more variety in a sexual life—a bit of the bonobo style, if you will. Alternatively, one might strengthen love and try to concentrate the sexual drive on a single partner. Either solution should reduce conflicts. But then again, while I'm at it, I would also remove the appendix and design a spine that was more suitable for sitting in a chair.

The only realistic alternative, as I see it, is to learn to live with human nature as it is. Jealousy is not the only cause of problems. Men and women have evolved in slightly different directions, and to understand the resulting dissimilarities, and to adjust to them, is part of the recipe for a successful marriage. I shall use the remaining part of this chapter to look at the disparities, because I believe a knowledge of them should dampen conflicts and improve relationships.

Separate Planets?

The evidence supporting the fact that men and women are in several ways different in design is simply too strong to ignore. Disparities cannot be attributed just to cultural stereotypes; it is in the genes. With respect to the anatomical differences, the conclusion is obvious, but it is less clear-cut when looking at "software" differences such as cognition and behavior. Yet, although the genes presumably do direct the brains of men and women in different ways, by the time the environment has done its task of molding us, male and female patterns of conduct grossly overlap. Moreover, the variation within genders is typically greater than the average differences between them.

From an evolutionary perspective, there is much to be gained if the two sexes can complement each other. In most mammals, the genders have diverged as a consequence of males and females engaging in slightly different tasks. Sexual selection, in the form of partner choice, may drive the sexes even farther apart than what evolutionary advantages should imply.

The mental and behavioral differences between the sexes are associated with two separate facets of life: The major distinction is concerned with features related to procreation, such as sex, pair-bonding, and childcare. A lesser distinction concerns sustenance, such as obtaining food and protection against enemies.

What follows is a brief description of some of the suggested differences, concentrating on the ones I believe are more useful to know about. Please bear in mind that such a description necessarily takes on the shape of stereotypes. For a more detailed discussion I would recommend reading one of the several books that cover the subject. One such popular book, by John Gray, is entitled *Men Are from Mars, Women Are from Venus*. That may be so, but as I shall argue, they both circle the same sun.[217]

The Major Distinction

The most obvious differences between males and females are those associated with procreation. As the major anatomical distinctions related to sex were discussed in Chapter 8, I shall concentrate here on mental variances. Please keep in mind that we are talking about differences in averages.

As discussed in Chapter 4, men are more promiscuous. It follows that men tend to be more forward, while female initiative is more along the lines of "putting up a lovely appearance." Men go hunting for women; women fish for men. Still, both have displays or other ways of making themselves attractive to the opposite sex.

Both hunting for women and fishing for men can be pleasant pursuits. A good chase, or having a big fish bite, can both be rewarding, regardless of what the next step might be. It should not be surprising, however, to find that the female is more likely to release the fish, compared to the chance of the male voluntarily allowing his prey to get away before he has been allowed to copulate with her.

The selectivity and restraints that characterize women's association with sex are there to avoid getting pregnant by the wrong person or at the wrong time. These features have made their sexual life more vulnerable: Women are more likely to be victims of both force and deceit. Thus, even when the sexual act does elicit rewards, the subsequent psychological reactions may put the overall experience on the negative side. It is generally more difficult for women to learn how to access sexual sensations, and to know when to even consider sex.

The fact that women can today avoid pregnancy without much difficulty has not changed the underlying, innate mental mechanisms. True, any inherent tendency can be overcome, but for the average woman sexual constraints will still be a significant force. The guru therefore advises women to pay attention to the emotional consequences of sex.

To return to the matter of jealousy, which appears to be present in every culture, both men and women can be jealous, but their possessiveness is vaguely different: The evolutionary rationale for male jealousy is basically the question of whether the child he is about to support carries his genes or not. Men are expected to look after a wife with the attitude that a single diversion could be enough. The jealousy involved is a kind of "crime against my property" event. Jealousy in women has a different rationale. A wife worries whether the male provider she is relying on will move on to other women; her jealousy is more of the type, "Does he still love me?"[218]

Evolution created jealousy for a purpose in both sexes. To understand that purpose, and to realize that it is a natural, if not always an equally useful reaction, will, I hope, make it easier to deal with situations that elicit this emotion.

In the long run we may actually be able to do more for those suffering. At least in prairie voles, male "jealousy" is displayed as aggression toward other males who approach a female the jealous male has had a chance to copulate with. The jealousy depends on the release of vasopressin—and the reaction can be blocked by antagonists against this neuropeptide. Thus, one day there may well be a pill that puts an end to human jealousy.[219]

A typical misconception is that a wife—based on her own emotional reaction to sex—assumes that the man's single escapade implies a serious threat to his care for her. Since male "one-night stands" typically do not involve any deep emotional affiliation, her jealousy may be an undue concern. Similarly, a husband may underestimate the emotional significance of a woman's extramarital affair.

According to the anthropologist Bronislaw Malinowski, men in the Trobriand Islands occasionally return after a couple of years at sea to find that their wife has a new child. The extra kid is cheerfully accepted as further proof that intercourse has nothing to do with pregnancies.[220] This conviction is not a very wise attitude for the sake of the husband's genes, but it is rather useful for his measure of Darwinian happiness. The genes' interests, however, are cared for in other ways: In this society, the primary male caretaker of the children is not the husband, but rather the wife's brother. This makes perfect biological sense in that your sister's children carry one-fourth of your genes while, under the circumstances, your wife's offspring may have obtained their genes from anywhere in the surrounding villages. Similar arrangements are to be found in other societies where confidence regarding paternity is low.

The Lesser Distinction

When you have finally found a proper partner at some distant village, the next question is whether the man or the woman should move. Anthropological literature tells us that in 80 percent of traditional societies the wife is expected to move. As pointed out by David Barash, the choice makes evolutionary sense: The wife's family never needs to doubt that the children born carry their genes, while the husband's family has more reasons to watch the daughter-in-law. Their genes are at stake if the woman cheats.[221]

After settling down as a couple, the Stone Age man and woman presumably practiced a certain division of labor: Men were responsible for most of the hunting, whilst women, who were burdened by pregnancies and childcare, did not venture too far from the camp. A woman's contribution to the food supply was primarily in the form of edible plants and insects. Most scientists believe this division of labor has shaped the two genders, so that today they have (on average) slightly different faculties.[222]

As hunters and as protectors against predators and enemies, males require physical strength and speed. It follows that men evolved to be stronger and to run faster. Hunting required a capacity for being able to get one's bearings; throwing a weapon at a target required an ability to "organize space." These demands may explain why men appear to do better at spatial tasks, and, as a possible further consequence, in mathematical logic.

In mammals, the female will always get a chance to breed, while the genetic success of males can vary enormously, depending on access to partners. This holds true for humans as well because we never became a completely pair-bonding species. It follows that men have more reason to protect a given territory and to shield their women from alien men. The same rationale explains why males tend to be more hierarchical: Status makes more of a difference in terms of reproductive success. These circumstances add up to explain the observation that men are stronger and more aggressive.

Women, on the other hand, are better at using their fingers, possibly as a consequence of their role in gathering food. Moreover, tending to children and collaborating with other females have led them to score higher at tasks involving linguistics, hearing, taste, and smell. It has been shown, for example, that mothers are more apt at recognizing their babies by smell than are their fathers. Women also tend to be more inclined to care for others, and will use more psychology and fewer threats or force to achieve something. It is commonly said that women are more interested in people, whereas men are more interested in objects.

If you look at the choice of occupation and diversions in males and females, the data certainly seems to support the above suggestions. However, cultural factors can have dramatic effects: Sometimes they turn the differences upside down, but more often they will expand on any inherent disparity. For example, if an occupation or a hobby has come to be considered a female thing, then it will draw more females, while men will at the same time tend to shy away from it.

The above statement adds support to the women's liberation movement: Present societies have probably, in some cases, pushed differentiation further than what would be suggested by innate dissimilarities between men and women. Moreover, gender differences should not restrain anyone from choosing a career or leisure activities. The guru does not discourage women from pursuing mathematics, or men to stay away from nursing; yet the average innate differences argue against insisting that half the accountants should be women, or half the pre-school teachers should be men. The following analogy illustrates the point: A shoemaker who insists on making shoes for women and men the same size has a problem—he needs to adjust his production to reflect the distribution of the size of feet in men and women.

We are better off accepting minor variations, but we should also allow each individual to fulfill his or her potential. So, it makes sense to counteract the cultural tendency of defining exclusive gender roles.

The fact that men are physically stronger and larger and taller than women could be taken to indicate that men were more likely to be tribal leaders. It is not that obvious. In both bonobos and humans, the females weigh about 85 percent of what the males weigh; still, the female bonobos seem to have considerable influence on group decisions, partly because they stand together.[223] My guess is that 50,000 years ago the distribution of power between the sexes was more equal than in most present societies.

Men probably spent more time away from the camp, suggesting that the women were running much of the show at home. But then, as the population density increased, tension among tribes increased. As a consequence, the strong, the aggressive, and the hierarchically oriented individuals gained power; tribes led by less assertive forces were not able to do so well. In short, leadership moved toward men.

Even if male leaders at one point were best for the genes, it is certainly not obvious that the quality of life today is best served by the same situation. Female leaders would presumably do better at improving the conditions for women. Furthermore, with the weapons available today, aggressive encounters put a heavy toll on all parties that engage in combat. In this situation assertive leaders can be a pest.

The Insignificant Difference

Human genes are located on 23 pairs of chromosomes. One of the pairs consists of either two X-chromosomes, in females, or an X and a Y in males. With one chromosome being completely different, is it not obvious that men and women end up on different planets? Actually the genetic dissimilarity between man and woman does not mean that much. In many species of fish and amphibians the anatomical and behavioral differences between the sexes are at least as obvious; yet, they are genetically identical!

In these animals it is the environment that decides whether the fertilized egg is to become a male or a female, and more often it is a question of temperature. The environment does what the sex chromosomes do for us. This is possible because it is the hormones that orchestrate the development of gender peculiarities; whether it is the temperature, or genes on the Y-chromosome, that induce male hormones, is not important. In fact, in several invertebrate species an infection of certain bacteria determine whether a developing individual turns into a female rather than a male type.[224]

In any case, the female form is the default or "prototype." Several species—for example aphids—can survive for long periods with only females who produce clones of themselves. Even in humans, all you need is a decent sperm depository to make men obsolete. (I hope some women disagree with that, but I have, on the other hand, seen them drive around with bumper stickers such as "A woman without a man is like a fish without a bicycle.")

What happens is that the activation of a key gene on the Y chromosome (the *SRY* gene) turns the production away from the prototype toward the shadier male version. The gene in question codes for a TDF (testis-determining factor) protein that causes the embryonic gonads to develop as testes rather than as ovaries. The testes subsequently produce the male sex hormones—primarily testosterone—that are responsible for all the other male characteristics. Many of the male (and female) characteristics are like seeds designed to sprout at puberty.

Jaak Panksepp claims that there are actually four possible "sexes," not just two.[225] His argument goes like this: Testosterone is converted to either dihydrotestosterone or estrogen. Both are important in shaping the embryo—the former is responsible for designing a male body; the latter for masculinizing the brain. If, for some reason, one of the two conversions fails, you may end up with a male body and a female brain, or vice versa. Together with the two normal versions, this adds up to four different genders. (Although such hormonal blunders can explain homosexual behavior, they do not imply that all homosexuals have had a history of hormonal aberrations during the pregnancy of their mothers.)

Nature has performed some remarkable experiments of this sort. A mutation that first occurred in the West Indies a couple of centuries ago causes the formation of a baby with female genitals, yet with male chromosomes. In this particular case, the big surprise comes as the individual reaches puberty—when the body starts to change into a male version! Naturally these individuals are brought up as girls. Much to the dismay of scientists who claim that nurture shapes behavioral characteristics, these "girls" readily take on a male role instead of the female role they are brought up with. Why? Simply because the "seeds" designed to sprout male brain features upon puberty are not disrupted; the mutation only changes the formation of genitals.[226]

Seahorse—the Exception that Makes the Rule

The biological definition of a female is that she invests more in the offspring when compared to the male. In some invertebrates, the difference is limited to the size of gametes; in rare cases the definition gets it all wrong.

The seahorse is a fascinating fish. You might think it is weird enough

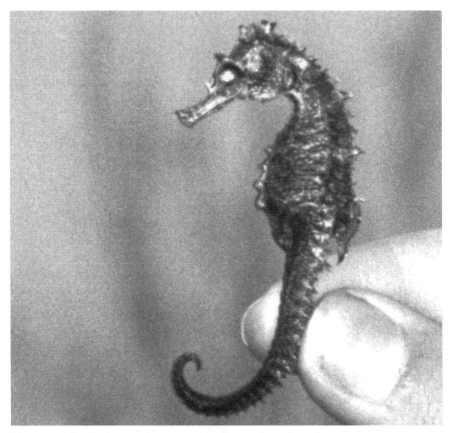

Plate 15. The Seahorse: the exception that makes the rule.

for a fish to look like a horse, but the seahorse has an even more eccentric feature; the female seahorse pulls off a stunt that would make the women's liberation movement obsolete. She maximizes her carefree lifestyle by placing the eggs inside the male! The male is thus compelled to care for the eggs.

For a biologist the most interesting observation is that this apparent violation of the above definition actually confirms the basic rule: The typical sexual dimorphism observed in so many species is reversed in the seahorse; not only is the female larger, but she is also the more aggressive gender. The male appears shy, flirting, and choosy about which females to engage with.

When evolution gave the male seahorse the major share in bringing up the offspring, it also gave him the behavioral consequences. Genetically speaking, the main difference is that in this case the male does not risk anything by taking on the burden of childcare: He is in the unique position of knowing for sure who the father is.[227]

Summary

In this chapter I have discussed the joys and the quandaries of forming a couple. Falling in love is probably the best dispenser of Darwinian happiness you will ever find—as long as it lasts. In order to retain the relationship as a positive asset, it helps to understand what bonding is all about, and what sort of glue can be added to make it stick. It also helps to understand how evolution has shaped men and women; to the extent that it is fair to state that we are from Mars and Venus, respectively, you should know what distinguishes these two planets.

I do not claim that the biology I preach can serve the role of a marriage counselor, since each couple has to sort out their particular problems. It may, however, serve as an extra resource when sorting out a relationship.

As witnessed by the seahorse, it may seem as if anything goes in the world of biology, but, upon closer scrutiny, most observations are backed by the logic of evolution: The principle of evolution is the sun that keeps both Mars and Venus on their particular paths.

CHAPTER 10

Good and Evil:
The Pleasure of Compassion

Friends in Gondar.

To Be or Not to Be Social

If love within the nuclear family were all the love we had, our crammed societies would be an unbearable place to live in. Fortunately we belong to a social species; evolution has made room in the human brain for kindness even toward non-kin. Without a solid capacity for communal bonds there would be no culture, and we would never have made the transition from ape to human.

Our innate tendencies create both opportunities and problems in organizing a community. The important question is whether or not present societies make optimal use of our propensity for collaboration and compassion. Could we, for example, be induced to associate with, and care for, all humans, or maybe all living things?

The world may never be one big family, but in order to make the most of the situation it is essential to understand both the gregarious and the aggressive aspects of human nature. This is the subject of the present chapter. As a first step I shall try to describe the evolutionary forces that shaped our social instincts.

While several species of monkeys enjoy social life, most apes prefer solitude, or form small family units; social behavior was thus probably not present in the lineage leading to apes and humans. The only apes with complex social interactions are the chimpanzees, and particularly the bonobos. Chimps and bonobos are believed to represent the last lineages to diverge from the hominids, which suggests that social behavior started to evolve around the time of that split.[228]

The social behavior of our ancestors may have been triggered by the fact that they began to live on the ground, rather than in the canopy of trees, as before. Since animals that live on the ground are more vulnerable to predators, forming groups offers a better chance for survival. The danger of predators raises the matter of both signaling an attack and organizing a defense. The observation that the tree-living apes, namely orangutans and gibbons, are solitary or live in pairs, while chimpanzees and bonobos form groups, supports this assumption; moreover, the same dis-

221

tinction is seen in monkeys. Gorillas only form small family units, but then their answer to the threat of predators was to grow big and strong. (They might be warned, however, that previous primate attempts at this strategy apparently ended with disaster, as witnessed by the fossils recovered of the now extinct *Theropithecus* and *Gigantopithecus*.)[229] In the human lineage, the socializing process was presumably boosted by other factors, such as the need for extended infant care and the advantage of hunting in packs.

According to the above description, evolution had a mere five million to six million years to install social behavior in chimps, bonobos, and hominids. The novelty of this feature helps explain why socializing in these three lineages appears to be of a somewhat different nature from that of monkeys. Chimps and bonobos have a rather complex social life; they display a larger variety of interactions than monkeys. The bonobos' peculiar use of sex for social bonding, mentioned in Chapter 8, is but one example. Bands of chimps definitely carry with them traditions akin to what we refer to as culture, and some of them have been observed to hunt together in a coordinated fashion.[230]

Humans obviously have an even more intricate social life. Yet the most important difference is that while monkeys and other mammals rely on instinctive tendencies to organize groups, humans presumably rely to a greater extent on feelings and emotions—including positive and negative sensations—and on intelligence. (I shall return to some other consequences of the emotional strategy for social life later in this chapter.)

In primates there seems to be a correlation between social complexity and brain size. A big brain is presumably more important for a social animal than for a solitary one, for the reason that intelligence would help the individual manipulate others and move up in the hierarchy. In our lineage, social life may have been a particularly strong force leading to the evolution of intellectual capacity: As behavior became more dependent on emotions and intellect rather than on instinctive tendencies, it became easier to cheat and fool others. Hence we needed to be good at social skills, including the ability to read the mind and intentions of our comrades. Sophisticated skills were required in order to secure a constructive social life based on reciprocity and trust.[231]

The size of our ancestors' tribes probably increased as their social skills evolved. Prior to the invention of agriculture, the typical tribe possibly numbered 20 to 80 members. Larger groups presumably tended to cause foraging problems, with the exception of locations having an abundance of food. Social life was not, however, restricted to one's own tribe: Neighboring tribes relied on each other for finding spouses. The exchange of females or, in some places, males led to *kinship* ties, and thus alliances beyond tribal boundaries.

Kinship is important in all cultures. We all care a lot about relatives, although exactly which categories of relationship are included, and what roles they play, vary. An individual is typically able to recognize some 100 to 200 persons as affiliates, and it is relevant to note that the list of affiliates traditionally includes people who are not kin, and that you are not raised with; for example, in-laws and members of the tribes of your in-laws.

Why Kamikaze Is for Bees and Not for Us

Ever since Edward O. Wilson published his book *Sociobiology: The New Synthesis* in 1975, the question of how evolution can allow real communal and self-sacrificing behavior to develop has been a hot issue for biologists. The book also led to a vigorous debate with social scientists on whether biological thinking could, or should, have any impact on our understanding of human behavior. It eventually did.

Wilson is an entomologist, a specialist on insects. Insects are the playground, the experimental theater, so to speak, for the evolution of behavior, and thus they offer interesting lessons in unselfish behavior. Any fantasy you might have about possible ways of behaving are likely to have a live version counterpart in the world of insects. For example, if you dream about living in a place where everybody is willing to do anything for the good of the community, join the Hymenoptera or the Isoptera: Certain species of ants, bees, and termites are the real champions of social life.

Social insects work unselfishly for the benefit of the group. Most individuals are not even capable of procreation; yet, they eagerly offer up their lives for the genes of those few that are capable. Moreover, like a

Plate 16. Termites are among the champions of social life. A mound like this in Northern Australia can house a million workers.

kamikaze pilot, a bee will kill itself for the benefit of the hive: A bee sting in your arm can be quite painful—enough to keep you away from the hive—but it leaves the stinger dying.

Why does evolution allow such self-sacrifices? Why would it promote even insignificant forms of helpful behavior, such as offering your seat to an elderly lady? To answer this question, let us look at the advantages of living in groups or colonies.

In the case of insects, the advantage has something to do with size. Evolution tends gradually to increase the size of animals; it is part of an arms race. Bigger means stronger, both in the case of conflicts with other species, such as predators, and in conflicts within species. Insects, however, have an external skeleton that derives oxygen from open channels in the body. This anatomy makes it difficult to construct large bodies. If it had not been for this anatomical restraint, we might have been terrorized by dinosaur-size ants reminiscent of old science-fiction and horror movies. Instead we are terrorized by a myriad of small ants. The anthill is almost like one mighty individual, with the additional advantage of being able to pop up in many places at the same time.

Just as the cells of your body cooperate for your benefit, bees and ants live for their community. Each cell in your body contains a complete set of your genes, and the cells collaborate beautifully without any selfish intentions. During normal development a large number of cells even commit "suicide" for the benefit of the "group"—for you that is. Unlike the cells of your body, the bee is a free-moving individual that theoretically could say to hell with the hive, and fly off into the sunset. Yet, there is a similarity between these two situations, which may become clearer if we look at the genetic answer to the question of why evolution can allow self-sacrifice.

Altruism, meaning unselfish behavior, was a paradox for evolutionary biologists until William D. Hamilton came up with the theory of *inclusive fitness.*[232]

The principle of inclusive fitness tells us that behavior benefiting relatives can be selected for, even if it is harmful to you, as long as the behavior helps the genes you share with your relatives. You share a lot of genes with your blood relatives, normally 50 percent in the case of siblings and children; thus, when evaluating whether or not behavior improves fitness, the analysis should not be restricted to personal advantages, but should also include possible gains befalling other individuals carrying the same genes. Behavior that supports your brother may not benefit you, but will nevertheless benefit half of your genes. If the inclusive fitness of the genes harbored in you and your brother is served by your assistance, then evolution will dispose you to help.

Remember that genes are what evolution cares about—the individual is simply the wrapping.[233] The cells of your body share 100 percent of their genes with each other; they have every reason to help the other cells. Bees living in a hive normally share 75 percent; they should thus be less dedicated to the hive than your cells are to you, but yet sufficiently dedicated to offer their lives.

The principle of inclusive fitness, often referred to as *kin selection*, is actually only one of four pillars that help us understand how genes benefit from cooperation and a social life. The other three are: *reciprocity*, which means that I help you if you help me; *mutualism*, implying that what is good for me happens to be good for you too; and *group selection*. While reciprocity and mutualism do not rely on unselfish behavior, kin and group selection give rise to the more remarkable forms of altruism.[234]

The notion of group selection, I should add, is controversial. Proponents believe evolutionary theory allows unselfish behavior benefiting the group to evolve. It is, however, difficult to find good examples, because groups usually include kin, and because acts that appear altruistic actually may bring personal benefits in the long run. For example, they may be explained by some sort of reciprocity. An act that benefits the group can, of course, also be useful for the individual who performed the act—that is, as long as the cost to the individual is less than that person's share of the advantage. The problem is that if you are not related to the other members of the group, the genes will theoretically prefer you to be a cheat: They prefer you to reap the benefit from somebody else's altruistic acts, but not lend a hand yourself. In evolutionary terms, acts that put you ahead of others are more important than acts that help both you *and* the others, as exemplified by the two sages running from the tiger. This problem has left many scientists skeptical about the idea that evolution can favor group selection.

The above four principles of cooperative behavior seem sufficient to explain the observed sociability of animals. Social behavior in humans, however, has certain qualities that are hard to explain within this framework. For example, although the genes may allow you to die for your children (it is genetically sensible if there are more than two of them, or you are unlikely to produce new ones), your genes are not likely to rejoice if you kill yourself for the good of your country. In this case, those who benefit are not closely related. Yet, as witnessed during the Second World War, Japanese pilots lined up for kamikaze attacks.

Suicide for the benefit of a country is not typical, but it is surprisingly common to donate money to help starving people on the opposite side of the globe. Why are we so kind to strangers? None of the pillars of cooperative behavior would seem to support compassion for totally unrelated individuals, particularly not for persons you are unlikely to ever meet. Neither can these pillars explain our concern for animals, with the possible exception of those animals that are there to benefit us, such as those we eat. (In fact, chickens and pigs are not treated with the same consideration as wild animals or pets.)

True, the power of cultural influence may shape people to be much more unselfish than what the genes would suggest, but the hallmarks of human altruism are reflected in all cultures—hence you would expect a definite genetic component to this behavior.

Morality—the Human Touch

One tenet that comes to the rescue of evolutionary theory is the notion of *indirect reciprocity*. The idea is that the return of a favor may not come from the person you helped, but from some third party.

Evolutionary theory allows, for example, that you help another person if the act is recognized by others and thereby improves your status and reputation. This form of behavior is evolutionary sensible as long as the improved reputation increases the likelihood of obtaining personal benefits.

Plate 17. The principle of inclusive fitness, which is central to explain altruistic behavior, implies that those who share genes, such as these siblings in Turkey, are inclined to help and care for each other. Our altruistic tendencies are part of the fabric that backs up morality.

Our almost irrational inclination to collaborate is partly explained by our concern with reputation. We want to be seen as virtuous. We worry about the impression we make on others. We dislike being observed doing something we know goes against the grain of social convention, even if we are unlikely to meet again those who saw us: When visiting a far away country, you prefer those you meet to think highly of you. Another trait that has boosted our cooperative tendencies is the evolution of docility: We are receptive to social influences and tend to submit to the will of the group or its leaders. A third important factor is that we seem to have an innate inclination toward punishing those who cheat or take advantage of others; that is, we have a desire to discipline those who violate norms.[235]

When discussing human kindness, it is also relevant to recall that evolution does not necessarily design for optimal utility. There is a real possibility that we have more innate compassion than is actually good for our genes, either due to some erratic evolutionary process or due to sexual selection. The preference for kindness in mates, referred to in Chapter 9, supports the latter idea.

The social inclinations of humans add up to one particularly potent feature: Our capacity for empathy and sympathy, combined with a concern for reputation and fairness, a willingness to submit to custom and command, and mechanisms for conflict resolution, are part of a curious and interesting phenomenon that we refer to as *morality*.[236]

Morality is a quality of human behavior that many believe to be a key feature separating us from animals. True, it is based on the human blend of intelligence and social behavior, but it can also be seen as an evolutionary adaptation that is, to some extent, shared with other animals. Frans de Waal suggests two requirements for the evolution of moral inclinations: The group must depend on each other for subsistence and defense, and there must be a need to cooperate in the presence of disparate individual interests. De Waal's observations regarding apes and monkeys indicate that behavioral traits reminiscent of morality are present in animals, particularly in chimpanzees and bonobos.

In evolutionary terms, morality may be "diagnosed" as based on kin and group selection with a distinct contribution from direct and indirect reciprocity. Reciprocity has presumably been instrumental in adding the feelings of fairness and justice to the human psyche. These facets of natural selection are sufficient to explain human ethics, but, as suggested above, other processes may have further boosted our compassion.

Some people seem to think that morality is a recent invention; something that separates us from the brutes, and possibly devised by the British nobility. They have these pictures of Stone Age people, soccer fans, and other savages constantly running around and bashing each other's heads in; laws supposedly forbid the common man to do what his instincts urge him to do. But this picture is not appropriate.

If morality had been a recent invention, and not something bestowed upon us by our genes, we would not be here today. In fact, it may prove difficult to find a population responsible for more deaths than the aristocracy of Western civilization.

True, the ethics you are brought up with are designed by your specific culture, but behind these rules of conduct there is an innate core laid down in our genes. Even if traces of morality are to be found in other species, morality is definitely an extraordinary adaptation in us humans. Moral behavior does add a distinct human touch to social life. It is a force that should be exploited for all it is worth, in order to benefit society—and to increase our measure of Darwinian happiness.

The Social High

I have pointed out why evolution may favor social and moral inclinations. We will never surpass the bees in unselfishness, nor replace the bonobos in sociability, but for a mammal we are not doing that bad at all. The main point in this and the following chapter is embedded in the last sentence of the former section: Our gregarious nature should be stimulated, not just for the benefit of mankind, but for the benefit of the individual as well.

The brain offers rewards in the form of positive sensations for compassion and companionship. The relevant brain structures involved in social affect can be assigned to two intermeshed modules: One yields negative emotions, typified by separation distress, loneliness, and (certain forms of) panic; the other gives you the pleasures of socializing, the joy of being with family or friends.

As indicated in Chapter 2, evolution requires a scaffold on which to erect new functions. Jaak Panksepp suggests that the social affect system—that is, the emotions involved in interacting with others—evolved from the following three features dating back to our reptilian past: place attachment; pain circuits; and homeostasis comfort. As we shall see, each of these features presumably included elements that helped evolution erect the present version of social affect.[237]

In the last chapter I mentioned that reptiles do not care much about their offspring, but they do get attached to a "home," particularly as a place for laying eggs. In the evolution of mammals this attachment was presumably expanded. When combined with a dash of sexual desire, it evolved towards mother-child attachment, and later, in some species, to love between parents. Social bonding presumably evolved as a further elaboration of the basic mother-child bond.

The distress of a child when separated from the mother should be associated with discomfort, because the infant must learn to avoid getting lost. The feeling of discomfort was apparently taken care of by involving the general pain circuits of the midbrain, a notion supported by the observation that the circuits responsible for separation distress are to be found in the same region. Similarly, the comfort of returning to homeostasis, such as finding a warm spot when freezing, presumably was the forerunner for the pleasure of social comfort, felt particularly intensively when children are reunited with their parents.

The split with our reptile ancestors dates a couple of hundred million years back, and the evolution of emotions has gone a long way since then. The three reptilian modules suggested as the underpinning of our social affect have been dramatically altered and expanded. Still, both neurochemical and neuroanatomical investigations support this evolutionary scenario, and there are various other observations that add further evidence. For example, pain is there to teach us avoidance, but that purpose does not explain why pain is displayed. Presumably it is displayed because of the connection between the archaic pain circuits and social pain, particularly separation distress: The display serves the function of eliciting care.

The evolutionary connection between depression and social affect is probably related to one of the two behavioral options of a lost child: It can either try to catch the attention of the mother (but is then at risk of getting the attention of predators as well) or opt to remain motionless in order to avoid being eaten and to conserve energy. According to the theory, choosing the low activity option evolved into a circuit that, if overactive, causes clinical depression. Again, the reaction should be uncomfortable in order to teach the child to avoid getting lost—just as we should try to avoid losing our affiliates.

One way of describing our social affect system is to say that it provides us with an emotional barometer to monitor the amount of social support we are receiving. The idea that it first evolved to help infants seek nurture from the mother, and the mothers to care for their infants, makes sense. Distress vocalization, ranging from the wails of an infant to cries of pain expressed by grown-ups, is a behavioral output initiated by this system. The vocalization is coupled with strong emotions in both the person crying and those listening.

The loneliness we feel as adults is presumably due to an activation of the social affect system. If a situation becomes too terrifying, the result can be panic. Infants can react with a "panic" feeling in case of a crisis; for example, if they suddenly lose contact with their parents. The unwarranted panic attacks that trouble some adults are believed to be due to an over-activity of the same module. Obviously, the negative branch of the social affect system is not a module you wish to kindle unnecessarily.

I shall briefly describe the neurochemistry of the social affect system and some of the positive effects it may engender, because it points to some interesting connections. The command neurotransmitter for the distress system, as for many other basic emotions, is glutamate, and antagonists to glutamate have been shown to stop distress vocalization in animals. However, we also know some of the more specific actors of social affect: One is the neuropeptide oxytocin, which, as previously mentioned, is "the nurturing hormone." An injection of this hormone into the right part of the brain leads to a decrease in aggression and to the promotion of caring behavior. The other neuropeptide involved, vasopressin, is associated with sex and mating. The observation that these neuropeptides are active in all forms of social interactions adds evidence to the previously suggested succession of evolutionary connections: sex—child care—couple bonding—and social affiliation.

Sex promotes oxytocin synthesis, which adds substance to the "make love not war" slogan. Humans and bonobos have exploited this link more than other species have, and both of us probably produce an extra portion of oxytocin when we have sex.

The main neuropeptides of the reward system, the endorphins, are called upon to give you the joys of social life. Presumably this opioid system for rewards first evolved for the "homeostasis" type of behavior, but was later coupled to a variety of other activities, including the whole gamut from sex to tribal devotion. Endorphins also alleviate separation distress, while a reduction in opioid activity will encourage you to seek social comfort. In fact, even autistic children display a bit of social response when given opioid antagonists.[238]

Animals that are separated from their companions are more likely to self-administer opioid agonists such as opium and heroin. And the withdrawal reactions heroin addicts experience seem to be neurologically related to separation distress.[239] This brings us to an important question: Is the misuse of these substances by drug addicts related to a lack of social comfort? In other words, do addicts crave heroin partly because they are unable to get enough social support, and is the shot of heroin to some extent a substitute for love and care? Moreover, if the social comfort is cared for by drugs rather than by interacting with people, does that explain why addicts seem to be prone to antisocial behavior?

Maybe the most important question is whether the problems of both addiction and antisocial behavior are consequences of the Discord social life in modern societies—particularly the way this Discord disrupts the normal development of nerve circuits engaged in social behavior. The link between opioids and the social reward system suggests that this Discord is increasing the likelihood of addiction, and, consequently, that by improving the conditions we might alleviate the problems associated with narcotics. It has actually been shown that touching each other is enough to stimulate the opioid reward system, and anthropological literature suggests that societies that allow a lot of physical touch and intimacy display less aggression. Presumably they also have more content citizens.[240]

Drugs and aggression are only two of the problems of Discord societies. Panic attacks, depression, autism, and sociopathy are presumably also due to malfunctions of the social affect system—malfunctions that probably are aggravated because of present Discord conditions. Moreover, patients seeking medical help are only the tip of the iceberg of socially related emotional problems. It is tempting to propose that much suffering could be avoided if society catered more to our innate social needs.

Why not Adopt Them All?

An intriguing feature of human behavior is our willingness to take care of children born to total strangers. "Willingness" is an understatement: For many couples it is more like a strong desire; they go through a lot of trouble in order to adopt a child.

Cuckoldry happens in the "best," the most pair-bonding, of species. For an evolutionary biologist it is not a problem that a cuckolded male cares for the child; after all, he does not know better. His genes are not sufficiently fine-tuned to realize the situation, or deal with it. But no animal "updated on Darwin" should willingly consider adopting the children of others. In fact, if a male has been able to annex somebody else's female, he is more likely to start the relationship by killing off her children—which makes sense genetically speaking, because they are a nuisance, a waste of energy. Moreover, a female is more likely to start ovulating if there are no children around to care for.

The point is this: If you have enough money, it is not much of a sacrifice to give some coins to the starving children of far away countries; but to adopt one of them is a huge, and genetically speaking absurd, investment. Why then?

There are two features that help explain our willingness to adopt children: One is related to human reliance on rewarding sensations for directing behavior. Thus, as discussed in the previous section, to nurture a child can be highly rewarding. Most parents find that all children look sweet, although their own children are of course generally just a little bit sweeter. Studies indicate that adopted children typically receive pretty much the same love and investment as ordinary children, while stepchildren may be slightly worse off.[241] It is to be expected that the relationship to a stepchild, or an adopted child, has a more difficult start: Pregnancy and birth are normally important in turning on parental love. However, the appropriate emotions generally develop in spite of bypassing these steps. You can fool your genes by using condoms, and you can fool your genes by adopting a child. Thus, although an adopted child does not advance your Darwinian fitness, it can do wonders for your Darwinian happiness.

To understand the second feature, it is useful to look at certain animals: Mice can accept unfamiliar pups as their own. If you add a pup to an existing litter, the mother will care for it. There is no noble adoption, or moral standard involved; mice are simply inept at distinguishing between their own offspring and those of others. Each mouse has her own nest. As long as there are no curious scientists around, it is highly unlikely that the offspring of a stranger will end up in that nest; thus the genes do not have to worry about wasting energy on genes belonging to other mice. Evolution has therefore not installed a mechanism whereby the mother easily recognizes, and favors, her own offspring. The motherly instincts are directed at anything within the nest that resembles a mouse pup.

Sheep live in large groups, and lambs from different litters easily get mixed up. The ewe therefore develops a strong bond with her particular lamb. In fact, in order to do so she needs to smell the baby within a couple of hours after delivery. If the lamb is removed at birth and returned the next day, she will most likely refuse to feed it.[242]

Humans evolved in a situation where children were unlikely to get mixed up. The typical tribe included several children, but they were not born at the same time. Moreover, due to the fact that they were all probably related, caring for them was not that much of a genetic burden. In fact, humans have probably evolved a tendency to collaborate in fostering babies. Hence, evolution did not need to direct our parental instincts exclusively toward our own children. The wonderful consequence of combining unrestricted parental instincts with mental enticement is that we can enjoy any baby. The only fly in the ointment is that people occasionally enjoy babies so much that they steal them.

With this discussion of the joys of adoption in mind, let us move back to our social disposition. As detailed in the above supplementary section on "The Social High," evolution made use of the emotions designed for mother-child interactions in order to create a social species and provided ample rewards for socializing. Although evolution primarily needed gregarious instincts that recognized members of the same tribe, the empathy should also include members of affiliated tribes. Thus, as in the case of children, it was not necessary to constrain compassion according to narrow criteria: It was easy for Stone Age people to understand where their loyalty should be directed. The risk of wasting resources on irrelevant strangers was remote; evolution therefore did not have to counteract this possibility. Furthermore, the advantages of communal life actually dictate that the individual should preferably form a positive relationship with everyone not showing hostile intent. In other words, it is in the interest of your genes to be part of a large and strong social web. As a consequence, it feels good to send food to victims of a famine, and it feels good regardless of who they are or how far away they live.

Social life is probably one of the more potent sources of pleasure, and the absence of a social life is an obvious Discord. A lack of friends easily turns on the circuits of loneliness and distress. Provided basic needs are met, the most significant external factor influencing the happiness of people is their social life. It is important to get along with family and friends. True, people can be the most awful stressors, but they are also the greatest soothers.[243]

Twenty years ago the psychologist Bernard Rimland did a simple, but illuminating, experiment; he asked people to judge the characteristics of others, including their degree of selfishness and happiness. Surprisingly, or maybe not at all surprisingly, he found that those considered to be unselfish were also assumed to be the happier. It can obviously be argued that content people are more likely to be unselfish, but it seems to work the other way around too: Being concerned about the welfare of others is a sure way of becoming happy. Why would this be surprising? Well, there is a definite logic to the opposite assumption—that selfish people put more effort into making themselves content and thus should end up feeling better. Fortunately, it doesn't seem to work that way.[244]

Socializing is of prime importance for other communal animals as well. The biologist Robert Sapolsky has shown that in wild baboons the males with the strongest social networks have the lowest level of stress hormones. In other words, the more socially savvy and affiliating personalities enjoy a successful and long life, both among baboons and humans.[245]

As in the case of adoption, we are potentially capable of feeling compassion for more or less anybody, and we are even rewarded for doing so— which helps explain why it is so easy to induce empathy for people on the opposite side of the globe. The obvious question is: Why not create the perfect peaceful society by having everybody adopt everyone else? Our capacity for empathy offers us a great foundation for a compassionate society, even boosting our Darwinian happiness in the process. Unfortunately there is a snag.

The Pleasure of Rage

Not only are we potentially able to generate compassion for all humans, but we happily care for animals and plants as well. Some people even develop a strong passion for inanimate things such as waterfalls. Personally, I love mountains. But what about rats, weeds, spiders, thugs, problematic neighbors, and fans of an opposing soccer team? Herein lies the problem: Evolution got away with giving us a flexible capacity for compassion by counterbalancing it with a flexible capacity for hate.

For the sake of society our aggressive tendencies are a drawback, but from your genes' point of view, they are at least as sensible as compassion.

Self-assertion in times of conflict is more common than unselfishness. Genes that make an animal too kind simply do not survive.

In humans both kindness and wrath are easily elicited, and both can result in extreme forms of behavior. People occasionally risk their lives for that of a stranger, but the same individual may have a fight to the death with the next person he meets. A picture of a starving child brings forth a lot of compassion, but then all it takes to induce anger is a dandelion on a spot where only grass is allowed. Evolution did not find it necessary to impose detailed instructions as to what stimuli should elicit compassion. The same holds true for aggression: Any perceived threat to ourselves, our affiliates, or our possessions will suffice.

The brain circuit most relevant in connection with aggression is referred to as the "rage" module, and its evolutionary history probably dates back to at least the early vertebrates. Thus, the primitive response to a threat is either to freeze or to become drastically active. The activity either scares away whatever is intimidating you, or aids your escape. This "activity" option was presumably the scaffold on which evolution constructed the rage circuit, while the "freeze" option was a forerunner of fear as well as anxiety and depression—as suggested earlier. The observation that we still value some physical output to vent our anger supports this theory.

The rage circuit runs from the amygdala to the hypothalamus and the midbrain. It is interesting to note that fear covers roughly the same subcortical regions, substantiating the proposed evolutionary link between the two. Certain serotonin agonists are known to inhibit aggression in animals (particularly those referred to as serenics), and are being investigated for possible therapeutic use in humans. Anti-psychotic drugs are used for this purpose today, but they act more like "chemical straightjackets"; their sedative effects simply make you less active. A naturally occurring neuropeptide (substance P) seems to specifically elicit rage; thus antagonists of this peptide should offer an alternative strategy for the design of medicine aimed at those who are unable to restrain themselves.[246]

As with any other emotion, rage can take on many shapes as a result of modulation by the cortex: Hatred, for instance, is probably a version of

rage that represents such modulation, a process that may also be referred
to as cognitive appraisal.

There are a variety of other derivatives of rage: Envy and revenge are
typical examples. It would seem as if envy had evolved to ensure that,
however much we have, we are constantly dissatisfied, because the feeling
is obsessed with the relative. We tend to envy those who are better off
than ourselves, regardless of how rich or poor we are. The nature of present
society—where there will always be someone who has more than you—
amplifies the burden of envy. Whether or not you have all the resources
you need, your measure of Darwinian happiness is unlikely to be boosted
by feelings such as envy, spite, or greed. Neither are these feelings anything to brag about when comparing the human species with other animals. The point is that there is no shortage of unfriendly feelings in the
human repertoire.[247]

Revenge, for instance, is interesting. True, some animals inflict punishment as a way of modulating the behavior of others, as when a wolver-
ine mother bites one of her young that becomes too demanding. And if a
wolf loses the battle for pack leadership, he may come back to try again.
However, neither of these behaviors is there for the purpose of settling
scores. The point is that the utility of these actions is rather obvious; only
humans seem to enjoy punishment as a form of revenge.[248]

The tendency to blame others is another contribution of our fabulous
cognitive capacity. The evolution of the human brain has prepared us to
externalize the sources of anger, meaning that we prefer not to recognize
our own contribution to a conflict. The truth is that other people do not
"cause" anger in any direct sense; they merely trigger particular emotional circuits in the person who gets angry. Thus, we might as well blame
evolution for having given us these circuits.

It is in the nature of both compassion and contempt to foster similar
emotions in others; if you smile to the world, the world will smile back.
Unfortunately, anger seems to breed a lot faster than amicability. Moreover, when people are not content, or are stressed, wrath and related feelings are the ones that move closer to the surface. They say a hungry man
is an angry man. Discord conditions are expected to have a similar effect.

Although curbing the various versions of rage may also be considered a Discord, you are advised to show restraint for the sake of your community. Actually, as I shall argue, the same advice may serve to increase your measure of Darwinian happiness as well: The good news is that only positive feelings—kindness, compassion, and generosity—are consistently accompanied by joy.

This, however, is not obvious, because rage can be very important for your genes. For instance, you should expect a large reward for crushing an enemy. My ancestors envisioned a heaven they called Valhalla; in their mythology only those who died weapon-in-hand could enter, and once inside they were allowed to fight all day. When night came, the dead and wounded were healed and they would all join in a feast—just to continue the battle the next day.[249] Maybe this is not the ideal paradise for everybody, but I am sure that a lot of men can acknowledge the idea that there are brain rewards to be harvested from fighting.

There are other rewards as well: One purpose of anger is to avoid having someone get the better of you; consequently it feels good to get the better of somebody else. Again, English is poor in words. In my language the term "skadefryd" ("Schadenfreude" in German), is used to denote this pleasure. Malicious joy is the English term that roughly, at least, describes what I am talking about. Of course, social pressure within a tribe restrains you from entertaining this feeling. Since today's societies typically want us to feel that everybody is in the same "tribe," we are pressed to not take pleasure from malicious joy at all.

It is possible that our Stone Age ancestors enjoyed the various forms of rage with a better conscience. Yet, I still maintain that compassion is a better source of joy and shall explain why I believe evolution has designed us to be happier hugging each other than hitting each other:

The important difference between the two categories of emotions is presumably rooted in their evolutionary history. Aggression is a very ancient feature, and most likely present in all vertebrates. The "rage" circuit appears to be a deep-rooted response conserved by evolution, requiring a great effort on the part of our free will to curb. As already mentioned, our social instincts appeared much later in the evolution of humans—at a stage where the evolution of behavior progressed due to the use of positive and negative sensations, rather than by hardwired responses. Wrath is more a legacy of our animal past. Therefore, although both combat and compassion can elicit agreeable sensations, the latter is more potent in this respect. Unwarranted aggression, moreover, is more likely to have dire consequences than unjustified kindness. Linking violence with pleasure is thus a dubious evolutionary strategy, because a person who really delights in hitting others will sooner or later end up as a victim himself.

So far so good, though regrettably other peculiarities of the human species speak to our disfavor. All mammals have a rage module, but the human version may be more touchy than the average: Most conflicts among animals of a particular species concern hierarchies and access to resources, of which territory and mating partners are the more important. Humans both live in hierarchical groups and are territorial. As a consequence, compared to less territorial and less hierarchical species, such as sheep or siamangs, our button for rage is probably rather more accessible. The short period of human history that carries a written record supports this assertion:

It is tempting to use the Israelites as an example, not because they were necessarily worse than others, but because they left more detailed chronicles.[250] If the Old Testament is to be trusted, the Israelites were highly proficient at both warfare and genocide: Under the leadership of Moses and Joshua they exterminated several tribes in what they had decided should be their promised land. In most cases all members were killed, but they did occasionally make exceptions for virgin women. Speaking from an evolutionary perspective, this is of course a sensible selection.

The Stone Age savage could have actually been less savage by nature than we are, as I suspect that selection for combativeness escalated along with an increase in population density and a concomitant increase in conflicts—a process that possibly started some 100,000 years ago. After all, the killer is more likely to pass on his genes than those who are killed.

Our compassionate and combative tendencies are best considered as separate modules of the brain. Selection that favors compassion does not necessarily change the innate tendencies of aggression, and vice versa. The two modules are triggered by particular stimuli, and take turns at manipulating the mind of an individual. It is therefore conceivable that humans today are both more combative and more compassionate than our ancestors were. Both modules are ready to stand up for you.

Unfortunately, there are a number of aspects of human aggression that cannot be resolved, even if people would agree that love feels better than rage.

For one thing, aggression is a much wider problem than simple rage: Assaults are very often motivated by impulses such as sex or money, rather than by justified anger directed at a certain victim. In other words, some forms of aggressive behavior are linked to rewards that have nothing to do with the rage system.

Hunting is an obvious example of a violent activity that is not under the management of rage circuits. Our ancestors probably began hunting at about the same time as we evolved our social bonds, which means that hunting took off at a time when it was more fashionable for evolution to use incentives, rather than brute instinct, to control behavior. It is strenuous and potentially dangerous to hunt down an animal; pleasant sensations are therefore important in order to motivate people to participate. Today people pay to be allowed to participate, and they pay a lot more than the value of the meat they may procure; in other words, they do it for the enjoyment.

Desmond Morris has suggested that one reason why it is so easy to have men volunteer for warfare is that combat functions as a substitute for hunting.[251] Both activities typically involve, and bring together, a group of males. Warfare might therefore recruit brain rewards from both the hunt per se and the gratification of social bonding. The latter aspect is boosted by the fact that nothing brings people as close together as the necessity of joining hands in the face of danger. Of course, it may help to motivate the soldier by stimulating anger directed at the adversaries, but this is apparently not required to make him pull the trigger.

Warfare and other forms of group-associated violence are the major problems troubling humanity, and the rage circuit is only partly responsible. To end up on the winning side is not that bad, in terms of Darwinian happiness, but I still believe that the greater delights are reserved for those who make other people happy. Therefore, the individual's quest for Darwinian happiness does not, fortunately, conflict that much with what is best for society.

Most people, unfortunately, do not pursue Darwinian happiness, but tend to follow whatever passion happens to be activated. Hatred is more hardwired. Thus, when the right button is pushed, people willingly oblige, not heeding the fact that it may destroy whatever joy they have left. May we hope that the idea of Darwinian happiness can come to our rescue?

Cowboys and Indians

As pointed out in Chapter 4, we are a highly homogeneous species—at least genetically speaking. Most of our genes are almost identical, so, according to the principle of "inclusive fitness," should we not feel solidarity with all humans? In fact, even the genes of chimpanzees differ from ours by only around two percent, so maybe the apes should be included as well. But unfortunately that is not the way the principle of inclusive fitness works.

Kin selection is based on the presence of non-kin who compete with kin for resources. The process distinguishes between the genes belonging to real kin and the almost identical genes of anyone else. We have this propensity therefore to classify people as either one of us or one of them. Regrettably, in order to obtain a robust solidarity, we seem to need an out-group as opponents. We want to play cowboys and Indians.

Novels and movies, particularly those coming from Hollywood, tend to portray people as good or bad, and it is reasonably easy, even for small kids, to find the right label for the different actors. We display the same tendency when dealing with real life humans; we prefer to consider them as either kind or evil, as friend or foe. In our tribal past this made sense: A person was either affiliated with you, or he was a possible enemy. As a precaution, it was safer to assume that a stranger represented danger. Sure, you ought to give him a chance, because you preferred to have him as an ally, but you should also be suspicious, and any sign of negative intent should classify him as an opponent. And, the more unfamiliar his looks or behavior, the way he dressed or the way he spoke, the more likely he did not belong to your group.

Today this tendency is unfortunate. We meet a lot of strangers, and, although it makes sense not to trust them completely, you are usually expected to interact positively with them. Moreover, the inclination to consider others as either good or bad distorts our picture of reality. People are not like that, simply because we all have the full complement of circuits catering to social interactions. The holy man sometimes hits an infant in a fit of rage, and even the most sadistic rapist probably loves his children. It is difficult for the average person to embrace the complexity of kindness and evil as well as the dual nature of human emotional life.

Modern society is a crucible where all sorts of humans are mixed together, but we still want to define an in-group. This is a Discord situation. Again and again we see that certain groups, which carry some recognizable feature, turn into units and find themselves at conflict with other units—basically the West Side Story all over again. By understanding the innate component of the phenomenon, we may improve our chances of curbing the conflicts.[252]

The Unbearable Lightness of Missiles

Whether it is a mountain lion trying to eat you, or a neighbor in bed with your spouse, conflicts are in reality a fight between genes. Your body is simply the unfortunate wrapping that ends up in the middle.

All animals are prepared to fight, but based on the historical record we humans appear yet again to be the worst kids on the block. More specifically, we are the champions when it comes to murdering our own species. No other animal kills its own with the same enthusiasm and efficiency. The success of the human brand of group violence can be seen in anything from two five-year-olds roughing up a third child, to hooligans fighting at a soccer match, and, needless to say, to mature young men performing at peak efficiency in times of war. As may be expected, most countries put a lot of effort into creating a potent and elegant system for organized murder.

Aggression in animals usually starts with a conflict between two individuals or, occasionally, between two groups of individuals. The animals in question face each other at close range; they show their muscles and growl and bare their teeth. In that way they can evaluate the power and the sincerity of the opponent. If one of them concludes that the other is too strong, or too fierce, he can signal defeat and thus save his skin. The opponent will rarely attack since even an inferior opponent is potentially able to inflict serious injury. If neither party withdraws, they can start a brief fight in order to further evaluate the power of the other. This is usually enough; one of them is likely to give up. Thus, under natural conditions, a conflict rarely causes severe injury.

Animals that are equipped with dangerous weapons, such as the teeth and claws of lions, tigers, and bears, tend to instinctively avoid "armed" conflicts. The more powerful the weapons, the greater the danger that both will get hurt; it is safer to just roar. Nature did not equip humans with much in terms of weapons; in fact, some people claim that our most deadly weapon is our tongue. We have, as a consequence, not evolved that much restraint when it comes to fighting each other. In fact, we enjoy sports like boxing where the purpose is to knock the opponent out cold. One important point is that, if we had just used the weapons nature designed us with, there would be no reason to complain.

In Chapter 4, I suggested that the invention of agriculture expelled us from the Garden of Eden. Actually, we probably took a good bite off the apple long before we started our own gardening. The first mouthful, the first step away from Eden, was when we realized that by putting something in our hands, we could become a lot more dangerous: The stone axe was invented some two million to three million years ago. Since then, human ingenuity has performed at a furious pace when devising tools for the purpose of killing.

Today we are far from the Garden of Eden—so far that we only look for it in a life after death, or in fairy tales. Which is sad. The latter part of our evolution may have boosted our fighting spirit, yet the main difference between then and now does not lie in our innate tendencies, but rather in our arsenal of weapons. Our genes probably do not code for more violence than what we can curb; thus the problem is not so much our propensity for aggression, but our access to deadly guns.

The weapons we use are anything from a stone or a spear to machine guns and atomic bombs, and they imply that even those who are physically weak, and at the bottom of the social and economic hierarchy, can kill anybody—and can do so with limited immediate risk to their own health. We may still snarl and throw words at each other, but, unfortunately, the power of a knife or a revolver makes the more harmless way of resolving conflicts less persuasive. The situation calls for attempts to regulate the distribution of weapons, and for rules restricting when and where people are allowed to carry knives and guns—which is much more of a hot issue in the United States than it is in Europe.

It is not that we are without restraints. Killing or wounding a defenseless person, or somebody who has not harmed us, is a Discord—it carries a mental burden. The way we organize death penalties illustrates the psychological toll of unwarranted killing: The executioner prefers the victim to wear a hood in order to avoid eye contact. And firing squads typically consist of several marksmen, of which only some have a real bullet in the chamber of his gun, in order to let each executioner assume that it was not his gun that did the killing.

Our latest, and biggest, bite of the apple came with the invention of long-distance weapons. We now have weaponry that works nicely without ever having to have that dreadful personal contact with the victim. We are no longer forced to evaluate whether violence is called for or not; it is sufficient to push a button, or to give a short order to a computer.

Firing a missile is so easy.

Summary—the Good and the Evil

To conclude, I shall list the factors that combine in shaping the problem of human aggression:

(1) We have a well marked and readily accessible rage button in our brain.

(2) We readily engage in violence for a variety of purposes, even in the absence of any cause of anger; for example, in connection with robbery and rape.

(3) We are social beings and thus inclined to form in-groups and out-groups with the concomitant preference for gang violence.

(4) The impact of hostility in present society is drastically worsened by the weapons we have invented.

(5) The Discord aspects of society create stress that is likely to lower the threshold for activating the rage button.

Is there anything we can do? First, to balance this sordid picture, we are also equipped with a generous dose of geniality that it is possible to kindle. It seems fair to consider the two opposing tendencies of geniality and rage as separate modules of the brain. The impact of each module on thoughts and actions is drastically affected by the stimuli received; thus, we may try to selectively activate geniality. Moreover, there is one major heartening aspect concerning these opposing forces: The good is more likely to be good for you, while the evil is more likely to be bad for you.

How best to deal with this situation is the topic of the next chapter.

CHAPTER 11

Community:
Making the Most of
Our Social Instincts

Essaouira—projecting the city from the sea.

The Tribe

The last chapter concentrated on the biological background of our compassionate and violent tendencies. The important question facing mankind is how to make the most of the human predicament.

Various cultures have been more or less successful at this task: The Yanomamö of Venezuela, on the one hand, have a reputation for being fierce fighters, and there seems to be a lot of aggression both within and between tribes.[253] On the other hand, the Trobrianders, who live on islands off New Guinea, are known for their peaceful coexistence.[254] It seems unlikely that there are any drastic differences in innate tendencies between these two tribal peoples; thus, the observed dissimilarity is presumably due to cultural and environmental factors. The obvious conclusion is that it should be possible to improve conditions by adjusting these factors. In fact, scientists are addressing the question of why features such as generosity and nastiness are unequally distributed when comparing societies around the globe.[255]

I believe one factor that makes a difference is how much Discord there is in the society: Even docile animals start maiming each other when stressed in captivity. A pervading idea of this book is that the typical conditions of modern society are stressful for us humans. A variety of conditions may contribute to this effect, but the social situation is presumably among the worst culprits.

In Chapter 4 I pointed out that present tribal people, which include the Yanomamö and the Trobrianders, do not have access to the environment of our Stone Age ancestors. The conditions for both tribes are more or less in Discord; yet, when comparing them, I do not claim that their differences in behavior should necessarily be attributed solely to Discord conditions. I propose that Discord conditions have an impact on aggressive behavior—not that this factor explains everything.

Most experts agree that hominids evolved to a life in a tribal setting. The tribe would typically include several family groups. There would be a certain number of individuals of each sex and age set, but usually well

Plate 18. The Masai of Kenya have had the courage to resist the temptation of modern society and try to retain their tribal way of living.

below a hundred in total. The most important feature of these tribes was that the members were generally very close to each other. No matter whether they grew up together, or came into the tribe as adults, they spent a lot of time in each other's company. They also relied on each other. Consequently they formed strong ties. They would occasionally meet with neighboring tribes, but only rarely would there be total strangers around. The different tribes depended on each other for the exchange of mates, and possibly for information and tools. Thus, in the absence of specific conflicts, they could trust the people with whom they interacted.

This tribal way of living began to disappear 10,000 years ago, and human social life has changed dramatically since then. It would seem that many people suffer from a lack of social security and belonging. In fact, I believe the lack of a tribal social setting to be the most significant Discord between present life and that of the environment our genes are adapted to (the EEA). It may prove to be an Achilles heel for the human species.

The biologist Lee Dugatkin argues, as I do, that our understanding of human social behavior based on an evolutionary perspective may help us generate a better society where people are more cooperative.[256] I sincerely hope the world will eventually learn to utilize this knowledge. At the end of this chapter I shall present a model suggesting how we may approach the problem of improving compassion. But first I shall look at political ideologies and at other aspects of modern societies in the perspective of human behavioral biology, beginning with a peculiar example of a vestige of our tribal past. The purpose of presenting these perspectives is that I believe some useful lessons can be learned from them.

Sheriffs or Honor: The Case of Japan

The "tragedy of the commons" is the story of a shared pasture, leading to its infertility and destruction. What happened was that each farmer put out on the "common meadows" as many sheep as he wanted to, and the combined stock destroyed the vegetation due to overgrazing.[257]

The story has been used as a metaphor for a dilemma: Should each individual be allowed to freely consume common resources, or should laws regulate consumption? The tragedy, of course, is that, left unregulated, the principle of sharing the commons will tend to ruin life-supporting resources—that is, unless the users are a sufficiently close-knit community, in which case universally accepted principles and morality should lead to the required restraint.

In a tribal setting the community was presumably on terms of sufficient intimacy to address the dilemma; today we are not. It is difficult to have people obey moral guidelines in a large-scale society; thus, to avoid the tragedy of the commons over and over again, we try to enforce regulations by enlisting the aid of sheriffs or the police. Do we have any choice?

One country stands out as different: Japan was brought out of its self-imposed isolation late in the nineteenth century. The country never had much in the way of natural resources, and at the time was industrially far behind the Western world. Yet Japan managed to produce one of the greatest economic success stories the Earth had ever witnessed. How did Japan manage to do this?

I wish to emphasize that economic prosperity may not necessarily increase Darwinian happiness. Thus, what I am interested in is not whether what Japan did was good, but rather why they succeeded in a task that most countries strive very hard to achieve, but with much less success. An explanation for Japan's accomplishment may help other countries achieve whatever aims they give priority to, not just to boosting their respective economies. For example, it might help society improve the quality of life for its citizens.

A closer look at Japan suggests that it is possible to have strong social affiliations that unite populations that are much larger than those of traditional tribes. Japan is (or was) a society governed by morality rather than by law. The point is illustrated by the observation that the United States has at least five times as many lawyers per capita. Factories and offices in Japan are organized as "tribal units" with close-knit ties; as a consequence the employees feel a moral responsibility for the welfare of each other and the work place. What is more, the country even managed to create a hierarchy of tribes with a god-like emperor leading a "super-tribe." Japanese culture is becoming more similar to that of the West, but at least Japan used to be a society where the social glue was composed of tribal feelings rather than law enforcement. I believe this feature helped the country achieve what it did.[258]

There are several misconceptions about Japan. First, a nation that starts a major war is unlikely to be regarded as peaceful. Yet, I believe nobody will deny that you are safer on the streets of Tokyo than of New York. As to violence, Tokyo is as close to the Garden of Eden as you are ever likely to get in a city of that size.

Another misconception about the Japanese is that the people lack feelings. The uninformed foreigner sees a lot of poker faces, disrupted only by occasional fake smiles, but that does not mean true emotions are not there. They are there—probably more so than in any other modern culture, for Japanese society is based on emotions. It is based on interpersonal relationships, which, as we shall see, actually explain the poker faces.

The emotional glue that keeps the community united is stronger than in comparable countries. Whereas we have complicated laws to tell us what to do, or rather what we are not supposed to do, and to enforce them, the Japanese more often rely on honor: Their society is based on the innate moral tendencies discussed in the previous chapter. The most horrible offense for a Japanese is to cause inconvenience to others; to be subsequently frowned upon by members of the community is considered worse

Plate 19. When appropriate behavior is enforced by the power of conscience, a police doll is sufficient to remind people to obey traffic regulations.

than a ten-year prison sentence. If the disgrace is sufficiently devastating, you are expected to commit suicide.

Who needs police if the crooks sentence themselves to capital punishment?

The density of the population, I believe, is the clue to why the Japanese are considered to be emotionally numb. In a society where feelings mean so much, it is important that people do not express their feelings at the wrong time and place. In other words, masks are more necessary in their culture, because the impact of an unmasked face is far greater.

Social life is centered around the work place. It should come as no surprise to find that having production units function as tribal groups yields greater productivity. The added productivity, however, is not the only advantage: To have a deep emotional commitment to those you work with is less of a Discord, and therefore helps to improve your quality of life. As stated by the anthropologist Roger Keesing, "If our human potential for self-realization and collective commitment is to be fulfilled, it will have to come in part from restructuring the experience of work."[259]

Moreover, any society would obviously prefer to be able to rely on friendly cooperation rather than having to depend on sheriffs with a fast draw. The Japanese experience suggests that this supplement to the more common solution to the problems of crime and violence has not been fully exploited in Western societies. It is a more difficult option to establish, but well worth working for.

In fact, I expect that obligations are more likely to be heeded if they are enforced by moral considerations rather than by law: It is often possible to escape the police, but very difficult to escape a guilty conscience. The power of our tendency to follow moral guidelines should not be underestimated: It is amazing how many criminals prefer to confess. You may choose to be a liar and thief, just as you may choose narcotics; in the short run both offer certain advantages, but neither works as a good long-term strategy for improving your quality of life. Narcotics too often turn you into an addict, and unsympathetic behavior not only affects your moral sense, but will eventually be discovered by your peers and will subsequently disable your social life. Since nobody has complete control of the unconscious, your real personality will tend to shine through.

I am not necessarily arguing for more leniency in our response to offenders. Where the system of moral obligations is not up and running, we need laws and decisive punishment. We need them to curb selfish behavior that hurts others, and we need them because we do have this innate feeling for fairness and revenge. The punishment of antisocial behavior is an important factor in building solidarity and erecting a culture where rules are taken seriously. Strong social mores should help us decrease the number of crooks—not the duration of their sentence.

There are lots of descriptions of tribal people living in harmony and contentment; the Japanese example is important because it demonstrates that some of the advantages of a tribal setting can be transferred to modern societies. The next question then is: Given that the tribal system did help the Japanese achieve their goals, why was the system restricted to Japan? Why did not Western countries take more advantage of innate moral tendencies? All cultures evolved from tribal societies, and we all carry the same natural capacity for emotionally based relations. Yet, even Japan's closest neighbors, South Korea and Taiwan, are completely different.

It is possible that Japan's particular history of isolation helped the country retain tribal values: During the period when Japan was transformed from a Stone Age tribal society to a large-scale feudal system, the country had limited contact with other populations. In most of East Asia, as well as in Europe, threats and conflicts with neighboring states were frequent, whereas no external conflicts spread to Japanese soil. Thus, the Japanese did not have to create particular ideologies or religions in order to keep the country united against physical and cultural foreign pressures.

European states needed religions, or other forms of excluding belief systems, in order to obtain national identity and thus national loyalty. And the message conveyed in most of these belief systems can be stated in a single sentence: "What we say is correct, what they say is wrong." As a consequence, principles took over the task of directing behavior. It is not that the Japanese found a new and ingenious way to organize society; they were simply lucky enough to retain the old one.

It should be mentioned that the Japanese system is not solely advantageous: The country seems to be characterized by conformity. The rule that you are not allowed to offend or upset anybody tends to restrict behavior more than our written laws do. Individualism may actually offer advantages in terms of happiness. Moreover, conformity tends to limit inventiveness: The Japanese are apparently good at adopting technology from other countries, but not so good at making their own inventions.

The Japanese way seems to be a losing option today, since the attitude of their culture is changing into a more Western one. Our approach is centered more in individual freedom rather than toward social pressure; as a consequence, work mates (and maybe even friends) are something we gather for a particular purpose, rather than for a lifelong commitment. Western culture offers more immediate gratification, and we live in a society where immediate gratification is king. In that respect our culture is a bit like a narcotic: It offers short-term pleasures, rather than stress-avoidance and long-term satisfaction. But who wants to go back after having eaten from the apple?

Maybe we should reconsider our priorities. The question we should ask is: When the consequences of the Discords have taken their toll, and a lifetime of happiness is added up, what type of society comes out on top? I believe we ought to learn something from the Japanese, rather than encourage them to adopt our dubious habits.

There is a difficult balance between building strong and healthy countries and having people feel solidarity for the population of the world. Having many "tribes" in the same region is likely to cause conflicts; thus I am not advocating tribalism for the sake of creating powerful and voracious nations. I am advocating that we try to stimulate the tribal feelings of solidarity and compassion, because those feelings can be redirected toward all members of our species, and because healthy nations are more likey to contriubute beneficially to the world.

The Biology of Politics

It is not easy to change a culture. Moreover, it is obviously easier to add a new "narcotic"—whether in the shape of a chemical or a cultural trait—than to remove popular items that are already widespread. You are more likely to gain acceptance for anything that satisfies immediate desires than for the idea of restraint and long-term benefits.

Is it possible to install tribal feelings in our gratification-hungry Western societies? It should be possible, because we all have genes that allow for solidarity and sociability. The problem is that instead of being able to rely on a continuous tradition dating back to our tribal past, as in Japan, Western countries must reintroduce these ideals; in fact, we have tried to do so with the use of ideologies.

When writing the political history of the twentieth century, two opposing ideologies take center stage: communism and capitalism. The two ideologies are discussed here because they offer a lesson in how best to exploit, for the benefit of society, two distinct features of our innate mental constitution—solidarity and self-assertion. That is to say, the two ideologies can teach us something about how these features can serve communal needs as well as tell us something about how best to go about changing a culture in the direction of solidarity. In order to extract these lessons, three very different cultures are used as examples. I have already presented the culture of Japan. In this section I shall expand on the issue by including the Soviet Union and the Western world in the discussion.

The conflict between communism and capitalism burned out toward the end of the last century. The compromise contained in Western-style social democracies emerged as the winner. The dismal reality was that the main communist power, the Soviet Union, never quite managed to handle the ideology for which they were presumably experts; capitalistic Japan was apparently more egalitarian.

The comparison of the Soviet Union with Japan is not entirely fair, because the Soviets needed to reinstall tribal sentiments in adults, which obviously is a lot more difficult than maintaining tribal feelings culturally introduced to the children, as was the case in Japan. Yet, I believe the Soviet Union would have done a lot better in instilling its communist ideology if it had based its attempt on an understanding of human nature. The Soviets made a couple of obvious mistakes: They decided that they wanted the State to be the most important level for people to associate with (whereas solidarity in Japan is based primarily on tribal-size units). Moreover, there are two features of sufficient power in the human mind to help pull off national solidarity from scratch: Feature number one is an external enemy, which the Soviets made sure they had; but they kicked out the other feature at the start—religion.

Marx claimed that religion is the opiate of the people, and his claim may carry some weight; but contrary to Marx I believe that, as a narcotic, religion has obvious advantages. If Lenin and Stalin had mobilized the church for their cause—instead of trying to destroy it—the result might have been a better and more egalitarian nation.

Capitalism, on the other hand, caters to our inherent tendency for self-assertion. This tendency is found in all organisms; genes that do not instruct their carriers to care for their procreation have a bleak future. The individual needs to obtain resources in competition with others. We do have a capacity for compassion, and this capacity can be encouraged, but any serious political system should take a level of egoism into account. Most humans primarily think of themselves (even if the less selfish people tend to be the happier ones). Those who are close to us are a good number two; and then, if everything is fine, an occasional thought and a handful of dollars are sent to starving children elsewhere.

Fortunately a bit of egoism is not necessarily such a bad legacy; it can actually be exploited to the benefit of society. Egoism can offer advantages to more than just the individual. For instance, a person who starts up an industry will tend to confer prosperity on those around him, on employees and clients and numerous others. Western social democracies have several tools that can be used to direct self-assertion so that society may benefit as a whole. What characterized the Soviet Union was a situation where the difference between rich and poor was probably as big as in some Western countries, but where the egoism that led the rich to riches gave less benefit to the masses. To channel the initiative and inventiveness of the individuals toward what is best for society is a very important, but rather difficult, task.

Self-assertion in modern societies appears to be primarily about obtaining money and possessions. For our hunter-gatherer ancestors, most tools were presumably readily available; and there was not that much difference between a Rolls Royce stone axe and a Lada stone axe. Diamonds and fat cigars were unknown, and they did not have banks to stow away riches. Within a tribe, the main resource that could be desired at the cost of others would be spouses. As suggested in Chapter 9, I believe this is one of the reasons why we have evolved as a pair-bonding species.

Obviously we do not have a particular gene for craving money and riches. We probably do have an innate tendency to hoard resources, since they offer some security; but I suspect that what drives the desire for money is not so much security or consumption, but rather the accompanying status and the joy of success. As a consequence, for people living in reasonable affluence, money itself does not boost Darwinian happiness that much.[260]

It is tempting to point out that no one in the Stone Age ever worried much about not having a color TV or a car—inventions that have certainly added plenty of frustration and unfulfilled desires to mankind. New appliances appear every day. In another hundred years, future generations will wonder how people managed to survive with the primitive state of technology in the year 2002. We are blissfully ignorant of future gadgets.

There is an innate drive toward obtaining a higher rank in most hierarchical animals. Selection made sure that a certain degree of status seeking is inscribed in the genes, as individuals high in the system tend to receive and obtain more resources, both in the form of food and mating partners. Again, humans are no exception. Anyone who has witnessed how girls flock around popular music stars should realize the importance of status. And as to gadgets, even a chimp can improve its status by possessing something that is rare—for example, an empty tin can. On the Trobriand Islands riches are displayed in the form of yam-roots, while the feathers of large birds gave status to the native Indians of America. Flashing diamonds and sports cars are just another cultural expression of a desire to display success.

Research on happiness supports the contention that money does not make you that much happier as long as your basic needs are covered. It is therefore tempting to assert that the contribution to Darwinian happiness afforded by money (that is, primarily the accompanying status and feeling of success, which should be potent sources of rewards due to their importance in procreation) can be obtained by other means. In other words, there are many "arenas" in which to harvest these rewards.

The choice of money, or other aspects of materialism, as the accepted currency for rank has unfortunate consequences. True, many products have a real potential for improving Darwinian happiness, but a society can do equally well without an excessive drive for consumption. It is difficult to feed six billion people without disrupting the environment or depleting vital resources; overindulgence is bound to increase the problem. Thus, society would be better served if status were based on deeds done for the good of the community. We might, for example, look to various tribal people where you gain prestige by giving away possessions.[261] As an extra bonus these people are awarded the joys of generosity and of helping others. Bill Gates, the founder of Microsoft, appears to have taken the hint.

In Stone Age tribes, innate tendencies functioned as they should. Confrontations, self-assertion, and the drive to improve status were balanced by compassion, cooperation, and subordination. Furthermore, at that time everybody was pretty much in the same boat. Studies on recent tribal societies suggest that tribal leaders are not the brutes you might imagine, but rather characterized by consideration and intelligence. Actually, some of the hunter-gatherers of today appear to have no class structure, and give little recognition to the role of leaders.[262]

It is interesting to note that while the chimpanzees are rather hierarchical, the bonobos appear to be a lot more egalitarian. Unfortunately, it is not possible to tell which one of these species most resembles the common ancestor of chimps, bonobos, and humans. Whether or not our ancestors were as hierarchical as the chimps, I believe it is likely that at some point in hominid evolution, leadership moved from dictators to collaborators. After that transition, decisions were made in a setting where personal relations prevailed; it was a compromise and consensus-type decision making. Leaders were not just directly accountable to those they led; they were also accessible. Moreover, the stone axe was presumably sufficiently potent as a weapon to make sure that tyrannical leaders did not sleep all too well. Although status at one point probably correlated solidly with reproductive success, in the later part of hominid evolution status became more a question of respect and reputation, and the correlation between actual power and number of children became less obvious.

Under present Discord conditions the situation is not as favorable. Despots flourish. The increasing size of societies and the invention of more advanced weapons, as well as walls to hide behind, shift the balance of power toward the side of the tyrant: A small army can deter a large crowd as long as that crowd does not possess the same armaments. The mighty and the rich throw away enormous resources while the poor lack even basic necessities. It should surprise no one to find that those at the bottom of the hierarchy do not always cooperate voluntarily. If they are given access to weapons, carnage is the likely outcome.

Desmond Morris once stated that directing a modern society is like having an elephant balance on a tight rope. We need leaders more than ever, and we need them to be very good. On the other hand, if we find the right persons, we do have the advantage that one individual can inspire the entire globe. It does not necessarily need to be a political leader; any person who is able to excite people has at his or her disposal a great tool for influencing their minds—a singer, a prophet, or an outstanding personality may do.

The social democracies of Western countries may not be perfect, but I believe they offer a decent starting point for future societies. They represent a reasonable compromise that exploits both egoism and altruism for the benefit of the community. They are, however, more Discord than what may be necessary—for example, in the way work is organized, in the social fabric, and in the way we deal with sexuality. Thus, although we could do a lot worse, further improvement is conceivable.

What the Internet Cannot Do

Several peculiarities of the present social situation add to the Discord between our genes and the way we live. And I believe this is worthwhile to look into, since any measure that decreases Discord is expected to reduce stress and to improve harmony in a society. While it may not be possible to recreate the tribal setting in an industrialized society, it may be possible to approximate certain features of tribal social interactions, as suggested by the following examples.

For example, the natural environment for sleep presumably consists of having the family stay in close proximity, typically within reach for physical contact, and the rest of the tribe should also be close by. The characteristic modern arrangement, putting the children in cribs and shuffling them into separate rooms, is a Discord. The genes presumably expect more closeness and touch than we get today, and we have seen that the lack of physical contact is likely to have consequences on mental development. Recall the discussion in Chapter 7 of rhesus monkeys and rat mothers licking their pups, and also the discussion in Chapter 5 on the requirement of serotonin receptor activity in infants in order to avoid later anxiety.

Another example concerns how children interact: In the tribal setting children spend most of their days throughout the year in each other's company. They come to know each other intimately. Rough-and-tumble play is important, and in the tribe it is not a problem since everyone knows the rules. If somebody crosses the line and acts in a way considered inappropriate by peers, children have effective mechanisms to set him straight. They also have ways of reconciliation. After all, there is nowhere to go; everyone knows that peers are likely to be around for the rest of their lives.

A good kindergarten should try to approximate the natural setting. For example, adults should not intervene every time two boys start mock fighting, and they should encourage children to resolve conflicts by themselves. To learn to socialize is like learning to speak: We have an innate propensity—a template, so to speak—but in order to develop our social capacity we need suitable input. Interacting with others molds our social competence. Play and conflict resolutions are important forms of interaction; if the situation is too much of a Discord, the input is unlikely to yield an adult with optimal social performance. The extreme cases of "feral" children, that is children growing up in the wild in the absence of human contact, or just locked away for many years in solitary confinement, exemplify the point. The romantic ideal of the noble savage, such as Tarzan or Mowgli, contrasts starkly with the reality—the majority of these children are mute, bestial, and egocentric.[263]

Life has changed in many ways for adults as well: For example, in Stone Age tribes there was no difference between paid work and work at home—everything was done with, and for, those with whom you had strong affiliations. Work was presumably not even considered to be "work," but just a part of life. Thus family concerns, community affairs, and the various activities were continuous elements in the daily round of life. The products of labor were either consumed by the producer, shared, or exchanged with associates. It is satisfying to work for your personal needs and for the needs of those who are close to you.[264]

There were no watches in the Stone Age, so the whole concept of time presumably had a totally different meaning. Or people simply did not relate to this concept. They may occasionally have felt compelled to rush, but they were presumably not exposed to the constant feeling of minutes and hours going by, of appointments to be kept, and the need to fill time with particular activities—matters that I believe are further examples of Discords.[265]

Social life in the Stone Age lasted from the cradle to the grave. Not only did you hang around with the same people, but the culture and ways of thinking were almost constant. You knew all the rituals. Society did not appear to change; you always knew what to expect.

Transactions were among affiliates and were a part of social life; you could therefore trust that social "contracts" were heeded. Today we are forced to deal with a range of people with whom we do not have personal relationships and whom we may never meet again. We fear that our trust will be misused. Often obligations are not heeded, with the consequence that one or both parties feel cheated, or suffer from a bad conscience.[266]

It has been shown that animals who have known each other for a long time display less aggression when grouped together. They accept each other's presence, and they know their rank so that potential conflicts can be resolved with a glance. The situation is less peaceful if you force unfamiliar individuals to interact.

To put a lot of strangers together is a Discord, presumably to both humans and animals. On the other hand, if those that need to interact get to know each other—for example, informal interactions at work—fewer conflicts will arise. Anything that activates the positive side of the social affect system will promote bonding—and thereby promote geniality. Thus, communal coffee breaks at work may not be such a bad idea; good-natured gossip that disperses information about fellow employees can improve cooperation and geniality.

Grooming in social primates is well known to stimulate positive relationships, and has been shown to boost opiate-related reward mechanisms in the brain.[267] Robin Dunbar even suggests that language evolved as a form of "grooming," and, moreover, that it helped facilitate social relations in large groups.[268] He points out that while physical grooming typically involves only two individuals at a time, oral grooming can engage several persons simultaneously. No wonder small talk is so popular.

I guess the bottom-line is that the coffee-break chat has the potential of both benefiting your employer and adding to your measure of Darwinian happiness.

The Internet and cellular phones have made interactions very easy, and technology certainly does improve communication; nevertheless, it also carries an aspect of Discord with it. Face-to-face, the physical presence, the smell and the touch—these are the social settings our minds are primed for; electronics has so far been unable to deliver them. Which is why we should strive to get a chance to hug each other.

The main point in this section is that, although present societies are far from what our genes have in mind, it is possible to reduce the Discord effect.

Cities—Just Another Narcotic

Many people have sensed that something is wrong with modern society. This dissatisfaction has led to the formation of a rich flora of alternative communes. Most are small in scale, utopian, and tend to vanish, but those that survive may have something to teach us.

For instance, a number of communes have tried to reinstall some of the elements of tribal life: They typically attempt to form closely knit communities of tribal size and with a stable culture.

The Hutterites, for example, have built their religious societies on the notion that groups of up to 100 to150 people can form well-functioning units with personal ties among all members. They recognize that social pressure can be used to control behavior and to resolve conflicts within units of this size. Although the number of members may be somewhat higher than those in the typical tribe, it makes sense when considering that tribes often had associates in neighboring tribes as well.[269] To my knowledge most of the more successful alternative communes, like the Hutterites, are based on religious doctrines—which testifies to the power of religion, a subject I shall discuss in the next chapter.

The observation that more secular communes have limited success is somewhat discouraging—particularly for those who believe, as I do, that the tribal-type commune is more in line with our genetic inheritance, and should thus potentially be able to improve our quality of life.

In order to defend the theory of Discords, I would like to make two points: First, to start a "tribe" with grown-ups, within the setting of a modern society, is a far from ideal situation. As suggested in the discussion of communism, it seems difficult to suddenly turn on tribal feelings among strangers. Second, people do not necessarily choose what is best for them; immediate satisfaction is closer to our heart than optimal choices.[270] As a consequence, it is difficult to retain members of a commune in competition with the lure of the outside world.

Although the available data are limited, there are some indications that communal life offers a better, more healthful lifestyle. For example, a study in Canada found significantly fewer psychoses among Hutterites when compared with the surrounding population.[271] I believe one reason why the presumed advantages of living in communes has not turned the United States into the "United Communes" is that the outside world of the cities works like a magnet. They may make you richer, but they are unlikely to boost your Darwinian happiness. In most statistics on crime and psychological health, the cities come out worse than rural areas. So why are people impelled to go there?

The question has a bearing on how to interpret the remnants of the oldest city found: The nine thousand-year-old city of Catalhöyük in Turkey had 10,000 inhabitants at its peak; the houses were so densely packed

Plate 20. Cities have always attracted people. The Mayan city of Tikal in Guatemala once housed some 60,000 inhabitants, but they all disappeared. Maybe cities are not always such a good idea after all.

that entrances had to be through the roofs. Yet, they apparently did not have division of labor, and they lived as hunter-gatherers with only rudimentary agriculture. In other words, people moved together because they wanted to stay close, rather than because the creation of specific vocations eased life by erecting a more advanced form of culture. Moreover, they appear to have moved together in spite of the fact that their subsistence suggested that a dispersed habitation would ease the gathering of food.[272]

It is possible that the Catalhöyük people bundled together for safety. The area was presumably starting to feel population pressure, and it is easy to imagine swarming hordes of bandits attacking small tribal units. Alternatively, the city could have been based on a religious movement, but the archaeologists have not found any signs of temples or other religious structures. These people most likely had some sort of religion, but probably not one that required a large congregation. It is tempting to speculate that crowded spots work much like a super-stimulus catering to our social nature, akin to how a bird prefers the bigger plastic egg rather than the real egg.

We do not necessarily choose what is best for our long-term happiness. If we did, why would so many of us have mental problems, or bad health, or spend our lives quarrelling, or committing suicide, or becoming drug addicts? We choose short-term pleasures and immediate desires. We possibly plan for the next day, but are less likely to care about the year after. And most of us never learned about human behavioral biology in school.

David Barash describes "rural" and "urban" rhesus monkeys in India.[273] The rural monkeys live in troops that range over the forested countryside, eat a variety of fruit and vegetables, and rarely fight with each other. Their urban cousins gather in temples where the Hindus feed them. Although the food in the temples will typically be more abundant than in the forest, the urban gangs fight and quarrel a lot. The rural monkeys seem to live a better and more happy life, yet there is no indication that the temple gangs wish to move back to the forest.

Temple life is probably stressing in a number of ways: It is more crowded, the monkeys lack a regular troop to belong to, and the food in the temple tends to be concentrated in particular locations, rather than being more evenly dispersed, thus causing more fights over foodstuff. In other words, there are several Discord factors associated with life in a temple. The point is that the monkeys choose to live there, even though it is a Discord, and even though it apparently does not do wonders for their Darwinian happiness. Not surprisingly, they prefer immediate indulgence rather than long-term contentment. Rats may do the same, and by manipulating these animals we are actually starting to learn about the brain circuits involved in this choice.[274] Humans are not necessarily that much better at making intelligent decisions.

The Pendulum Analogy

Human behavior can be modulated, but our versatility is restricted to the elastic limits set by the genes. I shall use the pendulum as an analogy to illustrate the relationship between innate dispositions and how we can modulate cooperative behavior. In this analogy, moving the pendulum to the right reflects an increase in gregariousness, while movement to the left implies more aggression. The accompanying figure illustrates the analogy. (See Figure 7.)

The position of the pendulum depends on two factors: One is gravity, which is analogous to the pull of the genes. The direction of this "field of gravity," however, depends on the conditions under which we live. In a natural environment, the gravity pulls straight down. In this case the default levels of aggressive and cooperative behavior, respectively, mirror the balance evolution has brought to our genes. Thus, the natural position implies a fair share of selfish and nasty behavior. On the other hand, when living in Discord conditions, the field of gravity is tilted to the left—that is, toward aggression—and the pendulum will, of course, tend to follow the pull of gravity. I believe modern societies are troubled by Discord conditions.

The second factor is our capacity to grab the pendulum and drag it in the desired direction, which corresponds to how we manage human behavioral resources. In other words, in order to move the pendulum toward benevolence we have two options: We can change our way of living toward what our genes are adapted to, and thus tilt the field of gravity, or we can try to haul the pendulum away from its point of equilibrium and

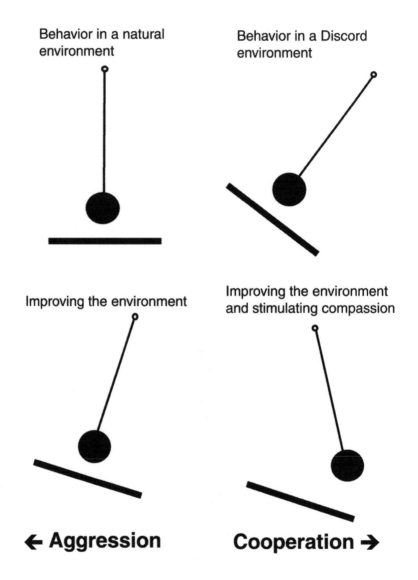

Figure 7. The pendulum as an analogy for the degree of aggressive versus cooperative behavior. In the default state of good mood the pendulum will follow the pull of gravity—that is, it will hang perpendicular to the line below. However, it is possible to inspire geniality either by lessening environmental stress, and thus tilting the direction of gravity, or by pulling the pendulum toward cooperation.

toward compassion. The importance of adapting our way of living to our genes is a permeating theme in this book. I have prepared some comments as to the second option—how to improve social behavior by stimulating our compassionate tendencies—in the next section.

Pulling the Pendulum

Thanks to the social sciences, we know a lot about how to stimulate geniality. In many countries these skills are actively exploited; consequently, although we presumably live under conditions quite different from those we are adapted to, present social behavior is not necessarily that bad.

There are a number of ways in which society can stimulate our caring and cooperative tendencies. Schools and the mass media offer excellent opportunities to nourish the public with stimuli designed to foster compassion; simple reminders of being kind and to smile at each other go a long way. Unfortunately, it is a lot more difficult to avoid stimuli that provoke our aggressive tendencies. It has been shown that the most cooperative societies are also the most generous; thus, collaboration apparently fosters geniality,[275] and what a government can do is to create the best soil for culturing positive stimuli.

Two conditions are particularly helpful in this respect: (1) There should be no unresolved conflicts within the group where you want to foster compassion, and (2) there should be a common enemy. It is important to have institutions that help people resolve disputes in a peaceful manner, and it would be useful if we were able to design a convincing and monstrous enemy. A concrete and highly threatening opponent is best, but anything that is potentially dangerous serves the purpose. We can feel solidarity even with a tree when there is a road construction team approaching, and we readily join forces against ants and mosquitoes. The easiest enemies to portray are obviously our fellow humans. Although such an enemy works fine for a particular society, it is less likely to enhance global peace. What we really need is an enemy that gathers all humans together: If you could convince people that the Earth is about to be invaded by Mars, it would serve beautifully. Unfortunately, aliens seem to be a dying race. Environmental destruction, an interesting alternative as a common enemy, has the advantage of being a more realistic foe than the Martians, but has the disadvantage of being less concrete. However, with the right approach, it may serve the purpose.

Did you know that the ancient Greeks personified the earth as the goddess Gaia? She has been called upon more recently by James Lovelock, who points out that the Earth can be viewed as one big creature.[276] The individual organisms that cluster our planet, be it animals, plants, or microorganisms, are akin to the cells of our bodies, or the ants of an ant-hill. In essence, all of us depend on each other. The popular portrayal of the foe might thus read: If we disturb the biosphere, Gaia will suffer. We are all part of Gaia, and somewhere there is an enemy that makes her weep. That adversary is the one we should unite to fight against, even if it is something inside ourselves.

Another alternative and interesting approach in dealing with violence is to consider surrogates. There are a variety of surrogates for compassionate behavior: pets, books, pillows, cigarettes, and teddy bears all offer consolation. Similarly, you may harvest the rewards of violence without crushing a single hair on an opponent, and without risking your own hair. Sports in general, and martial arts in particular, cater to our competitive and combative tendencies. So too do a variety of films and computer games.

For the sake of improving society, however, our socializing needs should preferably be cared for by people. Moreover, surrogates for our aggressive tendencies should be carefully chosen. Although the violence of films and games may relieve a desire to participate in combat, it can also inspire and stimulate brutality. Any stimuli that release agreeable sensations have a touch of narcotics in them, and, if offered a taste, we are inclined to crave for more. It is therefore not obvious whether the net impact of screen violence is to make us more, or less, likely to enter into real fights. This is an important question, and the answer probably depends on both the person and the context. Certain forms of surrogate stimuli will presumably tend to work more in the direction of diminishing real violence, while others will tend to stimulate aggressive behavior. More research is needed in order to decide which surrogates we ought to promote and which to discourage.[277]

I believe that handling the various innate tendencies associated with social life is one of the most important challenges of today. We may wish humans were different, that our true nature were all kindness, but it is not. We will simply have to deal with both the good and the bad.

In the long run we may be able to use our knowledge of the neurochemistry of social affect and rage to make suitable pills. Really good pills, however, will be hard to design, and even if we had them, we would probably not consider them to be ethically appropriate.[278] It is possible to induce more kindness than our nature suggests without resorting to chemical tools, but the task requires a resolute effort. Holding the pendulum away from the center of gravity demands a constant input of energy. Eventually you get tired, and at the moment you lose your grip, the pendulum swings to the other extreme, before returning to the point of equilibrium.

Summary—the Pendulum

Looking back at history it is not difficult to point out periods, or situations, where the pendulum has swung toward either benevolence or aggression. This is true whether you look at an individual person or a society. To learn how to control this pendulum, and to engage in the mission of moving it in the right direction, should be a task for each individual, but particularly for those in charge of society. If we can bring forth more kindness than suggested by the default nature of humans, we all stand to benefit.

In the next chapter I shall describe what is probably our best handle on the pendulum. It could serve us well, but then again, as demonstrated by history, this handle can be used to pull the pendulum in any direction.

CHAPTER 12

Religion:
If God Is in Your Genes

A Buddhist stupa in Kathmandu.

Does God Exist?

When Darwin first published his theory of evolution, some of his most vehement adversaries were members of the clergy. The church was trembling: Would his ideas demolish the biblical description of creation as well as the concept of Man as standing apart from all other creatures? When hearing of Darwin's theory the wife of the bishop of Worcester is said to have uttered "Descended from a monkey? My dear, let us hope that it isn't true! But if it is true, let us hope that it doesn't become widely known!"

In hindsight it appears as though the church did not need to worry. A recent survey concludes that people, including scientists, are just as much engaged in religious behavior now as they were a hundred years ago.[279] And the debate about whether humans are a product of God or of evolution continues. We are indeed devoted to our gods. So, is God with us after all?

There is a possible answer that links religion and science: Yes, God exists. He is right there, inside your head—encoded by your genes.[280] Some readers, or perhaps many readers, may disagree, but whether or not He exists, the more important question is actually: What can He do for us? Can religion help society and improve our measure of Darwinian happiness?

The Creation of Religion

Even the Neanderthals may have been religious: We have found Neanderthal graves more than 100,000 years old. Not only do the graves testify to the practice of burial, but apparently the Neanderthals deliberately added flowers and other objects to the grave of the deceased. The elaborate burials suggest that they assumed they would be given a second chance; perhaps they believed in reincarnation, or they may have had visions of an afterlife in the form of a Neanderthal heaven filled with flowers, fruits, and everlasting joy. The burial sites indicate that these people had the intellectual power required to understand the most devastating aspect of life: Its present version ends with death.[281]

The Neanderthals are most likely not the direct ancestors of present humans. Their line of descent presumably departed from that of our ancestors about half a million years ago.[282] If they were religious, it suggests that some sort of religious tendencies might have been present in hominids even prior to this date. It is tempting to speculate that a rudimentary disposition towards spirituality entered our brains in the distant past, maybe during or soon after the main period of brain development one million or two million years ago.

Before continuing the discussion about how we came to have gods, I should clarify what I mean by religiousness: The essential features of religiousness for the present discussion are: One, a belief system that helps explain observed phenomenon; two, supernatural forces with some sort of power; and three, a culturally inherited tradition. The latter feature implies that the belief system should be expressed in the community—for example, in the form of rites or prayers, and the existence of shamans or holy men. A fourth feature, which somehow seems to back up the above features, is the spiritual experience. I shall refer to this as a "transcendental feeling," since it is not obvious that a belief in spirits is required to have this experience. Other terms used for more or less the same experience include "Oneness with God or the Universe," "enlightenment," and "seeing the light."

Since the creation of the first supernatural spirits, worship has taken many directions. According to anthropological estimates, humans have developed a hundred thousand different creeds. The history of religion resembles an evolutionary tree: Early primitive faiths gradually transformed into more complex systems with advanced thought structures and intricate rituals. Most branches have vanished, but some have grown thick and strong. Today we find elements of religiousness in all cultures, from nomadic tribes to technically advanced societies.[283]

Religions of tribal societies are mostly animistic. In their case it is more a question of venerating nature, typically including a belief in spirits and forces that exert some sort of control on life. Although such faiths, too, can be used to reinforce morality, the more recent world religions

Plate 21. Mountains are often given a religious significance. (A view from Pico Aneto in the Pyrenees.)

have probably expanded on this function. The monotheistic religions that dominate the world today appear to be a rather recent invention; in fact, it is possible that the concept of an active, moral god arose in response to the needs of large-scale societies. As already mentioned, it is difficult to modulate behavior in societies too large for everyone to know every member well. The reason for the success of the concept of one moral god may have been that it strengthens the code of ethics in communities containing many people.[284]

For many scientists it is amazing that the concept of a spiritual power, or a god has survived so well. A scientific understanding of life and the universe, or, for that matter, the lack of scientific explanations for claims made by the clergy, has not managed to erode the vitality of faith. For those who believe, the power can be overwhelmingly strong—a force that far exceeds other leanings. Certain societies, for example those founded on communism, have tried to obliterate religiousness. The typical strategy involves the introduction of secular ideologies as substitutes. The genuine article, however, seems to survive all assaults, while the best the substitutes may hope for is reincarnation.

Are there any purely cultural traits that can claim a similar ability to permeate and survive? I believe the answer to be "no." The reason for the success of religions is, to my mind, that they are supported by a tendency inherent in the genes.

Religiousness: The Case for Genes

The cross-cultural validity and the power of faith are probably the most plausible arguments supporting the claim that religiousness is in our genes, but there is one more point worth mentioning. In biology you expect that the amount of resources allocated to a certain type of behavior correlates with the importance of that behavior for survival and procreation. Moreover, the more important the function is, the stronger you expect its genetic foundation to be. Observations of present societies, primitive or advanced, suggest that humans spend a lot of energy on religious behavior.

It is significant that most of the grandiose structures and great works of art that have survived from previous cultures are of a religious nature. There are temples, burial chambers, sacrificial altars, and objects designed to please or worship all sorts of spirits. Even in cultures such as those of nomadic people or hunter-gatherers, which do not construct objects designed to last, religious behavior consumes a significant amount of time and energy. People spend time worshipping; they have religiously motivated rituals; and they typically waste valuable food or other possessions as offerings to the gods.

If you accept that God may be in your genes, it should be pointed out that He is unlikely to reside in any particular gene. Traits such as blood type or the color of your eyes are determined by a few genes. In the case of religiousness, on the other hand, I suspect that a large subset of genes involved in the construction of your brain has been slightly modified for this purpose. I believe in spiritual genes in the same way I believe that genes back up our tendency to fight or to fall in love. Of course, some individuals never engage in any of these activities, but that does not disprove the case in terms of the genes.

For me, the above arguments are sufficient to assume a genetic influence. An alternative, non-genetic explanation for the observations outlined above is that religiousness simply fits with secular aspects of the human mind. This theory suggests that, as hominids evolved an inquisitive mind and a need for comforting explanations, religion was invented as a solution. That is, the spirits appeared as a secondary effect caused by an expanding intellect.[285]

It is pertinent to note, however, that the difference between my suggestion and the above "non-genetic" alternative is not that absolute. The proposed genetic changes required for religiousness to take root probably concerned brain arrangements involved in functions such as the following: submission to a higher power; the creation of thought constructs and adherence to the belief in them (whether or not they can be substantiated); the redirection of love and devotion toward abstract beings; and an engagement in rituals and other forms of spiritual socializing. The mind was probably equipped with versions, or rudiments, of these features prior to any religious commitment, so the advent of spirituality did not require any drastic changes. What may have happened was that certain features were slightly modified in the direction required to strengthen a commitment to spirits.

I shall illustrate the above notion with an example: In Chapter 11, I pointed out that leadership in the hominid lineage probably evolved from "dictatorship" to "democracy" long before the invention of elections. That is to say, as the need for cooperation increased, leaders became less autocratic. But our inherent inclination toward submission probably remained; in fact, the change toward cooperation rather than domination may have left this tendency partly "vacant." It is typical for evolution to base new properties on already existing structures; thus the tendency to practice obedience to a leader may have boosted the development of an inclination to bow before a spiritual power. Even in the absence of any genetic change, it would in this case be fair to state that religiousness is backed by the genes, because in the absence of spiritual functions the genetic tendency toward submission would presumably have declined. Today we often see the connection reversed: An emperor or a dictator who wishes to have obedient subjects tries to induce reverence.

One particular feature of our brains may actually have been designed as a direct consequence of the advantage of spirituality. The "transcendental feeling" referred to above—which is typical of the more intense religious experiences—has no obvious function outside the realm of religion. As described by Albert Einstein: "The individual feels the nothingness of human desires and aims and the sublimity and marvelous order, which reveal themselves both in Nature and in the world of thought. He looks upon individual existence as a sort of prison and wants to experience the Universe as a single significant whole." Although non-believers may have similar experiences, the feature is certainly suitable for the purpose of connecting with the spirits.

Brain imaging experiments, using deeply religious people engaged in meditation or prayer, suggest that this feature has a specific correlate to increased or decreased activity of particular parts of the brain. More specifically, there is an increased activity in the parts of the brain that regulate attention, and a decrease in a part of the parietal lobe of the cortex, an area presumably engaged in creating a sense of a self (as opposed to anything outside oneself). The interpretation of these observations are that the feeling of "Oneness with the Universe" requires the mind to be focused (but on no particular object), and at the same time to suppress the notion of being an independent entity.[286]

It is conceivable, however, that the transcendental feeling did not evolve for the purpose of religious use, but was simply a consequence of people discovering how to stimulate a particular mixture of preexisting brain circuitry. I believe the circuitries in question would include those involved in our default good mood, reward mechanism, and the systems that regulate attention and degrees of consciousness. In the case of submission and reverence discussed above, I argued that, although the nerve circuitry was there prior to religiousness, the advantages of religion played a role in retaining or strengthening the circuitry. Similarly, it is conceivable that, although rudiments of the capacity to enjoy transcendental feelings were available prior to religiousness, the advantages of an incipient religious tendency might have strengthened the relevant nerve circuitry. Because I believe our present genetic constitution has been affected by the evolutionary advantages of spirituality (in other words, I believe that there has been a selection favoring religious individuals), I consider it legitimate to claim that the concept of spirits is supported by the genes. In which case God has a place in our brain. As already mentioned, certain experiences associated with religious practice can be mapped to particular regions of the brain. Although some relevant nerve centers may be located in these areas, I would prefer to offer God a more spacious apartment—within the head.

An Advantage Worth Praying For

In order to substantiate my case for suggesting an involvement of genes in spiritual behavior, I ought to be able to explain why our genes have developed in this direction. That is, I need to answer the following question: Why did individuals and tribes who obtained relevant genetic changes prosper?

Aborigine tribes living in the inhospitable Australian desert survive by embarking upon long wanderings called "walkabouts." Every year they move about in a large circle, making sure that each season is spent at a location where food is available. However, when asked why they break camp so often, they do not state that moving is necessary in order to find food, but simply claim to be following the will of the spirits. What if some indolent member of a tribe came to the conclusion that spirits are just another fairy-tale and decided to stay put? His genes would have every reason for being mad at their host's attitude.

This example illustrates how religion can push behavior in a sensible direction. History shows that logical appeal exercises much less power than that derived from tuning your brain to supernatural forces. We are endowed with the ability to reason; yet finding our own answers does not always imply finding sensible ones. Our brains do not operate with the logic of a computer, and our thoughts sometimes only lead to an irrational stubbornness. Religion may guide people toward behavior that has proven to be sensible, but without their knowing why it is sensible. And, probably even more important, religion may unite people behind appropriate rules of conduct that would be difficult to enforce by any other means. A tribe where people cooperate and obey communal regulations will be more able to cope with both natural misfortunes and human enemies. In other words, a religion that lays down sensible rules, and, if necessary, delivers godly rewards or punishments in order to enforce them, should bestow an evolutionary advantage. Any factor that can help generate social harmony is valuable, and spirituality is certainly a potent factor.[287]

Most religions include features, such as the command to undertake seasonal wanderings, or various moral codes, which are functionally intelligent. It is obvious that the religious scripts, or belief systems, did not drift down from heaven with all these practical features included. The systems fit human and societal needs because they are shaped by them. For example, the explanation for ancestor worship is presumably that the young shall behave in ways that benefit the elderly. And rites of passage decide the status and function of a person—it is better for both the tribe and the individual that everyone know their place in society.

Modern societies have designed a lot of rules with similar practical purposes, and, while these rules can be a pain in the neck to enforce, believers adopt the rules of their faith with a minimum of external pressure. This difference, if nothing else, illustrates the power and the usefulness of religion.

The last million years of human history have witnessed many examples of one population replacing another; a tribe with a proper religion would be expected to fare well in such competition. Yet, it may be that the main advantage of having a well-organized tribe relates not so much to the occasional skirmish, but rather to a more harmonious way of living and a more efficient exploitation of natural resources, which, in turn, results in bringing up more children.

Individual Benefits

The above arguments are primarily concerned with advantages for the community. Within a certain tribe, the more religious members may obtain particular benefits: People with such inclinations are more likely to end up as (religious) leaders. The position typically enables them to acquire more than their share of resources, such as more food and more or better mates. The alpha males of baboons or chimpanzees ought to envy the power bestowed upon the clergy. (Catholic priests, with their requirements of celibacy and modesty, on the other hand, certainly do not reflect this pattern. The historical explanation for their restraint may be a reaction to obvious immodesty of earlier members of the priesthood.)

Spirits also offer advantages to those who do not obtain a high position in society: The combination of animal emotions and human intelligence may have traumatic consequences. For example, our ability to speculate may give rise to all sorts of distress. While animals sleep soundly after a good meal, or after escaping a predator, humans worry about whether they will find food tomorrow, and if they will escape the next time. Our understanding of the trials of life has brought emotional diseases in its wake. God provides a suitable dressing. He gives sensible (which, in this context, equates with comforting) answers to unpleasant questions. The recognition that we shall eventually die may be a heavy burden, but most religions have an answer: If a tiger eats me tomorrow, it is the will of God. And when the tiger has satisfied its hunger, I am in heaven. So why worry?

A decent religion offers a view of reality that explains all the phenomena you may observe, and leads you to believe that somebody is shielding you from an otherwise uncertain existence. God thus helps you find the default good mood. God may even go beyond that and give you ecstatic joy.

The soothing effect releases energy for the many functions of life, which again translates into improved reproductive potential. Satisfied people more easily find partners and offer their offspring better care. Satisfied individuals also create a better society. In ancient times, this was to the benefit of their genes; today, it is to the benefit of the quality of life.

The above discussion may sound like a leaflet handed out by some obscure sect, rather than coming from a biologist, but my main point is that religion offers definite advantages. In my evaluation, the potential gain is sufficient to explain why those with an incipient tendency toward religiousness spread their genes more efficiently than those without.

The Most Important Question

If God has His residence inside your brain, then how should you relate to Him? My main assumption in this book is that, as a rule of thumb, we are advised to follow the path laid down by our genes. If we do not, we tend to end up with the problems of Discords. If we do, we not only avoid stress, but we are more likely to experience rewarding sensations.

Yet, it is not obvious that a trait that happened to be advantageous to humans during the last two million years of evolution should be coveted today. Our way of life has changed drastically during the last hundred years; some traits that were beneficial in the past have now become inappropriate. When it comes to religiousness, however, I believe that at least some of the advantages are as vital today as they were for our tribal ancestors. Thus, you should believe in the Almighty as an independent being—not in your genes (and consequently not in me).

Western cultures tend to put science and truth on a pedestal. We are taught to consider the search for the most exact and objective explanations for phenomena to be a goal in itself, rather than as one of several possible means to obtain a better life. I myself am an almost hopeless case because lost in science; yet, I realize that although science has the power of giving you the most correct answers, it does not always give you the most constructive answers. In other words, you may be advised to find yourself a god and let him, or her, improve your quality of life. A decent god can help you obtain the state of default good mood, as well as the agreeable sensations associated with religious practice. Recent surveys indicate that spiritual people are indeed healthier and happier.[288]

An important aspect of religious behavior is to communicate with the spirits. A practitioner occasionally calls for help, but it is interesting to note that people often do not expect tangible benefits, meaning that the experience of closeness to the spirits is cherished in itself. Which is what I would expect: If evolution placed religiousness in our genes, there should be an accompanying reward mechanism in the brain. And so there is: the transcendental feeling, the bliss of God. If you ever heard somebody sing "Hallelujah," or if you joined in, you must have sensed the joy sweeping through the congregation.

The methods used for getting in touch with the spirits typically stimulate rewarding sensations even in the absence of a religious context. Music, dance, meditation, and feasting are popular ingredients in formulas developed for approaching the gods. The stimulation of two or more independent reward systems presumably offers a particularly powerful experience and a concomitant strong motivation toward participation. Chanting is a good example: In this case you combine music with devotion to a god.

Some of the benefits mentioned in this chapter may be even more important today than they were for our ancestors. Present societies are more complex and probably even more in need of principles that can inspire the good behavior of their citizens. And the destiny of the individual is as uncertain as ever. As discussed in Chapter 7, our minds get burned. We may not have to worry about tigers, but we are surrounded by guns and dangerous cars; and we do worry about exams, electricity bills, and lots of things that our ancestors could not have envisaged in their wildest dreams.

As before, the answers offered by a god may prove more useful than those provided by logic. For example, religion holds a clue to relief from anxiety, and most religious communities cater to our unfulfilled social needs, and our need for someone to love. God is worth His weight in gold. And the heavier He appears to you, the more valuable He is. Yet, I would choose my god carefully.

Ideally, religious belief should adjust to human behavioral biology— that is, it should take into consideration all our inherent tendencies. Many religions have the drawback of unnecessarily trying to steer us away from natural behavior, as exemplified by how most Christian movements relate to our sexual life. The guru in your genes recommends God to say that sexual desires are natural and good, but that they should be practiced in ways harmless to others.

A Gift for Mankind

Religion involves intense emotions, but one unfortunate consequence of that is the possibility of strong and emotional disagreements. A common religion for all of mankind, or simply having religions that are sufficiently open-minded to embrace local variants, should make the Earth a better place to live in.

As early as in the sixteenth century the Indian Mogul emperor Akbar tried to create a synthesis of all the creeds he knew. In the nineteenth century Bahá'i appeared with a similar mission. Unfortunately, neither initiative got as far as it deserved. It seems as if religions rely on a certain measure of assertiveness and egoism in order to survive and prosper. The two winners of our time, Christianity and Islam, know how. For a biologist that sounds familiar: Evolution works that way.

There is no shortage of creeds today, but going back ten thousand years, the diversity was probably even greater. The belief systems available at that time were presumably less complex than those of present religions, but the number of independent creeds was probably considerably higher. The evidence regarding this hypothesis comes from linguistics:

Throughout human history, particular cultures have expanded and gained domination over larger regions, leading to the loss of cultural and linguistic diversity. The most dramatic elimination of languages apparently occurred between 3,000 and 10,000 years ago.[289] It came about as a consequence of the expansion of agriculture; in other words, it was a consequence of the success of large-scale societies in subduing or extinguishing tribal cultures. It is likely that a concomitant elimination of creeds occurred. Now, the present trend is toward ever-greater domination at the hands of a few major religions—which is not necessarily a bad thing. It could serve the Earth well if we managed to gather all people under a single god.

Whether science can be combined with religion is a highly engaging issue, and several famous scientists have expressed strong opinions, either for or against. Richard Dawkins, who has been called the chief gladiator of science in the fight against religion, has notoriously claimed that anyone who believes in a creator god is scientifically illiterate. Einstein, on the other hand, once said that a limited scientific understanding tends to move us away from God, while a deeper understanding of the universe brings us closer to God.

Based on human behavioral biology, I have come to an alternative stance: For me the troublesome aspect of the conflict between science and religion is not the question of what religion may or may not be able to explain, but rather that *science has the power of laying bare the nature of reli-*

giousness. Unfortunately, it appears inherently difficult to believe in what I am saying and at the same time believe in the Almighty. If you find God in your genes, there is not much room for Him elsewhere.

You are advised to try. Religions do have a lot to offer, no matter whether it is appropriate or not to claim that we have a genetic bias toward religious belief. You should therefore go for the alternative favored by the majority; and your community is well advised to support the congregations they believe work for the benefit of society.

A synthesis that puts together the best elements from each creed, taking into account our inherent tendencies, as well as the particular needs of modern civilization and the cultural heritage of individual societies, would be a great asset for mankind. I believe a suitable religion could do wonders. We could unite all humans and make them feel solidarity and responsibility, not just for each other, but for our planet and for future human beings as well. And, at the same time, make them happy! Unfortunately, the idea seems rather Utopian at present.

Inducing people to *believe* in a constructed faith may be the minor problem. I actually see a prospect for coping with the dilemma that engaged Dawkins and Einstein—that is, how to accommodate both science and religion: The Christian bible suggests that humans were created to believe in God, and we may claim that the genetic changes that made religion possible were initiated by a heavenly power. As to the brain's capacity to engage in transcendental feelings, it seems logical to point out that if God designed human genes, He would be sure to include the means for communicating with Him.

The story becomes even more plausible (but possibly less religious) if we state that the heavenly power is not an actual figure, but rather a personification of the universal laws of nature. It is tempting to point out that even minor changes in the laws of physics would make the universe obsolete.[290] Not to mention life. Is that God? Did He stretch out His hand and create the laws of physics on the first day?

Based on the atrocities connected with religious disagreements over the past centuries (and even today), the impassable obstacle may be to have people *agree* to the task of erecting a global religion. The design of a proper belief system, and to induce people to believe in it, may be the

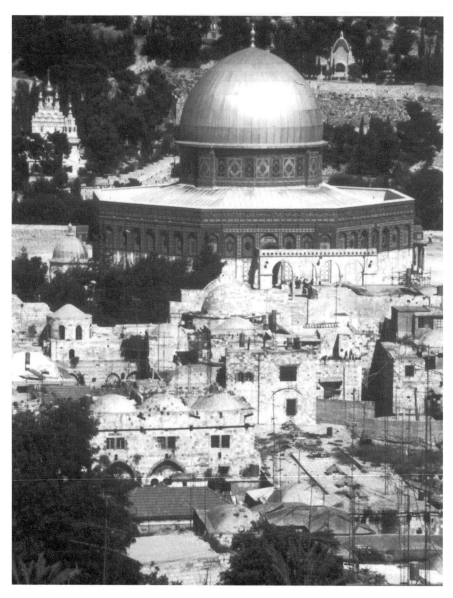

Plate 22. Religions do not always benefit mankind, and sometimes they just seem to promote conflicts, as in the dispute between Jews and Muslims in the Middle East (The Dome of the Rock—a Muslim shrine on the Temple Mount in Jerusalem).

minor problem. But, as science improves our understanding of mankind, we may, some day, find a way.

Summary—Let God Be With Us

Religiousness has followed man to every corner of the world; yet, there are some who feel this to be an archaic feature that it is about time to shed. True, much harm has been done in the name of various gods, but, in my opinion, if all the gods were to stand trial, most—if not all—would come out on the positive side: In general, more good has come from religions than evil.

My conclusion here is that we should cultivate the constructive aspects of religiousness, and make the most of this tremendous force for the benefit of human society. This would mean that we ought to support the various churches, but also that we should try to direct religious practice in directions that give the most benefit—and more specifically, to merge the various practices with the wisdom reaped from human behavioral biology in order to decrease Discord and help bring out joy. Moreover, we should prefer faiths that can accept, and live side by side with, alternative faiths—until one day they will all be shades of the same Belief.

Of course, nobody said this would be an easy task.

CHAPTER 13

The Art of Seeing: Visual Delight

Beauty is a quality that gives pleasure to the mind.

The Dawn of Creation

Religion has been a pivotal force in bringing out the artistic capacity of humans. Dating back to the oldest recovered paintings and sculptures, much of the art left behind from previous cultures appears to have served religious purposes. Furthermore, most present religions, and presumably the ancient ones as well, make extensive use of music. Yet, both visual art and music have a lot to offer mankind regardless of religious context.

This chapter and the next are dedicated to our delight in the visual arts and in music, respectively. My purpose is based on the notion that knowledge is power—that is to say, knowledge of our innate propensity to enjoy these aspects of human nature will help us extract related rewards.[291]

The questions I wish to address include: Why are we obsessed with decoration and beauty? In other words, why do we bother to make things visually pleasing? Various animals are able to manipulate their surroundings—birds by means of building nests, chimpanzees by inventing tools, and so forth. But the features present in our human brain opened the way for something more eminent; with hands no longer required for locomotion, and with a brain possessed by a burgeoning intellect, mankind faced an opportunity not to be missed: No other animal uses tools to create new tools, and, as a consequence, no other animal is able to produce the variety and complexity of objects that we do.

Even the most primitive gadgets are of obvious importance for survival, whether they take the form of clothing, cooking utensils, containers, or weapons. When we look more closely at man-made objects, however, we find one surprising feature: *We are not satisfied by merely producing tools with an optimal utility value.* It seems we desire something more from the objects we make.

For some reason our ancestors started to decorate pots, clothes, rock surfaces, and their bodies. A pot without decoration would be just as handy, and would require less effort to produce. A cave painter may have expected something in return from the spirits, but would it not have been sufficient to make a rough sketch concentrating on the resemblance to the object in question? These assumptions may well be true; nevertheless, we are able to recognize an "aesthetic intention" both in the pots and in the artistry depicted on cave walls. In fact, some form of aesthetic intention seems to be present in practically all cultures examined by anthropologists.[292]

So, a second question is: When did our interest in visual aesthetics begin? The archaeological record suggests that the artistic capacity of humans got started some 40,000 years ago. From then on we find the famous cave paintings and decorated pieces of bone as well as figurines. The sudden appearance of advanced art coincides with the penetration of modern humans into regions previously inhabited by Neanderthals. Speculation has centered on whether this is just a coincidence or if art served a particular function for the newcomers. Was it perhaps spurred by an attempt to distinguish themselves from the Neanderthals—an effort to demonstrate a different, and superior, culture?

The production of art carrying symbolic meaning may have started 40,000 years ago, but I believe the tendency to beautify dates back much further than that. We have found human skeletons more than a hundred thousand years old that bear signs of intentional beautification, such as filed teeth or deformation of the skull. There are also indications that people decorated their graves with flowers at that time, and recently a couple of 77,000 year-old red ochre stones with carved geometric designs were unearthed in a cave in South Africa. The red ochre was presumably gathered to be used as a pigment for decorative purposes. The tendency to appreciate beauty, it seems to me, is innate and has been with us for a very long time.[293]

I propose, therefore, that the answers to the first two questions are: (1) we decorate and make art because we evolved a capacity to derive pleasure from aesthetic experiences, and (2) it all started gradually, perhaps as long ago as several hundred thousand years. While I admit that these answers may not seem that informative, they do, however, lead to a third, more significant question: (3) Why did humans evolve this particular capacity for pleasure?

In order to substantiate the claim that our competence for aesthetic

Plate 23. These animal figures were carved in the rock by Norsemen some 5,000 years ago. Their purpose may have been to induce spirits to aid in the hunt, but the design suggests that the artist also appreciated aesthetics.

enjoyment lies in the genes, an explanation based on the theory of evolution is called for: The genes are expected to have a reason for why they push us in a particular direction. They would not have supported a delight in particular visual impressions unless there was a purpose, such as a link to improved survival. Anything else would have been squander. Identifying the evolutionary advantage of an aesthetic sense is not only of interest in terms of a scientific question, but the evolutionary benefits should guide us toward an understanding of the constituents of beauty, and thereby improve our ability to derive pleasure from visual input.

Before I expand on why I believe certain types of visual experiences evolved to be agreeable, let us take a closer look at the aesthetic disposition of humans and what I believe are the two main aspects of art. The constituents of beauty—that is, the elements of aesthetics—will be dealt with later in the chapter.

The Nature of Aesthetics

Our creative urge is so strong that we are not satisfied by just decorating utensils: We make works of art with no apparent practical value at all.

Actually, an artist will probably claim that paintings do have a function, that they are a means of communication. However, apart from the utility of the pottery or the ideas communicated by a picture, the skilled artist consciously or unconsciously incorporates something extra: This additional something is what I shall refer to as the *aesthetic elements*.

For purposes of discussion, I believe it is important to distinguish between aesthetic elements and other features of art. More precisely, the functional value of an object, and the specific associations or ideas fostered by a work of art, should be distinguished from the more intuitive aesthetic delight it gives.

Some art theoreticians argue that art is nothing but communication. I maintain that the aesthetic qualities we prize are not added primarily for the purpose of conveying a message: These qualities can be explained independently of both the functional and the communicative aspects. They are there because they elicit positive feelings; and they may do so for both creator and spectator. While it is not so difficult to suggest possible evolutionary advantages of communication and practical tools, the rationale for the aesthetic elements is far from obvious.

Webster's New College Dictionary gives a definition of beauty that I appreciate: "Beauty is a quality that gives pleasure to the mind." The aesthetic intention is present in the features included to make an object more attractive. A beautifully designed car, toothbrush, or painting is more pleasing to look at than a similar object in which design is based solely on practical criteria.

Both the non-associative (roughly what I refer to as aesthetic elements) and the associative (the thoughts and ideas that a work of art inspires) aspects of art excite feelings. While the feelings aroused by looking at a vase may mainly be non-associative, the emotions that a typical painting stimulates tend to be more associative. Thus the aesthetic aspects are more obvious in the design of a vase, because the associative content is less important; however, the principles guiding the potter also apply to the painter. The same principles are relevant for other visual arts as well, such as theater or film, but here the associative aspects are even more overwhelming.

Most art scholars seem to agree that universal guidelines for beauty do exist. If you bring in objects from various cultures and let experts with different backgrounds evaluate their aesthetic qualities, there is a certain degree of agreement. The difficult part is deciding on how to describe this consent; that is, how to describe aesthetic ideals.

If we can understand why we have a capacity for aesthetic enjoyment, I believe we will come closer to explaining these ideals.

Sensations Evoked by Aesthetic Elements

Earlier I discussed how the brain influences your actions by delivering rewarding and punishing sensations. *In biological terms, aesthetics has to do with reward-eliciting sensory input.* But why should aesthetic elements translate into rewards?

I should start my explanation by pointing out that not all rewards are as obviously pleasant as orgasms or cupcakes; in some cases our feelings are clearly positively or negatively charged, whereas in other instances the value is less obvious. From the point of view of your genes, it is desirable to allow your mind to engage in whatever feelings a situation calls for. If the right thing to do is to mourn, then that's fine; if it's time to fall in love that may be even better. Proper utilization of feelings is therefore connected with a reward, and, as argued in Chapter 3, even sadness may "feel good."

Another important point to recall is that the rewards are not necessarily adaptive in our present way of life. An orgasm feels good regardless of the use of contraceptives. Likewise, adding aesthetic value to a work of art is not necessarily adaptive behavior. *The brain offers rewards because directing your attention to particular types of sensory input was adaptive at some time in our evolutionary history.*

The essential feature of our aesthetic sense is thus to evoke agreeable sensations, but the feelings need not necessarily be cheerful. We may enjoy a sad painting just as well as we enjoy a sad film. The quality of art should be measured more in terms of how efficiently and elegantly such feelings are elicited, rather than in terms of the actual nature of those feelings. In short, the main question for the present chapter is why evolution connected certain types of visual input with positive sensations. As we shall see, several aesthetic elements can combine to give aesthetic pleasure.

Before I describe some putative elements, it is pertinent to make a note of our visual system.

The Visual Limits Set by our Eyes

When discussing aesthetics, you should bear in mind that our capacity for vision reflects the purposes for which it evolved. Our eyes and the associated brain centers both modulate and set limits to how we experience the input of light.

I shall not attempt to outline all that is currently known about vision, but rather shall point out a couple of important features. These features are relevant to the following discussion, but they also serve to remind you that our senses are bodily functions with inherent strengths and weaknesses.[294]

Not all animals are able to recognize light of different wavelengths as colors: For certain nocturnal primates the world is monochromatic—what we would call black and white. Other primates have dichromatic vision. Humans and apes have a particularly advanced system for detecting colors: the trichromatic eye. The main difference between dichromatic and trichromatic vision lies in the number of different colors that can be distinguished. We have three types of pigments that are sensitive to different wavelengths of light, and these allow us to differentiate between a large variety of colors within the visible spectrum of 380nm to 780nm wavelength. Some animals can see wavelengths outside this spectrum and are thus able to see "colors" that are invisible to the human eye.[295]

Human vision does not analyze light in a logical or mechanical way. For example, the same color sensation can be produced by very different physical stimuli: A mixture of red and green light of the proper intensities is perceived as yellow, even though the wavelengths are not at all those of true yellow; and pairs of pure complementary colors will produce the same sensation as white light if mixed together. Furthermore, the way we perceive a color depends on neighboring colors. These effects are related to the fact that our ability to differentiate between colors is based on the particular qualities of our light-absorbing pigments, and on the brain's ability to process signals initiated by these pigments.

Moreover, the way our brains process visual input offers the artist opportunities to create special effects. For instance, it is believed that the brain has three systems for deciphering signals coming from the eyes: One is concerned with colors; another with movement; and the third distinguishes objects from each other by looking for variations in light intensity suggestive of shadows or contours. It is possible to deceive these systems. For example, you can create a feeling of unrest by adding dots of different colors, but with similar light intensity; the color system recognizes the individual dots, but the contour system does not, since it relies on variations in light intensity. The brain therefore finds it difficult to determine the location of the dots; the impression created is one of unrest or of motion.[296]

Color—an Element of Visual Aesthetics

The perfect start for the seeds of tomatoes is to end up in human feces. At least this used to be the case. Today, tomatoes are faced with a very difficult challenge: How to adapt to modern sewage systems.

Plants that wish to recruit the help of animals in dispersing their seeds have to fulfill two requirements: The seeds must be packed in something nourishing in order to make them worthwhile for the animal to eat; and some effect must be added to make the fruit easily detectable, such as a distinct color, or, occasionally, an odor. The animals in question have evolved the ability to respond accordingly; they have taste buds linking the taste of the fruit with a pleasant sensation; and they have a visual system that enables them to spot ripe specimens.

Fruits and berries have always been an important source of food for mankind. To induce us to find them, we have presumably developed an appropriate, agreeable sensation connected with the sight of anything looking like fruit. This reward stimulates us to pay attention to colorful objects, which, I believe, constitutes one element in the biology of aesthetics.

Research has been carried out to ascertain whether the average human has a preference for particular colors. Typical experiments involve allowing subjects to choose among colored cards. Although the choice depends a lot on cultural and individual peculiarities and backgrounds, investigators typically find a preference for warm hues, such as red or yellow, rather than brown or blue.[297] If an object is to be conspicuous in the green-brown environment of vegetation, then red, orange, and yellow are suitable colors, and these are indeed the most common colors for ripe fruit and berries. The fact that the earliest pigments found to be associated with human decoration are red and yellow adds evidence to the idea of a general preference.[298]

Red may actually be preferred for another reason as well: The female genitalia are red or pinkish. In certain primates the buttocks of the female swell and turn pink when she is in heat, a signal employed to attract males.[299] Furthermore, most lipsticks and powder contain red pigments. Thus, males may appreciate the conscious or unconscious associations accompanying something red, while females may appreciate the color for its ability to attract men. No wonder red lights are so popular in "red-light districts."

Brown tends to be less popular. This could be related to the fact that brown is the color of feces and rotten fruit, both of which ought to be avoided. Most nuts come in shades of brown or gray. They are nutritious, but in contrast to fruit, not designed by the plant for animal consumption. The color of nuts may be partly intended as camouflage but may also reflect an attempt by the plants to make them less desirable.

It is likely that we also have a preference for colors that are easily distinguished, and, moreover, that we prefer light rather than dark hues: Bright, fresh colors tend to be regarded as pleasant, while darker and muddier colors are more depressing. Humans are diurnal animals: Daylight is more useful for our activities than the dimness of the evening or early morning; we therefore thrive where there is plenty of light, and tend to become depressed in its absence.[300]

An artist, of course, may not intend to evoke cheerful sensations; and, as previously mentioned, even sadness can have a positive connotation. An acclaimed painting may therefore very well be dominated by dark brown. The main concern of the artist, moreover, is not centered on the individual color, but rather on the combinations of colors. Thus, the effects of single colors as discussed above are probably of limited importance in determining the quality of art. Nevertheless, I believe that the above effects are real, that they contribute to our response to art, and are therefore relevant to an understanding of aesthetics.

A Question of Curiosity

As discussed in Chapter 6, humans are pushed toward behavior that is exploratory. We enjoy gathering information because our curiosity is connected with brain rewards, and our eyes are our most important tools for obtaining information regarding our surroundings. We cherish inspecting objects just for the sake of finding out more about them.

It also seems likely that the "wanting" (or "seeking") module of rewards can be aroused by visual investigation, even if there are no obvious objects of desire to be found. Of course, when we do spot objects of possible value, such as a bright red circle that just might be an apple, the "wanting" system ought to kick in. You may recall from Chapter 7 that such reactions start in the unconscious mind, and that they can influence our mood even when conscious appraisal tells us that it is just a blot of red paint.

The term "boring" is often used in an aesthetic context to describe a situation where there is too little variety or novelty. A painting may lack sufficient diversity in color or form to attract our attention; there are no surprising details to feed our curiosity and not enough content to make a visual scrutiny worthwhile. A suburb consisting of a single type of housing is considered to be depressing. On the other hand, originality and complexity—richness of detail and novelty—stimulate our curiosity and are therefore pleasing.

Then again, we may react negatively if the picture is too complex. The mind needs clues to help it organize and understand the visual signals. Thus, there should be a degree of coherence in the diversity; we need to find patterns or connections to make sense of the visual information. The confusion of not understanding an image can be uncomfortable, because strange or unfamiliar objects and settings could possibly imply danger. Moreover, too many signals and impulses may just lead to an unpleasant "overload" in the conscious processing machine.[301]

In the aesthetic tradition of the Chinese, there is a concept called the "Rule of Five." Based on the limitations of the human attention span, the rule suggests that the mind is able, without too much effort, to handle five objects or elements at a time. If more elements are needed to extract comprehensible information, the effect may be unpleasant, meaning you become confused. A painting containing too much unconnected information will be considered overly complicated rather than complex. As a rule of thumb, the complexity involved should not exceed the attention span of the human brain.

Steven Pinker has pointed out that our visual system is tuned to look for certain basic forms, or elements of recognition—for example, lines and basic shapes such as squares or circles. He suggests that we get pips (meaning small bits or pieces) of microsatisfaction each time we identify such items.[302] This idea would help explain the popularity of Cubism as a school of art, but the principle applies to any form of art, and is related to the above suggestion that it pleases us to find comprehensible information.

Depth and Movement

In contrast to most mammals, the eyes of primates are situated more on the front of the face rather than on each side. Having both eyes pointing in the same direction limits the field of vision, as the area covered by the eyes largely overlaps. The advantage, on the other hand, is that it allows for a more binocular vision, which allows for better perception of depth. The primate design is presumably connected with the requirements of living in trees, where moving from branch to branch demands an ability to measure distances accurately. However, the ability to gauge depth and calculate movements requires practice. I imagine that what the brain must do, in order to help the individual gain that practice, is to provide rewards for engaging in the processing of relevant visual input.

A typical criticism of amateur paintings is that they appear flat. We appreciate the skill of a painter who manages to create an impression of depth. We are also fascinated by images that give an illusion of depth, such as holographs.

It is also important for the visual system to detect and to estimate movement, which means the brain should reward us for practicing this skill as well. Moreover, we should take an interest in moving objects because they could imply danger in the form of predators, or opportunities in the form of prey.

Sculptures occasionally include actual movement, but this is not practical in a two-dimensional picture. However, as previously mentioned, it is possible to lure the brain into perceiving motion by adding dots of different hues but of similar light intensity. Furthermore, a picture may contain "lines" that the eyes are induced to follow. In a culture where people are trained to read from left to right, lines running from the upper left toward the lower right are perceived as going down—and thus tend to give a depressing effect—while lines running along the opposite diagonal are interpreted as being elevating.

If a painter manages to create the illusion of depth and movement, the effects add to the quality of the painting in the sense that it obtains an additional capacity to induce agreeable sensations in the observer.

Balance and Symmetry

One of the few rules of aesthetics that has won a certain acceptance is the principle that the main motif in a picture should divide the canvas into two parts, approximately in a ratio of 3:5. What the principle probably suggests is that placing the object in the middle is boring, while placing it near the edges produces an unbalanced appearance. The ratio of 3:5 is supposedly the optimal compromise between these two undesirable extremes.

The disagreeable effect of an unbalanced picture may be connected with our fear of falling. Falling is not a major problem for an animal based on the ground, but our ancestors did at one time live in trees; moreover, even ground-dwelling animals need to be aware of the possibility of an unsteady rock tipping over and making them stumble. A dominant object on one side of a picture gives the unpleasant impression that the whole picture is tilting toward that side; something is needed on the opposite side to provide a counterbalance. On the other hand, a perfectly balanced picture lacks excitement.

In some cases an exact balance actually adds value, for both humans and animals seem to appreciate symmetry. Our choice of the ideal mate typically reflects this preference; perfect symmetry is a sign of health and gene quality, and thus desirable. Existing data actually suggests that symmetrical input stimulates our visual system in a particular way, and this extra stimulation would be expected to yield another drop of micro-satisfaction.[303]

The positive aesthetic value of symmetry is most obvious in architecture: Many buildings considered to be great works of art have strictly symmetrical features. The effect is also witnessed in the delight of children when taught how to make symmetrical images by applying paint to a sheet of paper and then folding it in two to create the same image on both sides of the fold.

Functionality and Perfection

The oldest reference to the word aesthetics is in the writings of the German philosopher Alexander Baumgarten. In his treatise *Reflections on Poetry* (1753), he describes beauty as a comprehensible representation of the perfect. That is to say, art should try to improve on nature.

His description suggests an aesthetic element that I believe is also reflected in the more recent style known as functionalism—a style that was particularly popular in the architecture of the 1930s. A central doctrine of that style is that form should follow function. There are obvious reasons why looking for functionality and perfection should be connected with an agreeable sensation: For example, consuming sick animals or rotten fruit may be dangerous, whereas eating the best specimens ought to keep you healthy. It is also important to learn to recognize the features of a tool that actually make it functional. It therefore makes sense that the brain should reward us for viewing objects that appear to be of high quality; the pleasant sensation stimulates us to distinguish good from bad, and to obtain what is good.

The organistic theory of art is another school of aesthetics that is relevant in this respect: It holds that all the details of a painting are closely related and must be viewed together as a whole. All aspects of the object should be consistent and should contribute to its overall unity. According to the organistic theory, the main objective is not so much the perfection of function, but rather the perfection of the work of art as created by the artist.[304] The relevance of this principle is exemplified by the fact that a minor fault in an otherwise great work of art drastically decreases its value. The fault could be due to the artist's lack of concentration or to later damage, such as a tear in the canvas.

Our evaluation of human appearance may be used to further illustrate the point. Experiments where people are asked to choose among a large number of photographic portraits indicate that the visually most attractive persons not only have symmetrical features, but also display average features. As a rule of thumb, regular and prototypical features imply health, while abnormalities are interpreted as signs of bad genes or of a sick body.[305]

We prefer a healthy spouse just as we prefer an unspoiled apple. Yet special characteristics, such as a distinctively shaped mouth or bigger than average eyes, may add value because they catch attention. They stimulate our curiosity. Unexpected traits that cast doubt on the person's health, such as a wart or a scar, are less likely to be appreciated.

The Picasso of the Apes

My understanding of aesthetics is related to a philosophy of art sometimes referred to as the hedonist school: The central idea underlying this philosophy is that aesthetics is about creating images that induce pleasure.[306] The notion dates back at least to Aristotle, who held that the aim of life is happiness, and that the main function of art is to provide human satisfaction. My description of aesthetics adds substance to the teachings of the hedonist school. It also helps resolve the following paradox: Why do so many of the great works of art express melancholy and tragedy when art is meant to make you happy? This incongruity is resolved if we realize that most emotions, including sadness, can be appreciated.

Even though delight is an important component of art, not all pleasant sights should be referred to as art. Our visual system, including the accompanying sensations, evolved for the purpose of viewing nature, not man-made objects. We can thus derive just as much aesthetic pleasure from a stroll in a forest as from walking down the aisle of an exhibition, but we simply restrict the word "art" to human creations.

Furthermore, pictures that are produced to create associations do not need any aesthetic qualities in order to be appreciated: No additional artistry is required to create a picture of a nude woman that delights a man. In my view, aesthetic qualities are present when the creation of an object involves the use of elements, such as those outlined above, in order to create desirable sensations.

The preference of a typical art lover is probably more influenced by nurture than by nature. Moreover, the associative content of a work of art is typically more important than the purely aesthetic ingredients. Thus, the reader should take note that this text focuses only on one minor aspect of the enjoyment of art: Our inborn tendency to enjoy particular types of visual inputs regardless of the context they are in.

The most potent art, I believe, uses aesthetic elements to enhance its associative content. The aesthetic and the associative rewards are then added together, creating particularly strong sensations. For example, the portrayal of a murder is typically rendered in dark brown, while flowers and fruits appear in vivid colors. When painting a symmetrical house, you may choose to put it in the middle of the canvas, while a painting of someone climbing a rock could include highly unbalanced features in order to add drama. There is a parallel to the combination of aesthetic and associative elements in the way dancing enhances the experience of music.

Two aspects of art deserve further comment: One is the importance of "the human touch." As discussed above, we are curious about most things, but we are particularly curious about other people—we are naturally nosy—but we are also rather fond of other people. As pointed out in Chapter 10, to associate with others both diminishes negative sensations (loneliness) and adds agreeable feelings (geniality). An object of art contains clues regarding the mentality of the artist, and by viewing them we may sense a form of companionship with him or her. What makes a sad picture agreeable may be partly related to the pleasure of nurture; people appreciate the chance to offer mental sympathy to the poor person depicted on the canvas, as well as to the artist who appears to be in such a depressed state. Again, such sentiments do not need to reach our consciousness in order to have an impact on our mood.

The aesthetic elements that I have presented in this chapter are presumably consequences of natural selection. The second aspect that should be discussed is whether our artistic propensity is also partly a result of sexual selection. That is, if men and/or women have preferred to mate with individuals who display artistic talent, then evolution will have intensified both the capacity to create art and the desire to do so. The question of a human touch and the question of sexual selection relate as much to music as to visual art. I shall therefore return to them in the next chapter.

Art depends on both the ability to appreciate visual inputs and the ability to create them. The reward mechanisms I have suggested may actually be present in other mammals as well, but non-human animals

Plate 24. Both infants and apes delight in the use of crayons and paint, but when children reach two to three years of age they start making figurative art, something apes apparently do not master.

usually lack the opportunity to create. There are exceptions. Desmond Morris describes the chimpanzee Congo who became so fond of painting pictures that he earned the nickname Picasso. Although Congo never moved into figurative pictures, he did show an appreciation of color, and he did prefer a balanced picture composition. Interestingly, his favorite color was red.[307]

Congo was an action painter. He painted because he enjoyed the process, not because he expected that he, or anybody else, would ever appreciate the result. Children do the same. Hence art is not solely intended as communication; it is also there for the immediate joy of the creator.

Summary

In this chapter I suggest that our inclination to add aesthetic elements to works of art or other objects is a consequence of how our brain influences behavior. Our brain is designed to reward us when we focus our attention on objects with particular visual qualities. I have described some of these qualities, but the list is not necessarily complete. I believe both the artist and the spectator may benefit from an awareness of these visual signals, inasmuch as knowledge should help us tune in to our aesthetic propensities. In other words, it should help us use our eyes for the purpose of extracting Darwinian happiness.

It is important to note that, for the sake of curiosity or excitement, the suggested aesthetic elements may be deliberately ignored. People who pay to ride a roller coaster, where they experience the horror of falling, may also enjoy the thrill of an extremely unbalanced picture. Thus, the theory I present obviously does not restrict the artist to narrow rules. My aim is to help people delight in any visual input, whether from mediocre art, fine art, or nature—rather than providing a recipe for the creation of masterpieces.

Taking delight in art and aesthetics should improve your quality of life. However, whether you paint for yourself or look at the work of others, it requires practice to derive maximal benefits. A comprehension of what it is all about should help you improve that skill.

CHAPTER 14

Sounds and Song:
Musical Satisfaction

Listening to the koto.

The First Flute

Birds sing, but do they delight in their song? Probably not much, since for them song is simply a form of communication. We, for whom the song was never intended, may in fact be the most appreciative listeners, because we take particular pleasure in a certain type of sound. Our great delight in sounds that have particular qualities, what we refer to as music, is a rather odd phenomenon that requires an explanation.[308]

Although musical appreciation is clearly influenced by nurture, there is strong evidence suggesting that the capacity to appreciate music is innate and of ancient origin. The most important line of evidence for a genetic influence is the universality of musical appreciation. Most cultures make use of music, if not with advanced instruments, then at least in the form of song and rhythm.[309] Playable flutes that are almost 9,000 years old have been found in China,[310] and a piece of bone discovered at a Neanderthal site had several holes drilled into the hollow part, suggesting that even they made flutes.[311]

Hominids probably used percussion "instruments" long before the first flutes were made; and even prior to that we presumably made music with our voices. Thus it is conceivable that the ability to appreciate music has been present in hominids for a very long time.

The observation that musical appreciation apparently arises spontaneously in infants offers further evidence in favor of an innate tendency.[312] The powerful effect that music has on the human mind offers yet another indication. This effect is documented in a variety of studies, ranging from neurological and physiological consequences to the use of music as therapy, as relaxation, in enhancing physical performance, in promoting social interaction, and in creating an attentive or receptive mood in connection with advertisements and shopping. Music can produce an emotional response of an intensity rarely experienced in everyday life.[313]

How about animals? Do they enjoy music? Several studies suggest that music can have a relaxing effect on animals;[314] yet, it seems fair to assume that the powerful emotional response to music is a specific human

Plate 25. Even snakes can respond to music, but deep appreciation is most likely restricted to humans.

trait. There are various accounts of animals, such as birds, dogs, and apes, taking an interest in music, but dogs who "join in" when people sing probably do so because they have a tendency to howl with the pack rather than because they enjoy a particular song. Male voices should be in desperate demand before signing up a dog to sing in your choir, as the canine has not evolved the ability to produce tones of the purity required.[315]

Although vocal communication is rather important in chimpanzees, and they apparently take some delight in making sounds, their oral activity would hardly qualify as song in terms of human standards. Actually our more distant relatives, the gibbons, are better at singing.[316] However, the important distinction between human music or song, and the sounds produced by other animals, including birds and gibbons, is that our communicative needs are cared for primarily by a separate way of making sounds—the spoken language. What we refer to as "song" in these animals is their particular way of communicating. We generally know what is the function of bird song and gibbon song, but the strange phenomenon that requires an explanation is *why we* sing.

The brief answer is to say that we create, and listen to, song and music because we obtain positive sensations by doing so. Accepting that our obsession with music is based on an innate tendency that developed primarily after our lineage split off from that of the apes, the question remains: Why is the brain designed to connect certain forms of auditory signals with pleasurable sensations? In other words, what sort of evolutionary forces have carved this tendency into the human mind?

As with visual aesthetics, I believe that the answers to these questions will enlighten our minds as well as help us derive more pleasure from our being. And, as with visual aesthetics, I suspect there are several factors that combine to yield the sensation of joy. Before I try to describe these elements, I shall briefly discuss how it is that we perceive sounds.

A Sound Is Not Always What It Sounds Like

Just as the eyes set limits for visual input, the ears and the associated brain centers limit the types of sound we are able to recognize, and how we perceive them. Below are some examples[317]:

A young person can normally detect sound waves (minute, rapid changes in air pressure) in a frequency range between 20 and 25,000 hertz (oscillations per second). The eardrum transfers the signal to an internal chamber where sensory "hair"-cells react to the waves and send messages to the brain. The auditory centers process the signals and help the higher mental functions interpret the sound. The signals are filtered along the way, meaning that only a subset of the sounds hitting the ear actually reaches the conscious mind.

To be more accurate, the processing of signals coming from the ear is not just a question of filtering: The way we perceive sounds is not always directly related to the quality of the sound waves traveling through the air. If, for example, you strike a piano key to produce a 100-hertz tone, the generated vibrations are a mix of this frequency and overtones such as 200, 300, and 400 hertz. Yet your brain tells you that you are hearing a pure 100-hertz tone. Surprisingly, even if we remove the 100-

hertz vibration, the particular series of overtones will lead the brain to believe it is the 100-hertz note you are listening to. The sound you hear is not even necessarily the sound that is there. If the signal is loud enough, the ear may itself produce signals reflecting tones that are not at all present in the air.

One more example: By interpreting variations in sound intensity, we can calculate how fast the source of a sound is either approaching or moving away from us; however, we tend to overestimate the speed of the approaching sound, but not that of the receding sound. This makes sense, because something moving toward us is more likely to indicate imminent danger, and in that case it is better to react too soon rather than too late.

The above observations illustrate that precision is not the prime objective behind the evolution of the senses. Evolution only aims toward accuracy when accuracy is important for survival. For the subsequent discussion it is important to keep in mind that our auditory sense (as in the case of vision) evolved to care for particular functions.

Exercising Your Ears

The way human infants develop the capacity to create sounds is rather different from that of birds; the sound-producing ability of birds tends to be more fixed. True, many birds are able to learn by imitation and to elaborate on themes, thus creating both dialects and individual signatures; yet their way of singing—and their capacity to learn—are based more on genetically determined brain circuits. It is to a larger extent wired into their brains.[318] We, on the other hand, need to learn by voluntary practice.

We are born with a competence for language, but it is a flexible template that each individual needs to spend a considerable effort developing.[319] Language is complex, difficult, and of paramount importance to survival, so we need a lot of practice in order to speak fluently and to understand the spoken words of others. Again, it makes evolutionary sense for the brain to provide rewards to stimulate such a process. As a consequence, humans make sounds for fun—just observe a babbling baby. And it does not stop there: We fill concert halls, sing under the shower, and spend money on recordings and musical instruments as if they were edible. Is it all just to improve our capacity for language?

In his book, *The Descent of Man*, Charles Darwin himself discussed a possible evolutionary connection between music and language, and several more recent publications support this connection. For example, in one set of experiments it was demonstrated that children who learned to play a musical instrument subsequently became better at remembering words.[320]

A strange disease further substantiates this idea: People with Williams syndrome lack some genes on one of their two copies of chromosome seven, and are, as a consequence, retarded. However, they are surprisingly clever when it comes to two sorts of tasks: They are very fond of talking (although the messages conveyed may not always be coherent), and they have the ability to enjoy and create music. People with this syndrome tend to be short and "elf-like" in appearance. It has been suggested that they were the inspiration for the singing and storytelling elves and fairies of folklore. Their brains are smaller than normal, but one area of the brain may actually be larger. As you might guess, this particular part of the brain, which lies adjacent to the primary auditory cortex, is believed to be important for both music and language.[321]

The two halves of the human brain have actually somewhat different functions relating to the processing of sounds: The right hemisphere is considered to be the one more involved with music, while the corresponding part of the left hemisphere concentrates on language. This division of labor seems to be associated with the handling of, respectively, environmental sounds and sounds with communicative intent, but the division is far from complete. Rhythmic analysis is apparently handled primarily by the left hemisphere.[322]

For most vertebrates, smell and visual signals are more important than sound as means of communication. However, a greater reliance on sound developed independently in at least three lineages: In two of these, namely birds and cetaceans (which include whales), olfactory communication is impractical. The air and the open sea are unsuitable for depositing chemical signals, and, what is more, some of these animals travel vast distances. The third lineage is the anthropoids, which include humans and apes. Although apes use more complex auditory signals than monkeys, man is the only representative of this lineage in which the importance of language has reached an unprecedented level. The environment of our anthropoid ancestors was more suitable for chemical communication than that of birds and cetaceans; thus the shift toward sounds was probably due to the advantages of evolving a system able to handle elaborate information.[323]

As discussed in Chapter 6, infants have evolved a fondness for play behavior in order to develop the various capacities of the brain. It makes sense to suggest that focusing the mind on the production and interpretation of sounds is adaptive behavior because it helps develop the required nerve circuitry. The sound-processing neurons in the auditory cerebral cortex do indeed require a proper input of signals in order to mature, and the lack of auditory signals during a critical language-learning period can severely limit a child's potential for developing communicative skills.[324]

The above theory makes sense—but not complete sense. It may, for instance, be argued that a preoccupation with music as a form of play behavior should be associated primarily with children: The main period in which auditory signals are required for the development of relevant neural circuits is thought to last until the age of six or seven, but our interest in music apparently peaks much later. The following argument may help explain this discrepancy. Even when the circuitry has been established, the mind still continues to pay attention to sounds for two reasons: First, we may still need to exercise our sound-producing and interpreting capacity as adults; and second, we are driven toward exploratory behavior regardless of age. We take an interest in sounds because auditory signals, particularly in the form of language, are important for survival. However, as will be evident from further discussion below, I believe there are also other reasons why adults are so keen on music.

In order to present a convincing theory of musical appreciation, the following questions need to be addressed: If sounds, especially sounds of language, are important for mankind, why do people rave about sounds with the particular qualities we call music? If it is a case of exercising our ears, would not any sound do just as well? Or, if there is a preference, why do we not concentrate on the spoken word? Moreover, considering the awesome power of a symphony in inducing feelings, can music really be nothing but an ear exercise?

It is important to keep in mind that what separates us from the other sound-producing animals is the complexity of our language, and that *we have song and music as behavioral elements in addition to language*. Although song and music clearly have communicative functions, this is apparently not the primary purpose—at least in the present stock of humans. Actually, song may have served as the major means of communication in early hominids, a question I shall return to later in the chapter.

Purity and Harmony

The tendency to distinguish between pure sounds and scrambled disharmony is a central element in the enjoyment of music. Studies of children suggest that a preference for purity, and possibly consonance, is innate.[325]

One reason why these qualities are favored may be because they enhance oral communication. The capacity to produce pure sounds is most advanced in animals such as songbirds and certain cetaceans, in which the prominent form of communication is oral. A pure tone presumably carries farther. Although language typically includes a mixture of relatively pure (vowels) and dissonant (consonants) sounds, purity, and consonance are expected to reduce ambiguity. The brain centers involved in the production and processing of sounds are probably primed to prefer the qualities that are most suitable for communication.

Several languages, including Chinese, are referred to as tone languages, which implies that the meaning of a particular sound depends on the pitch. Speakers of these languages appear to be better at recognizing variations in pitch compared to speakers of non-tonal languages.[326] A third of the world's present population has tone languages; thus, it is conceivable that the first languages to evolve depended on pitch, a suggestion that would help explain a concern for the frequency of sounds.

To summarize so far, I propose that humans are rewarded by the brain to take an interest in sounds, because the brain needs practice, and because we need to explore the sounds present in our environment. The basic rewards may not be very obvious, and the typical environment of modern communities is probably so filled with background noise that the system is overloaded. We are therefore unlikely to appreciate every sound we hear. Qualities such as purity and harmony will enhance the rewards, yet these qualities are not sufficient to induce really powerful sensations. After all, your alarm clock and telephone are not the acoustic highlights of the day. In other words, there appear to be additional factors that contribute to the human appreciation of sounds.

What More Can You Wish for in a Symphony?

As with visual art, a certain complexity presumably has a positive effect on the listener.[327] Humans are inherently curious; they wonder about, or intuitively speculate on, the significance of sounds. A single, pure tone is not interesting to explore; it is to be expected that a measure of complexity is required to excite human curiosity and exploratory tendency. Sounds that are too complex, however, tend to be overwhelming. As with visual aesthetics, we presumably prefer some sort of coherence, a principle that connects the various sounds and makes them comprehensible. Otherwise we just call it noise.

A main feature of human language, as opposed to oral communication in apes, is the importance of the temporal patterning of sounds. Single sounds tend to be without meaning; but when put together in a specific sequence, they form words and sentences. Temporal patterning is equally important in music; if the tones are not in some way sequentially tied together, people are unlikely to show appreciation. The temporal patterning is related to what musical literature generally refers to as a melody. It is conceivable that music requires this similarity to language in order to be valued, because it then utilizes more of the brain resources involved in processing the spoken words.

Using computer technology and electronic instruments, we can generate a complete orchestra from a single box. The tones are guaranteed to be mathematically pure, the rhythm correct to less than a thousandth of a second, and we can program the timbre of anything from oboes to ukuleles. Great. Do we need musicians?

One of the more significant elements in the enjoyment of sound is probably the communicative aspect, for music should have a "human touch." We are obsessed with understanding our fellow humans; when a person creates sound, we expect to be able to infer something about that person, something connected with his emotional life. A voice always gives us the opportunity to do so. The same goes for an instrument in the hands of a skilled musician, whereas it is difficult to program a computer to display emotions. In other words, the complexity should have a human flavor to it. As with paintings, the communicative aspect of music may be more important than the purely aesthetic aspects.

It is interesting to note that people tend to agree on what emotions a given sequence of music reflects.[328]

The human touch is also highly relevant for another important function of music: It keeps us company. Music is a companion somewhat like a pet; it reduces loneliness and presses the buttons for receiving socializing rewards. The effect may help to explain why music is so popular among the young of the companion-starved Western societies.

The Music of a Crying Infant

The above suggestions may explain a general appreciation of music, yet the emotional response occasionally appears to be more overwhelming than what would be expected. The sensation referred to as a chill, or a shiver down the spine, is surprisingly strong.

It is not a good evolutionary strategy to encourage a certain type of behavior in excess of what is adaptive: A person who is preoccupied with song or music pays less attention to other tasks at hand or to possible dangers. Thus, the rewards associated with any sounds should not divert our attention to a greater extent than what the contribution to survival suggests: The chill appears to be excessive encouragement.

Certain qualities of the music that tend to produce chills point toward a possible explanation: Chills are evoked more often by sad music than by happy music and more by familiar music rather than an unknown piece; intense passages such as crescendos are particularly chilling. Furthermore, women experience chills more often than men do.[329] Based on this information, Jaak Panksepp has suggested that the chills appear because music hooks directly into the brain's primitive emotional circuits—more specifically, the right type of music has some sort of relationship with the call of an infant crying for its parents.[330]

Wailing as a consequence of separation would be expected to evoke powerful feelings in parents, and especially in mothers; after all, nothing is more vital to your own genes than the genes you have packed into the next generation. Panksepp points out that human separation calls have properties related to chill-producing sounds: The cry of a baby is at once intense, familiar, and sad. He also claims that he has been able to evoke sensations reminiscent of chills in parents by playing recordings of their infant's cries.

As pointed out in Chapter 10, the nerve circuitry causing the distress associated with separation, as well as delight in the case of comfort (for both parent and child), may have arisen from our more ancient homeostasis regulating units, including the one in control of body temperature. Panksepp suggests that this evolutionary connection could explain why chills involve that particular feeling of "cold that makes hair stand erect."

Another feature that seems to be associated with chills is the creation and subsequent violation of expectancy. Composers typically make striking themes and then repeat different variations several times in the course of the composition. The creation of expectancy implies a certain familiarity, which may be related to the fact that a parent reacts more strongly to the cry of his or her own baby than to the cry of an unknown baby.

There are several ways to create a surprise in music; in addition to changing the intensity, you may include sudden alterations in tempo, tone color, as well as other effects. Of course, changes in the expected patterns may also be appreciated because they stimulate our curiosity: We tend to investigate the unfamiliar until it becomes familiar. Music offers a series of interesting surprises set against a background of expectation.

As to the preference for sadness, it is also relevant to refer to the discussion on melancholy regarding visual aesthetics in the previous chapter. Both visual art and music offer the possibility of harvesting the rewards of sorrow and empathy without having to undergo and deal with the bereavement that normally precedes these feelings.

One more problem is this: Neither the sounds resembling those of an infant child, nor the sounds just demanding our attention, produce much of a chill, at least nothing resembling what the theme from Beethoven's Ninth Symphony can give. Thus, a more elaborate explanation is needed. The connection with language may help us out.

Long before the development of language, our ancestral genes had presumably designed the brain to offer ample rewards to ensure attentiveness to the call of infants. It is possible that the chill is an accidental sensation evoked when music happens to approach the sounds we are programmed to react to as caretakers. However, it is also conceivable that the chill can be explained by the way evolution tends to utilize structures already present for novel purposes, as exemplified by the way legs evolved from the fins of fish. The need for rewards to encourage the processing and production of sounds, which appeared as a consequence of our dependency on language, may have caused evolution to exploit the emotional pathways associated with parents' attention to the cries of their babies. In other words, a slight reorganization of the wiring in the brain put some of the emotional response to a child within reach when we hear, or produce, sounds of the right quality. An important point is that the right quality of sounds for language purposes means purity of pitch and tone, and thus music instead of crying. What Beethoven's Ninth does is to combine the attributes of baby sounds and the attributes of sounds intended for efficient communication.

Safe and Relaxing Sounds

The appreciation of music probably depends on a variety of qualities, and I do not expect the language connection to explain them all. For example, as pointed out above, music can have a relaxing effect on animals as well—an effect that obviously cannot be ascribed to language.

One interpretation of the relaxing effect is that music is continuous—as opposed to dangerous sounds, which in a natural environment tend to be sudden and unexpected. Quiet, peaceful sounds calm you down; they are similar to the background of irrelevant sounds in a natural environment. As to the soothing effect on humans, it may also be pointed out that music is intuitively understood to be man-made, and as such not related to dangerous situations—with the exception of music culturally associated with violence, such as war drums. Music can therefore serve as a "comforting companion."

The unconscious part of the brain has a particular system designed to kick in when oral or visual stimuli are deemed to require special attention. The system is based on "sentries"; that is to say, the sentries sound the alarm by arousing you and by directing potentially dangerous stimuli to the conscious part of the mind. For example, when the corner of your eyes detects something remotely resembling a snake, you jump and then focus on the object. The sentries tend to direct any abrupt sound—even including sounds that are repeated at regular intervals—to the conscious mind. It is stressful to receive too many calls from the sentries, since it is nerve-racking to have to "jump" all the time. Relatively soft discontinuous sounds can therefore be unpleasant—like the dripping of a leaky tap—even if we are consciously aware that the sound does not signal danger. A continuous soft sound, on the other hand, relaxes the mind.

Rhythm and Movement

One of the most characteristic features of music is rhythm. Rhythm does not need to be a distinct beat, but it does require a regularity, or a pattern of timing.[331] In the more primitive forms of music, beat instruments are the central element, but even elaborate music seems to require some sort of rhythm in order to be generally appreciated.

One reason for appreciating rhythm is that it offers the mind something to hold on to whilst analyzing the sounds. It helps the brain to organize and make sense of the signals coming from the ear.

Another possible reason is that rhythm has a calming effect related to the beat of the mother's heart registered by the fetus.[332] The rhythm, or timing, is also important for adding a human touch to the melody.

Most of us have probably felt the compulsion to move when listening to music; it can actually be quite difficult to resist. All bodily movements, including running and walking, are apparently in some way associated with rhythm: A regular contraction and relaxation of muscles presumably calls for a smoother and more efficient way of using muscles; and movements, as well as other functions controlled by the brain, are coordinated by rhythmic activity patterns in brain circuits.[333] Rhythm might thus be rewarded, as it is a preferred way of coordinating activities. Music may help you to harvest these rewards.

I believe that dancing can both exaggerate the sensations evoked by music and add extra drops of microsatisfaction related to the joys of using you body (also discussed under sports in Chapter 6).

Plate 26. The first musical "instruments" were probably used to create rhythm, and rhythm is still a core element of music.

To Play or Not to Play

I shall briefly summarize what I suggest to be the main innate elements of musical appreciation. The pleasant sensations associated with music depend on the combination of several features: one, qualities that we are favorably disposed to because they are relevant in connection with the acquisition of language (purity, harmony, melody and temporal patterning); two, qualities that stimulate our curiosity or feed our imagination (complexity, the human touch, love songs); three, the link to rewards associated with caring for infants (familiarity, intensity, sadness); four, relaxing and comforting effects (companionship, security, continuity); and five, rhythm and bodily movements.

The power of the sensations evoked presumably depends on how efficiently the sounds exploit these elements. Music is designed to maximize the sensations afforded by these features; it is therefore not surprising to find that music is more potent in this respect than language in the form of the spoken word.

Although the above summary implies that music should be analyzed as a conglomerate of several factors, I believe the evolution of language—or oral communication anyway—was pivotal for developing the strong positive sensations associated with music. That is, the more specific rewards evolved originally to induce us to concentrate our minds on sounds with qualities relevant for communication. Given the importance of language, the rewards make sense.

The life of dogs depends on a keen sense of smell. Your dog would never insist on going to a concert, or an art gallery—but most dogs would love to visit a "stench-gallery" where they can wander around sniffing interesting odors. Likewise, humans love music and art because sounds and visual input have been particularly important in the evolution of our lineage.

My theory of musical appreciation does not require all music-related behavior to be adaptive. Furthermore, the various functions that have been associated with music in the literature on ethnomusicology may be valid,[334] even though they do not necessarily reflect advantages that led to the evolution of a preference for musical sounds. That is to say, music may very well take on secondary functions such as the maintaining of social cohesion or communication with spirits. And it is conceivable that these cultural effects of music have contributed to the proposed evolution of a genetic disposition for musical appreciation; however, I expect that the elements listed at the beginning of this section preceded possible cultural benefits.

In Chapter 13, I suggested that it is also possible that artistry was selected for in the absence of any advantage regarding survival. Geoffrey Miller has pointed out that men and women who are proficient in art or music probably are preferred as mates.[335] In other words, art functions as an ornament to attract members of the opposite sex. The theory sounds relevant: Artistry could easily boost status, or just add an attractive quality. The picture of rock stars and their groupies comes to mind, but even before the days of groupies, sexual selection might have promoted the evolution of artistic competence.

We know that sexual selection is responsible for much of the visual displays in many species of animals, including the peafowl. Likewise, much of the oral communication in birds and cetaceans is about mating. The most musical of the apes, the gibbons, do wonderful duets with their sexual mates. It would not be entirely surprising to find that sexual selection has been instrumental in shaping human auditory and visual signals: The ability to produce pleasant sounds, and to follow a rhythm, could very well be relevant in human courtship as well. The idea would help explain why love is by far the most popular theme for songs.

Is our capacity for aesthetic acrobatics just the human version of the peacock's tail feathers? The reason for the present enormous interest in art and music obviously has a lot to do with properties such as status and money. However, my point is that neither sexual selection, nor status and money, are likely to have *initiated* the human interest in art and music. Sexual selection can be very good at expanding existing features, but this evolutionary force is less likely to invent novel traits. The peacock would not have gained its enormous tail if there had been no tail feathers prior to the onset of a sexual selection favoring large and colorful feathers.

On the other hand, it is conceivable that human evolution went through a stage where oral communication was similar to the song of gibbons, birds, or whales. In these animals the more elaborate song evolved for mating purposes; and sexual selection would certainly be expected to take part in the evolution of complex mating calls. Did the human race sing before it could talk? And was our first song a love song? It's an attractive idea.[336]

The Sami—the indigenous people living in the far north of my country—has an oral tradition referred to as "yoiks." Yoiks are a traditional way of singing using a lot of nonsense syllables, but yoiks can also tell stories—typically of historical relevance, or as a way of expressing an opinion about somebody. I could easily imagine the tradition to be a remnant of a more singing way of communication.

Could it be that advanced language evolved at a later stage of human evolution, as a consequence of the advantages of a more versatile and exact form of communication? The point is that the postulated "song" stage of humanity could very well have left relics of behavioral propensities—for example, in the form of an "irrational" interest in music.

In our present languages, the vowels are suitable for singing, while consonant sounds tend to be less melodious. However, the consonants have the advantage of adding variety to the sounds created. It is theoretically possible that the requirement for increased complexity of content was cared for by introducing more consonant sounds. In other words, there would have been a trade-off between melodiousness and the complexity of the message; that is, our communication moved from song to the spoken word as a consequence of requirements associated with an increasing intellect.

The idea of a more musical stage in the evolution of human communication, and the possibly concomitant role of sexual selection, do not contradict the language connection. In fact, I believe all the factors mentioned above may have participated in shaping our delight in music.

A musician may feel that reducing musical appreciation to an inherent trait does not do music justice. It is important to stress that the innate force postulated is no more than a general influence; musical appreciation depends on this influence, but has gained a life of its own. The rewarding sensations suggested in this chapter promote a preoccupation with sounds and direct our preferences toward what can broadly be referred to as music, but the individual's particular taste is governed by personal and cultural traits. Thus, the observation that the same music may produce pleasure in one person and discomfort in another does not contradict the ideas I propose.

Our appreciation of sounds with qualities resembling what we today call music presumably evolved because it was adaptive for our Stone Age ancestors. The rewards of music are not necessarily an optimal design for survival in modern society. Both visual, aesthetic elements and music can be regarded as supernormal stimuli: They are designed to hit the particular brain circuits with maximum power; in other words, they offer exaggerated signals akin to the way a nesting bird will prefer a plastic egg if it is bigger than the real egg, or a larger than normal chick, such as a cuckoo in the nest.[337]

The reward model for musical appreciation is supported by the observation that listening can take on an addictive character.[338] Stimuli that release agreeable sensations have a tendency to initiate excessive consumption if they are easily accessible, and in modern society, music is readily available at any time and at any intensity. For some people, listening to music is reminiscent of the maladaptive behavior associated with addictive substances; for example, they knowingly insist on playing music so loud that it results in a loss of hearing, or so often that it prevents the execution of more important tasks.

As an addictive substance, however, music is about as good as it gets. It is certainly less hazardous than most chemical alternatives, and the positive contribution to Darwinian happiness seems to be far greater than the negative aspect.

Twin studies suggest that the variation in the ability to be enthralled by an aesthetic experience is at least 50 percent heritable.[339] The important point is that we all have a capacity for delight, and however lucky you have been with your particular genes, it is always possible to enhance that capacity. I believe knowledge about the biology of aesthetics is more relevant to this endeavor than as a formula for the design of outstanding works of art. Thus, the purpose of this chapter on music is similar to the purpose of the previous chapter on visual aesthetics: It is meant to give the reader an increased awareness of possible joys to be harvested, to hint at what these joys are about, and to indicate how they can be obtained.

If evolution has bestowed upon us a capacity to derive superfluous rewards from music, we should rejoice and listen. As suggested by Panksepp, for those who seek long-term health and happiness, the question is: To play or not to play?

Summary—The Eternal Source of Beauty

We make aesthetic decisions each and every day. We choose which clothes to wear or how to set a table. Maybe we buy a flower or a picture, tune in to the radio, or play a CD. We also receive a steady stream of unsolicited impulses with varying degrees of aesthetic value. Your guru asks you to seize the opportunities and to make the most of them.

As long as your basic requirement for sustenance is covered, you have the opportunity to delight in the luxury of aesthetic enjoyment. Unfortunately many people seem unable to raise their gaze above the daily chores, or to escape the emotional stress that restricts their potential for non-essential forms of enjoyment such as art and music. The rewards connected with aesthetic enjoyment do not force themselves upon you. The signals are easily ignored, but they are also possible to nurture.

Evolution has given us a variety of opportunities for joy and appreciation that go beyond what could reasonably be expected from a process that prudent—music and art being among the more interesting options. But do not despair if there is no art available, because nature is an eternal source of beauty. It has been claimed that what the artist does is to select some bits and pieces of nature and flavor them with his personality; the original source of aesthetic enjoyment remains out there. As long as you can bear the lack of human touch, a single flower has the aesthetic power of a Mona Lisa, and a nightingale the power of a violin. Almost, anyway.

CHAPTER 15

Is the Future Just History?

How can we help our planet?

So, What Are We?

In the theater of life we are without doubt the leading character of the present act. Our future, as well as that of another million or so other species presently inhabiting the earth, depends on how we develop our role.

We like to think of ourselves as the hero—a supreme being—but our character has so far been none too heroic, and in addition to the appendix and spine the body carries a number of other dubious design details.[340] It may be useful to remove the pedestal we are standing on, in the hope that a more humble hero will take his role more seriously.

Science has already delivered a few blows to our ego: Copernicus taught us that our planet is not the center of the universe, that Earth is just another something in space, among billions of bigger and more energetic objects. Darwin taught us that we are not a superior form of life, belonging to a different realm than all the other species, but rather a conceited ape in need of a body toupee.

Even so, many people still consider man to be the pinnacle of evolution. They see evolution as a force that strives toward ever greater complexity, with mankind, the one and only, being the greatest triumph. They consider the birth of the human species to be the most spectacular event on this planet. Is that really the case?

There is one type of organism that can claim continuous success almost since the beginning. A life form that has survived all the catastrophes ever witnessed on earth—a life form that will most likely still be around whatever happens to us—is a reminder that we are not the true champions of this theater: The title goes to the bacteria and other prokaryotes. Numerically speaking, they have certainly been the most successful: You have more bacteria in your intestines than there have ever been humans alive on this planet. And whatever destructive power we may release, they are likely to survive.

Furthermore, the evolution of humans is not the most dramatic episode in the theater of life—at least not if such judgment is based on biological creativity and novelty. The basic body construct on which we are designed has been around for 500 million years. Moving from fish to amphibians, onward to reptiles, and lastly to mammals and humans, required only a succession of minor modifications. These modifications are really not that much to brag about, compared to the three really smashing evolutionary milestones that took place.

The Earth came into existence some four and a half billion years ago, and less than a billion years later the first milestone, or miracle, of evolution occurred: Living cells that were capable of reproducing formed. For the next two billion or three billion years bacteria-like organisms had the Earth more or less for themselves.

Then one billion years ago, evolution came up with the second bright idea: It discovered the advantage of putting cells together, not just as an aggregation of cells, but for the purpose of division of labor between the cells—a concept akin to the invention of large-scale human societies. Physical constraints forbid unicellular organisms to grow larger. Multi-cellular organisms, on the other hand, are able to evolve into gigantic forms.

The third milestone was a very extraordinary event, or feat, that began like this: After the invention of multicellular life, evolution slowly and painstakingly moved forward in the process of creating higher complexity in regard to the division of labor among the cells, and larger and more powerful organisms. Life had been evolving in water, and the oceans were still the scenario for the theater of life. (You would have to go for a dip in the sea to appreciate all the strange ways of multicellular body organization that evolution decided to give a try. Actually you will not find them all: The list of innovative forms tested at some time includes several that unfortunately did not make it.) At one point, however, the slow process of evolution was curiously broken. That particular instant, which actually lasted some million years, occurred approximately 530 million years ago. What happened then was that within this relatively short period most of the main types of multicellular animals appeared.[341]

Most subsequent evolutionary events are just tedious routines in comparison. Plants did give birth to some innovative transformations after they went ashore 300 million to 400 million years ago, and within the animal kingdom you might also applaud evolution for the design of land vertebrates and insects, but as far as variety of gross anatomy and strategies of living goes, the last 500 million years have not really witnessed much novelty.

Vertebrates are assumed to have moved ashore soon after the plants did. This change of habitat had, of course, dramatic consequences in the long run, but the first step was nothing spectacular. As pointed out by Myles McLeod, it was "One small step for fish, one giant leap for us": Fossils and some rare present species of fishes suggest that the main functions required for a dry land life were already there. Certain fish already had lungs (presumably for survival in oxygen-drenched waters) and primitive legs (possibly for locomotion along the beds of seas and lakes).[342]

If there is anything in evolution to suggest a creative force reminiscent of the hand of God, the three events described above would designate the time that hand really did strike.

True, we are different from other animals. The most important difference lies in the cognitive power of our brains. But, if judged by a creature less tuned into mental acrobatics, the human brain is no more different from the brain of a chimpanzee than the neck of a giraffe is from that of an elk. Each species has its own peculiarities, and each species is different from all other species. Yet, genetically speaking, we are almost identical to the chimpanzees and bonobos, and not really that different from a frog. (In fact, the most noticeable difference between us and the typical frog is that the frog has a larger genome than we do!)

Never before has so much influence been allocated to just one actor on planet Earth. And humans are about to use that power to turn Earth upside down! But this is a cultural rather than a biological event, and I'm not so sure that it is something we should be proud of.

There is, however, one thing we might want to brag about: The six billion people with us today possibly contain more biomass, roughly 250 million tons, than any other species of animal ever had before. Our common ancestral mother, who lived 150,000 years ago, might be pleased to hear about the success of her children; however, since she was no doubt intelligent, she probably would also worry. If you plotted the change in population starting from her time to the present on a normal sheet of paper, with time on the x-axis and the number of humans on the y-axis,

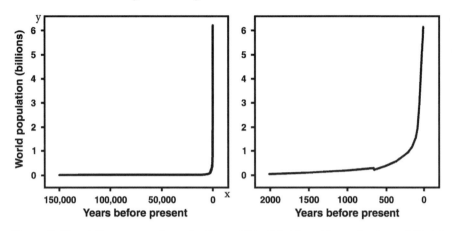

Figure 8. Population curves, from the time of "Eve" (left) and from the time of Christ (right). The population at the time of Eve is estimated at 100,000, while the population at the time of Christ is estimated to have been 100 million. The slight dip in the right curve corresponds to the Black Death, where possibly 50 million people died.

there would be no "curve." What you get is a horizontal line that abruptly changes to a vertical line. (See Figure 8.)

You need neither be a mathematician nor a biologist to realize that a population cannot increase forever. Common sense suggests that what goes up fast will come down fast. Humans have already caused the extinction of a number of our primate cousins, and about half of the 230 or so remaining species of primates are endangered due to our activities.[343] Be not too sure which half your species belongs to.

Who Can Tell What an Elephant Is?

A famous parable tells about three blindfolded sages who are presented with an elephant and asked to describe what it is. One of them gets hold of the leg and states that an elephant is a large trunk with a soft and wrinkled surface that is able to move itself. Another sage finds a tusk and says: "No, no, an elephant is a hard and smooth conical shaped thing." The third sage finds the tail, and, of course, disagrees with the former two; for him, an elephant is a giant paintbrush with a flexible shaft. Obviously they all end up fighting about who is right. Now, which one of them has come up with the correct description? They all have, and yet none of them has!

There is nothing we try so hard to understand as ourselves. Philosophers and scientists have raved and argued for thousands of years about what we are. I believe what Darwin did was to give us the option of removing the blindfold; we are now able to describe what the "elephant"— or mankind—really is.

The biological perspective connects the field of interest of the various sciences studying humans to a unifying whole. Unfortunately, biology does not seem fashionable today. Other subjects are more popular at colleges and universities, and the general public knows little about life on Earth. Many find the natural sciences difficult. This is sad, as we are ready to understand a very interesting part of biology—how the human brain functions, which is a subject that includes how our innate tendencies affect our behavior. True, the subject is a bit complex, but a basic understanding should be no more toil than the math we have to learn in school. And I believe an understanding of human behavioral biology is a lot more relevant for our quality of life.

A Peculiar Tool

I have offered a short resume of the theater of life and of where we stand today. The question is: Where are we going? While evolutionary history was never known to recreate an old scene, some people claim that human history repeats itself. Is that so?

There are achievements that are simply beyond the capacity of humans, certain limitations that are simply beyond the capacity of our intelligence to overcome. We cannot produce the amount of food necessary to sustain mankind without at the same time affecting the environment; we cannot find enough fossil fuels to last us an eternity; and we cannot free ourselves from genetic influence. The latter point may actually prove to be the most important one: Our innate aggression and selfishness will remain there as a force to be reckoned with—perhaps to be curbed, but not to disappear.

Human life and human culture will always carry a flavor of our innate behavioral tendencies. New cultures are born, change, and vanish, but our genes remain pretty much the same. That is why you recognize emotions in the faces of people brought up in different countries, and that is why many aspects of history repeat themselves. All cultures move within vague confines imposed upon them by the genes. We create intricate and heterogeneous communities, and we invent all sorts of strange tools. But behind the cultural mask—behind the gadgets—there is always a human face. Knowledge about the biology of human behavior not only helps us to grasp what and who we are, but provides us with a basis for understanding past societies. It may also help us to predict the future. More importantly: *It may help us to shape the future!*

For many years we have tried to compensate for the detrimental aspects of industrialized society. A central political dogma has been to create a so-called sustainable development, meaning the creation of an industry that does not deplete natural resources or destroy the environment, thus leaving the Earth in a more or less intact state for the benefit of future generations. This is important, *but adapting society to human nature may be an equally important principle for improving the conditions of mankind.*

It does not mean that all cultures should be alike. Our personal and cultural upbringing has shaped us to be dissimilar, and we live under different environmental constraints. Each individual and each culture will, and should, remain unique. The whispering of our genes does not dictate exact conditions, just vague confines. Sometimes the limits ought to be stretched, in order to allow for the advantages of a modern society; in other situations stretching them causes needless strain on the individual.

I believe the following cautionary note (often referred to as the naturalistic fallacy) has been included by nearly every biologist writing on human nature: What is sensible from an evolutionary perspective is not necessarily sensible from a practical or moral point of view. Warfare can be great for the genes of your tribe (as long as you win), but that is no reason to promote it. The evolutionary perspective I try to promote would, on the contrary, state that warfare should be discouraged, since it is unlikely to improve the average Darwinian happiness of those involved. And biology is not deterministic: We are in a position to curb warfare. The point is that we should know what we are up against, and know what is required to move the pendulum in the right direction.

The main tool we have for shaping the future is a very peculiar property that evolution has bestowed upon the current star of the theater of life (that is, us)—our measure of free will. It is a property so sublime that we take it for granted. Few people ever stop to reflect on what it really implies. Armed with free will, and a complete conception of the "elephant," we can try to control some of the more destructive aspects of human nature, and to stimulate our heroic and caring qualities. We do have the competence to shape the role we are given, and to help bring the present act to a happy ending. We know basically what is required to retain the variety and harmony on our green stage. We are all members of the cast. It is in our hands, and within the capacity of human nature, not just to save the Earth, but to create a decent quality of life for all humans. It is possible. It will not be easy; it may not even be likely; but it is not something that simply cannot be done.

Evolution Never Stops

Evolution has been at it for three or four billion years. It has made some astonishing accomplishments: you, for instance. It has also made some apparently stupid moves; sometimes it has got away with it, and in other cases it has not. Ostriches, moas, and related flightless birds presumably evolved from flying predecessors, and, although some of them have survived, a number of these species have become extinct. The removal of wings was a dubious move. If I had been employed as an adviser in the evolutionary process, I would have objected. But then again, I would also have tried to intervene in the evolution of amphibians, pointing out the instability of having just four legs when two or more are required to be off the ground at the same time in order to move efficiently, and noting the more robust design of six-legged insects. Leaving all locomotion to just two legs would seem to be careless evolution, and I would probably have resigned in protest. Some of the dinosaurs tried that, but they are no longer here. In fact, some of our ape relatives apparently tried it, and they too went extinct.[344] Yet, this was the move that facilitated the evolution of human intelligence.

The process of evolution never comes to a halt. Thus the human pool of genes, including the genes that support our precocious brainpower, as well as the genes that balance our caring and aggressive tendencies, will eventually change. With regard to the balance between compassion and

Plate 27. The present population of six billion people seems to be more than this planet should wish for. There is not much readily arable land remaining, and we live in expanding cities under increasingly Discord conditions.

violence, sexual selection presumably favors the former, while natural selection favors the latter: We prefer caring mates, but benevolent people are more likely to be killed in times of conflict. It is not obvious which of these selective pressures will have the greater impact, but I fear we are not being bred to compete with angels.

Is it possible (and if yes, should we try) to intervene and change the course of evolution? Which way human evolution is headed may not be our immediate concern. On the other hand, if evolution is heading in an unfortunate direction, it will at some point aggravate our problems. It therefore makes sense to consider the question of intervention.

We are the first species ever to interfere consciously with the process of evolution. We do so already and very keenly, and with dramatic effects, in dealing with pets and farm animals. The practice of breeding animals for particular purposes has been going on for thousands of years: The

Plate 28. We have interfered with the evolutionary process for thousands of years in that we shape other animals to suit our needs. The genes of the dozen or so species to which we have given most attention might appreciate what we do. There would not be that many horses and mules around without our interference; however, it is less obvious that the quality of life we offer those animals should make the individual animal equally happy about the arrangement.

capacity of cows to produce milk, for example, has been increased many fold; and dogs are shaped into all sorts of creatures to serve our wishes. If cows and dogs had any awareness of what was going on, they might disprove of what we do; their genes, however, have no reason to complain. Thanks to human intervention there are a lot more copies of them around.

We are also in the position to interfere with our own evolution. We actually interfere a lot more than we would like to think: Every time we take medicine, whenever we use contraceptives, or decide on a spouse, it has a potential impact on evolution.

Several societies have at some point pursued ideas about how to retain, or improve, the quality of their race. Such ideas are referred to as *eugenics*.[345] Some of the resulting policies have been based on racist views, but even when based on science—such as when discouraging the birth of babies with serious inheritable defects—many consider the underlying ideas to be unethical.

The disrepute of eugenics has a lot to do with the policy of Nazi Germany. It should be pointed out that the ideology supporting that policy—based on the notion that the "Aryan" race is genetically superior—has no support in the sciences. On the contrary, it may be suggested that people of the Third World, whom Hitler apparently despised, have more healthy genes, since they have not been exposed to the blessing, and genetic deterioration, of modern medicine to the same extent that we have. Moreover, survival and procreation in Calcutta may require more intelligence than it does in Berlin, Oslo, or New York.

Eugenics has a very bad reputation in another way, too; human evolution is something we are not supposed to even think about, let alone talk about or tamper with. Sticking both feet, and your head, deep into the sand is the obvious solution to avoid stepping on something. But is it the best way to evaluate a potential problem?

Evolution is based on the combination of mutations and selection. New mutations appear regularly, and most of them are either neutral or have a negative impact on the attributes of an organism. This is because they strike randomly at very complex machinery. Hitting your computer with a hammer could theoretically improve its functions, but do not count on it.

Most mutations do not strike as hard as a hammer, simply because most of the genome seems to be of little importance. Even the small part of the genome that comprises your actual genes can take quite a bit of pounding without malfunctioning. Still, the bottom line is that mutations are more likely to be harmful than beneficial; thus, in the absence of selection, all the accumulated features a species has acquired will gradually degenerate.

To sum up, mutations are a necessary source of variation required to make evolution progress—but, unfortunately, improvement also depends on the harshness of selection.

It is not that the principles of selection no longer apply to our species, because selection is basically a question of who gets how many children. The important point is whether those features of our species that we treasure are still selected for, or selected for with sufficient intensity to avoid decline. For example, to have genes that today specify good health is not as important for survival and procreation as is was in the time of our Stone Age ancestors. Why? Sedentary farming communities presumably offered their citizens safer surroundings, leading to the fact that qualities such as strength, stamina, and resistance to disease gradually became less important. The decreased selection for robustness culminated in the development of modern medicine. The more lethal mutations will still be selected against, but minor variations in a large proportion of our 40,000 or more genes will presumably cause slight deterioration in how well we fight off infections and how easily we are hit by other ailments. With our present lifestyle and present health care system, most of these alterations will not correlate with having fewer children—even nearsighted asthmatics may obtain maximal payoff at the discotheques and the delivery rooms.

The human body moves around with spare tires. Not only do we have two copies of each gene, but many genes apparently have a capacity to compensate for ailments in other genes. We all walk around with several mutations that can cause ailments, and some of them may even prove to be potentially lethal, but on the whole they do not have much impact on our health. However, as with the driver who tours deserted roads with a spare tire, the situation really becomes unpleasant the second time he has a puncture.

The predecessor of the moas presumably lost its wings, not so much because wings were selected against, but rather owing to the absence of selection favoring their retention. It is possible that domestic hens are becoming less apt at brooding on their eggs, again not because the inclination is selected against, but simply because it is not retained by active selection: Today, machines care for most of the eggs. Where is human evolution heading?

Evolution may well prove to be a tyrant for the human race. As traditional parameters of selection, such as strength and health, become less important, it is conceivable that sexual selection will be more momentous in shaping the future human species. We should hope that kindness will still be favored. Furthermore, the popularity of singers may help forthcoming generations to end up as excellent choir members. Besides kindness, another mate-choice preference may be intelligence. This sounds like good news, since a more intelligent species would presumably stand a better chance dealing with problems. On the other hand, it is not obvious that the more intelligent couples will beget more children.

Actually some people believe we are close to the end of the road for the evolution of brainpower anyway, as there appear to be no more obvious improvement paths available.[346] The limits imposed by the female birth canal, the apparent requirement of nerve cells to be formed prior to birth, and the constraints in obtaining a higher blood supply, make it difficult to expand the brain in size. It is of course conceivable that the performance could improve without an actual increase in terms of size or structural complexity. An option could well be to drop archaic utilities, such as the nerve circuitry involved in making goose bumps, in order to supply space and energy for refining cognitive functions, or simply to clean up the messy wiring resulting from million of years of more or less clumsy evolutionary craft.

It may be difficult to create brains with more intellectual power than the best we have around today, but it is certainly theoretically, and technically, possible to move the average toward that extreme. It is also possible to select for better health. The question is whether we wish to engage in any such endeavor, considering the ethical dilemma involved in controlling pregnancies.

A policy for the future evolution of humans could, in theory, be adapted either for the purpose of counteracting the presumed problem of genetic deterioration, or even going beyond that, to try to improve the species on the whole. Human evolution can be dealt with by the same means that are applied to shape our domestic animals, namely by controlled breeding. Semen and egg cell banks combined with artificial insemination are technically easy solutions, but ethically questionable. Moreover, for eugenic efforts to have a real impact on the human gene pool, a majority of individuals should go along with the relevant measures. Of course, these would be very difficult to implement.

The modern methods of gene technology are more difficult (and ethically no better). It is possible to insert novel genes in the egg, and even to destroy existing genes, but the techniques are not just laborious; they do not always yield the desired result. If applied to humans, we should expect to end up with several defective fetuses. Moreover, you can only correct one, or a few, genes in each fetus. Thus, although gene technology can be used to change genes in the context of treating diseases, it is not, at least in the foreseeable future, a practical alternative for improving the human gene pool.

With regard to the more serious genetic diseases, there is also the possibility of advising parents who harbor the same defective gene, either not to have children, or to have the fetus genetically examined and aborted in case it carries the double dose of the gene. Certain countries have actually tried to implement such measures—for example, Malta and China. It should be pointed out that while this policy does decrease the number of persons who have two copies of the gene-causing disease, and thus suffer from the disease, it hardly has any effect on the total number of disease genes in the population. This is because the vast majority of the disease genes are hidden away in healthy people who carry only one copy.

All of us presumably have a couple of such bad genes hidden away in the genome, but normally only one of the two copies is bad, which in most cases does not cause any harm. With 40,000 or so genes, the chance of having two people with the same bad alleles meet, is, fortunately, rather small. More and more of these bad alleles are being identified, but it would be an impossible task (with present technology) to screen each individual for all bad alleles.

Anyway, if we had had the power to effectively control evolution, I fear that popular demand would not seek intelligence and kindness, but rather a surplus of Elvis Presleys and Britney Spears.

There are plenty of valid arguments in deploring any form of eugenic measures. It is therefore not my intention to advocate an active role in the evolution of our species, but I do believe the issue should be brought out of the closet and examined objectively. The conclusion would most likely be that the problem is not acute. The worry, if any, has a time span of at least hundreds or thousands of years. It is nevertheless tempting to quote the Bible, which states that the meek and poor shall inherit the Earth. From a distant perspective, this may be an accurate prophecy: The rich deteriorate genetically; the poor may die like flies, but in the process they improve their genetic quality.

The question of the future evolution of our species is certainly not the most severe problem on our planet; it does, however, exemplify a more general concern. Our intellect has made us able to consider a variety of dilemmas, and has made us technically capable of dealing with them. *Yet evolution did not necessarily prepare us psychologically to handle these situations.* It seems that the technological solutions are the minor obstacle when it comes to handling problems facing mankind. *The will to do something, and the will to cooperate, are the major limitations.*

Human behavior will continue to move within the vague boundaries set by our genes. Still, the future is not just history: We do have plenty of navigational room within those confines. We can choose the best part of the history of mankind, and go for that, rather than reincarnate all the mayhem of the past. Unfortunately, I am not sure if this will be our choice.

Paradise Society

People keep searching for a purpose in life. There is no purpose, which is why it is so hard to find one.

If nature had supplied us with a goal, you would have known, and there would be no need to seek high and low for it. What nature has supplied us with is self-awareness. When this quality is combined with an intellect, and an urge to do things considered to be useful, we assume there must be a purpose, or we wish for a purpose. We look for a meaning in order to justify our existence, because otherwise we get this terrible feeling of futility and emptiness.[347]

If you ask your genes for direction, of course, they will supply you with an answer: The aim of life is to offer them eternal existence in as many copies as possible. But if you wish for a grand plan of life to satisfy your personal desires, the genes are not the ones to turn to; an intelligent priest can provide you with a more convenient solution.

I offer an alternative answer to your quest: I believe the desire for meaning to be a valuable tool, and suggest that we make the creation of a Paradise Society our ultimate goal. A Paradise Society should be a community designed to maximize Darwinian happiness, a place that combines the advantages of the Garden of Eden of our Stone Age ancestors with modern-day comfort.

I believe we need to consider the following questions in order to establish a Paradise Society:

(1) How can our way of living be brought more in tune with our genetic dispositions?

(2) How should we best appeal to the positive aspects of human nature and at the same time curb the negative aspects?

(3) How do we teach people to find joy and contentment?

If we are successful in arriving at answers to these endeavors, we may find that it is possible to offer everybody the basic needs for sustaining life, as well as a reasonable measure of Darwinian happiness, and at the same time give the future a chance.

I fear we cannot create a happy ending to the present act by just telling people to be nice to each other at their own expense. This is not a stable strategy because human nature is marred by selfishness. With the principles of Darwinian happiness we can overcome this problem; it is a choice plum, ripe for the individual's taking, and the principles behind this concept work well for society. They work well because they are based on science, because compassion is an excellent source of joy, and because a high score does not require affluence. It is certainly easier to solve environmental problems if we can curb materialism, just as it is certainly easier to curb aggression if people are content.

If we cannot present a vision—and a way to get there—I fear the global theater may resemble the classical Greek tragedy: The act will close with the "Titanic" sinking over and over again. The rich may survive for awhile, but the poor will drown in a holocaust of wars, famines, epidemics, and environmental disasters.

A Paradise Society should definitely not listen to the voice of evolution when it comes to one major aspect: The aim should not be to generate as many human genes as possible, since the present population is already more than the stage can readily cope with. Crowded communities tend to breed poverty and powerlessness; if too many people inhabit the Earth, contentment will be hard to find.

Studies by Frans de Waal suggest that chimpanzees, and presumably humans, as opposed to most other mammals, are actually less aggressive when briefly crowded together.[348] This reflects an emotional restraint, reminiscent of how people interact in an elevator: They reduce friction by minimizing body movements, eye contact, and vocalization. Apparently we do have a natural talent for dealing with crowded areas, which works just fine as long as we are reasonably content, and the situation is not lasting. On the other hand, chronic crowding combined with scarcity of resources is something altogether different. Furthermore, many of the indirect consequences of a crowded society are Discords and, as such, are stress eliciting. We may cope in the short run, but in the long run aggression is likely to increase, and our measure of Darwinian happiness diminish.

We have only this one planet—a place we preferably may think of as our friend and goddess Gaia. Saving Gaia is a formidable assignment. Our great feats of engineering, from building the pyramids to sending a man to the moon, have been the easy tasks: *The real challenge in shaping the future Earth lies in dealing with human nature.*

The human species possesses properties that can be used to set up a paradise. Incidentally, we also possess properties that can turn the entire planet into a living nightmare and a subsequent biological refuse dump. The real question is whether or not we will be able to harness human nature for the benefit of all living things. We have witnessed the breakdown of the tribe, and we are now seeing the breakdown of the family and the ever more frequent breakdown of society. Will we opt for paradise or will the theater of life enact the final breakdown, the scene where humans create their own personal version of hell?

Neither the situation nor our genes are likely to improve by themselves; thus if we cannot deal with the problems of today, we are unlikely to do any better tomorrow. Fortunately we do almost have the power of gods—the question is whether we have their wisdom.

It is not typically human to give up. We are innate optimists; we continue to look for heaven even while burning in hell. And we ought to be optimists, because I believe our knowledge of human behavioral biology does point us toward a path leading to a place more like paradise than anything we ever had before.

Earth is unlikely to be the only planet in the universe to harbor life, but I doubt that any other planet has ever witnessed a drama as exciting as the act we are witnessing today. I just hope it will bring applause for the performance of its leading character.

ENDNOTES

GLOSSARY

INDEX

Three islands off the coast of Norway—pointing toward the horizon.

ENDNOTES

I have concentrated on references to printed works, assuming that for those who have access to the Internet it is relatively easy to locate suitable information there. Moreover, where appropriate, I have tried to list literature that is reasonably accessible for non-specialists. Where there are more than three authors, only the first is included.

Chapter 1. Introduction: On Genes and Gurus

1. See G. P. Moberg, *Animal Stress* (American Physiological Society, 1985), for a general text on problems of keeping animals in captivity; and A. Lord, "No way out," *New Scientist* (26 January 2002): 34–38, for a discussion on stereotypical behavior.

2. For an introduction to the science of the brain, I can recommend J. E. Dowling, *Creating Mind: How the Brain Works* (W.W. Norton, 1998).

3. A. Whiten et al., "Culture in Chimpanzees," *Nature* 399 (1999): 682–25.

4. A. Kitchen, D. Denton, and L. Brent, "Self-recognition and abstraction abilities in the common chimpanzee studied with distorting mirrors," *Proceedings of the National Academy of Science USA* 93 (1996): 7405–8.

5. D. Barash, *Sociobiology: The Whispering Within* (Harper & Row, 1980).

6. The book by E. O. Wilson, *Sociobiology: The New Synthesis* (Harvard University Press, 1975) spurred the debate to what extent biological knowledge should be applied to human behavior. It is still considered an excellent introduction to the social behavior of animals. (A 25th anniversary edition was printed in the year 2000.)

7. For introductory books, I can recommend: D. M. Buss, *Evolutionary Psychology: The New Science of the Mind* (Allyn & Bacon, 1998); L. Cronk, N. Chagnon, and W. Irons, *Adaptation and Human Behavior: An Anthropological Perspective* (DeGruyter, 2000); A. Stevens and J. Price, *Evolutionary Psychiatry: A New Beginning* (Routledge, 2000); and I. Eibl-Eisenfeldt, *Human Ethology* (De Gruyter, 1989).

Chapter 2. Evolution: The Theater of Life

8. C. Darwin, *On the Origin of Species* (John Murray/Harvard University Press, 1859/1975) is still an interesting read, and in my mind probably the most important book ever written, but for a more updated and accessible introduction to evolution, I suggest J. Maynard-Smith, *The Theory of Evolution* (Cambridge University Press, 1993).

9. H. Cronin offers an excellent introduction to sexual selection in, *The Ant and the Peacock* (Cambridge University Press, 1991). For a recent discussion on the importance of sexual selection in shaping the human psyche, see G. Miller, *The Mating Mind* (Doubleday, 2000).

10. A. Atholl, *Prodigious Birds, Moas and Moa-hunting in New Zealand* (Cambridge University Press, 1990).

11. R. Dunbar and L. Barrett, *Cousins* (BBC Worldwide, 2000).

12. See R. Dawkins, *The Selfish Gene* (Oxford University Press, 1976) and *The Extended Phenotype* (Oxford University Press, 1983) for enlightening discussions on the relationship between genes and individual organisms.

13. For a general book on aging, I suggest S. N. Austad, *Why We Age: What Science is Discovering about the Body's Journey through Life* (John Wiley & Son, 1997).

14. K. Hawkes et al., "Grandmothering, menopause, and the evolution of human life histories," *Proceedings of the National Academy of Science USA* 95 (1998): 1336–39.

15. For a discussion on the problem with the spine, see R. A. Deyo "Low-back pain," *Scientific American* (August 1998): 28–33.

16. I recommend I. Wyllie, *The Cuckoo* (Shire Publications, 1999) if you want to learn more about this fascinating bird.

17. J. Alcock, *Animal Behavior: An Evolutionary Approach* (Sinauer, 1997) is an excellent textbook.

18. For recent discussions on the evolution of social behavior in humans, see L. Dugatkin, *Cheating Monkeys and Citizen Bees* (The Free Press, 1999); or J. Cartwright, *Evolution and Human Behavior* (MIT Press, 2000).

19. Although the concept of "Darwinian happiness" is not taken from the writings of Darwin, he did write extensively on the application of evolutionary principles to human behavior, particularly in *The Expression*

of the Emotions in Man and Animals (University of Chicago Press, 1872/ 1965), and *The Descent of Man, and Selection in Relation to Sex* (Hurst & Company, 1874).

Chapter 3. Darwinian Happiness: Why We Should Listen to Our Genes

20. The increasing interest in happiness is reflected in the dedication of the January 2000 issue of *American Psychologist* to "positive psychology"; in D. Kahneman, E. Diener, and N. Schwarz (eds.), *Well-Being: The Foundation of Hedonic Psychology* (Russell Sage Foundation, 1999); and in the new *Journal of Happiness Studies*, as well as in *The World Database of Happiness* (http://www.eur.nl/fsw/research/happiness/), the latter two edited by R. Veenhoven. With regard to the evolutionary perspective, the only serious contributions I am aware of are: D. M. Bush, "The evolution of happiness," *American Psychologist* 55 (2000): 15–23; J. H. Barkow, "Happiness in evolutionary perspective," in N. L. Segal, G. E. Weisfeld and C. C. Weisfeld (eds.), *Uniting Psychology and Biology* (American Psychological Association, 1997), p. 397–418; B. Grinde, "Darwinian happiness: Biological advice on the quality of life," *Journal of Social and Evolutionary Systems* 19 (1996): 249–60; and B. Grinde, "Happiness in the perspective of evolutionary psychology," *Journal of Happiness Studies*, in press.

21. See D. G. Myers and E. Diener, "The pursuit of happiness," *Scientific American* (May 1996): 54–56; or, for more comprehensive treatises: D. G. Myers, *The Pursuit of Happiness* (Avon Books, 1993); and D. T. Lykken, *Happiness: The Nature and Nurture of Joy and Contentment* (St. Martin's Press, 2000).

22. See Moberg, under note 1; or D. Carroll, *Health Psychology: Stress, Behavior and Disease* (The Falmer Press, 1991).

23. C. Crawford and D. Krebs, *Handbook of Evolutionary Psychology: Ideas, Issues and Applications* (LEA, 1997); or for an early discussion of the concept, D. Symons, *The Evolution of Human Sexuality* (Oxford University Press, 1979).

24. K. Widdows, *Myopia and the Control of Eye Growth* (Wiley, 1990); and G. E. Quinn et al., "Myopia and ambient lighting at night," *Nature* 399 (1999): 113–14.

25. M. F. Teaford and P. S. Ungar, "Diet and the evolution of the earliest human ancestors," *Proceedings of the National Academy of Science USA* 97 (2000): 13506–11.

26. See O. Lundberg, "The impact of childhood living conditions on illness and mortality in adulthood," *Social Science & Medicine* 36 (1993): 1047–52; or, for a more general treatise, J. P. Shonkoff and D. A. Phillips, *From Neurons to Neighborhoods: The Science of Early Childhood Development* (National Academy Press, 2000).

27. The concept of stress was first introduced by H. Seyle in *The Stress of Life* (McGraw-Hill, 1956); for a more updated dissertation, see M. J. Friedman, D. S. Charney, and A. Y. Deutch, *Neurobiological and Clinical Consequences of Stress* (Lippincott-Raven Publishers, 1995). I can also recommend the discussion of stress by R. M. Sapolsky, "The physiology and pathophysiology of unhappiness," in D. Kahneman, E. Diener, and N. Schwarz (eds.), *Well-Being: The Foundation of Hedonic Psychology* (Russell Sage Foundation, 1999), p. 453–69.

28. See S. B. Eaton, M. Konner, and M. Shostak, "Stone agers in the fast lane: Chronic degenerative diseases in evolutionary perspective," *American Journal of Medicine* 84 (1988): 739–49; or L. Pani, "Is there an evolutionary mismatch between the normal physiology of the human dopaminergic system and current environmental conditions in industrialized countries?" *Molecular Psychiatry* 5 (2000): 465–75, and references therein.

29. R. M. Nesse and G. C. Williams, *Why We Get Sick: The New Science of Darwinian Medicine* (Vintage Books, 1996). See also W. Trevathan, J. J. McKenna, and E. U. Smith, *Evolutionary Medicine* (Oxford University Press, 1999); A. Stevens and J. Price, *Evolutionary Psychiatry: A New Beginning* (Routledge, 2000); or N. Boaz, *Evolving Health: The Origins of Illness and How the Modern World is Making Us Sick* (John Wiley & Sons, 2002). Boaz uses the term "adaptive normality" for the conditions humans are adapted to, which is related to the use of "Discord" in the present text.

30. M. Cabanac, "Emotion and phylogeny," *Japanese Journal of Physiology* 49 (1999): 1–10.

31. I first presented the concept of Darwinian happiness in B. Grinde,

"Darwinian happiness: Biological advice on the quality of life," *Journal of Social and Evolutionary Systems* 19 (1996): 249–60.

32. For an easy-to-read discussion on the effect of stress on health, see E. M. Sternberg, *The Balance Within* (W. H. Freeman, 2000).

33. Data presented at the meeting of the *International Society for Human Ethology* (ISHE) in Salamanca (2000) (abstract available at ISHE's web site).

34. The idea that our sensations tend to be either positive or negative is discussed by R. M. Nesse, "What good is feeling bad," *The Sciences* (November/December 1991): 30–37; or see note 29.

35. R. Spanagel and F. Weiss, "The dopamine hypothesis of reward: Past and current status," *Trends in Neurosciences* 22 (1999): 521–27.

36. For a scholarly treatise on grief, I recommend J. Archer, *The Nature of Grief: The Evolution and Psychology of Reactions to Loss* (Routledge, 1999).

37. D. J. Mela and P. J. Rogers, *Food, Eating and Obesity: The Psychological Basis of Appetite and Weight Control* (Aspen Publishers, 1997).

38. For a discussion on our propensity for happiness, and the problem of finding it in modern society, I suggest D. G. Myers, *The American Paradox: Spiritual Hunger in an Age of Plenty* (Yale University Press, 2000); or O. James, *Britain on the Couch* (Arrow Books, 1998). As to Down syndrome, see R. J. Robison, "Learning about happiness from persons with Down syndrome: Feeling the sense of joy and contentment," *American Journal of Mental Retardation* 105 (2000): 372–76.

39. Described in introductory psychology text books such as R. L. Atkinson et al., *Hillgard's Introduction to Psychology* (Harcourt Brace & Company, 1997).

40. M. Csikszentmihalyi, *Flow: The Psychology of Optimal Experience* (Harper Collins, 1991).

41. See note 21.

Chapter 4. Human Origins: The Age of the Dangerous Hero

42. A. Hallam and P. Wignall, *Mass Extinctions and their Aftermath* (Oxford University Press, 1997), deals with the extinctions; F. Pearce,

"Wind of change," *New Scientist* (2 May 1998): 35–37, discusses the "big fart" hypothesis.

43. R. F. Kay, C. Ross, and B. A. Williams, "Anthropoid origins," *Science* 275 (1997): 797–804.

44. For an easy introduction, I suggest R. Lewin, *Human Evolution: An Illustrated Introduction* (Blackwell Science, 1999). I might point out that there is no such problem as a "missing link." Compared to most other mammals, we have a substantial collection of human fossils covering most periods since the split with the chimpanzee. The problem seems rather to be too many fossils, and the question of which are on the branch leading to us and which are on the branches of extinct hominids is hotly debated. For brief discussions, see, for example, L. C. Aiello and M. Collard, "Our newest oldest ancestor?" *Nature* 410 (2001): 526–27; or A. Gibbons, "In search of the first hominids," *Science* 295 (2002): 1214–19. As to early apes in Asia, see A. Gibbons, "New study points to Eurasian ape as great ape ancestor," *Science* 281 (1998): 622–23.

45. S. Horai et al., "Recent African origin of modern humans revealed by complete sequences of hominoid mitochondrial DNAs," *Proceedings of the National Academy of Science USA* 92 (1995): 532–26.

46. See note 3, or A. Whiten and C. Boesch, "The cultures of chimpanzees," *Scientific American* (January 2001): 49–55.

47. A. Gibbons, "Tracing the identity of the first toolmakers," *Science* 276 (1997) 32; and S. Semaw et al., "2.5-million-year-old stone tools from Gona, Ethiopia," *Nature* 385 (1997): 333–36.

48. H. Thieme, "Lower palaeolithic hunting spears from Germany," *Nature* 385 (1997): 807–10.

49. This is a much-used example of evolution at work, mainly because of its pedagogic qualities; however, certain aspects of the moth story have been questioned. For a discussion, see A. Sibatani, "Industrial melanism revisited," *Reviews in Biology* 92 (1999): 545–47.

50. For an overview of the Grants' research on the Galapagos, see the excellent book by Jonathan Weiner, *The Beak of the Finch: A Story of Evolution in our Time* (Random House, Inc., 1994); and P. R. Grant, *Ecology and Evolution of Darwin's Finches* (Princeton University Press, 1999). The interested reader may also consult: P. R. Grant and B. R. Grant, "Unpre-

dictable evolution in a 30-year study of Darwin's finches," *Science* 296 (2002): 707–11.

51. For the sounds and language of chimpanzees, consult J. H. Gill, *If a Chimpanzee Could Talk: And Other Reflections on Language Acquisition* (University of Arizona Press, 1997); and J. C. Mitani, K. L. Hunley, and M. E. Murdoch, "Geographic variation in the calls of wild chimpanzees: A reassessment," *American Journal of Primatology* 47 (1999): 133–51.

52. L. Spinney, "Bodytalk," *New Scientist* (8 April 2000): 30–33.

53. For a general discussion on the evolution of language, I can recommend S. Pinker, *The Language Instinct* (HarperCollins, 1994).

54. See note 25.

55. For "culture" in species other than chimpanzees, consult E. Avital and E. Jablonka, *Animal Traditions: Behavioral Inheritance in Evolution* (Cambridge University Press, 2001).

56. E. S. Lander et al., "Initial sequencing and analysis of the human genome," *Nature* 409 (2001): 860–921.

57. C. G. Kurland and S. G. Andersson, "Origin and evolution of the mitochondrial proteome," *Microbiology and Molecular Biology Reviews* 64 (2000): 786–820.

58. See note 45; and H. Kaessmann et al., "Great ape DNA sequences reveal a reduced diversity and an expansion in humans," *Nature Genetics* 27 (2001): 156–57. Actually similar analysis of Y-chromosomes suggests that Adam was present at about the same time: A. Gibbons, "Y chromosome shows that Adam was an African," *Science* 278 (1997): 804–5.

59. M. Krings et al., "Neanderthal DNA sequences and the origin of modern humans," *Cell* 90 (1997): 19–30.

60. A. C. Wilson and R. L. Cann, "The recent African genesis of humans," *Scientific American* (April 1992): 22–27.

61. Both genetic, linguistic, and archaeological data bear evidence on the exodus from Africa that presumably eventually colonized the entire world. See, for example, M. F. Hammer et al., "Out of Africa and back again," *Molecular Biology and Evolution* 15 (1998): 427–41; or C. Renfrew, "World linguistic diversity," *Scientific American* (January 1994): 116–23.

62. K. Douglas, "Our distant ancestors' fondness for a swim may

explain why humans are such unusual primates," *New Scientist* (25 November 2000): 29–33.

63. C. Stringer, "Coasting out of Africa," *Nature* 405 (2000): 24–27.

64. See Kaessmann et al., note 58; and Lander et al., note 56—which indicate that present humans are some 99.9 percent genetically identical.

65. A. Yoshida, V. Dave, and H. B. Hamilton, "Imbalance of blood group A subtypes and the existence of superactive B gene in Japanese in Hiroshima and Nagasaki," *American Journal of Human Genetics* 43 (1988): 422–28.

66. B. Hamilton, "African running dominance: What is behind it?" *British Journal of Sports Medicine* 34 (2000): 391–94.

67. B. Harris, "Evolutionary changes in the supraorbital ridge," *Impressions* 1 (1980): 6–12.

68. J. McCrone, "Fired up," *New Scientist* (20 May 2000): 30–34.

69. N. Takahata, Y. Satta and J. Klein, "Divergence time and population size in the lineage leading to modern humans," *Theoretical Population Biology* 48 (1995): 198–221; and H. C. Harpending et al., "Genetic traces of ancient demography," *Proceedings of the National Academy of Science USA* 95 (1998): 1961–67.

70. For information on climate changes after the ice age, and their effect on the distribution and subsidence of humans, check L. G. Straus, B. V. Eriksen, and G. Erlandson, *Humans at the End of the Ice Age: The Archaeology of the Pleistocene-Holocene Transition* (Plenum Publication Corporation, 1996).

71. H. Pringle, "The slow birth of agriculture," *Science* 282 (1998): 1448–50.

72. See note 25; Boaz, under note 29; and S. B. Eaton et al., "An evolutionary perspective enhances understanding of human nutritional requirements," *Journal of Nutrition* 126 (1996): 1732–40.

73. M. C. Stiner, "Thirty years on the 'Broad Spectrum Revolution' and paleolithic demography," *Proceedings of the National Academy of Science USA* 98 (2001): 6993–96.

74. A. Gibbons, "Bone sizes trace the decline of man (and woman)," *Science* 276 (1997): 896–97.

75. M. Balter, "Why settle down? The mystery of communities," *Science* 282 (1998): 1442–45.

76. See note 7; or L. Cosmides et al., *What is Evolutionary Psychology: Explaining the New Science of the Mind* (Yale University Press, 2001).

77. A collection of anthropological data on various cultures can be found either in the compilation of G. P. Murdock, *Outline of World Cultures* (Human Energy Press, 1983); or, continuously updated, in the *Human Relations Area File* (available as CD-ROM, or on the Internet under Yale University).

78. To learn about what twins can teach us, I recommend N. L. Segal and T. J. Bouchard, *Entwined Lives: Twins and What They Tell us About Human Behavior* (Plusock Mesoamerican Studies, 2000). The Minnesota Twin Study, probably the most extensive project on twins, has data files available for research purposes (contact the Psychology Department at the University of Minnesota).

79. As to the role of shared environment, see D. B. Cohen, *Stranger in the Nest: Do Parents Really Shape Their Child's Personality, Intelligence, or Character?* (John Wiley & Sons, 1999); and as to the "social multiplier" effect—that is, how slight genetic differences may be blown up to vast performance differences, see W. T. Dickens and J. R. Flynn, "Heritability estimates versus large environmental effect: The IQ paradox resolved," *Psychological Review* 108 (2001): 346–69.

80. For an introduction to behavioral genetics, I can recommend P. Bateson and P. Martin, *Design for Life: How Behavior Develops* (Jonathan Cape, 1999).

81. R. J. Greenspan and J. F. Ferveur, "Courtship in Drosophila," *Annual Reviews in Genetics* 34 (2000): 205–32; and N. G. Kamyshev, K. G. Iliadi, and J. V. Bragina, "Drosophila conditioned courtship: Two ways of testing memory," *Learning & Memory* 6 (1999): 1–20.

82. T. Strachan and A. P. Read, *Human Molecular Genetics* (John Wiley & Sons, 1999).

83. J. P. Alsobrook and D. L. Pauls, "Genetics and violence," *Child and Adolescent Psychiatry Clinics of North America* 9 (2000): 765–76.

84. For an introduction to ethology, I can recommend P. J. B. Slater,

Essentials of Animal Behavior (Cambridge University Press, 1999). See also J. L. Gould and C. G. Gould, *The Animal Mind* (Scientific American Library, 1994), for an introduction to animal cognition.

85. F. de Waal and F. Lanting, *Bonobo: The Forgotten Ape* (University of California Press, 1997); but see also T. Kano and E. O. Vineberg, *The Last Ape: Pygmy Chimpanzee Behavior and Ecology* (Universal Microfilm International, 1992).

86. S. Parmigiani et al., "Selection, evolution of behavior and animal models in behavioral neuroscience," *Neuroscience and Biobehavioral Reviews* 23 (1999): 957–69.

87. J. Panksepp, *Affective Neuroscience: The Foundation of Human and Animal Emotions* (Oxford University Press, 1998) offers an excellent authoritative overview of the field.

88. For hormones and sexual behavior, check D. W. Pfaff, *Drive: Neurobiological and Molecular Mechanisms of Sexual Motivation* (MIT Press, 1999); or P. T. Ellison, *On Fertile Ground: A Natural History of Human Reproduction* (Harvard University Press, 2001).

89. See note 85.

90. T. H. Clutton-Brock, P. H. Harvey, and B. Rudder, "Sexual dimorphism, socionomic sex ratio and body weight in primates," *Nature* 269 (1977): 797–800.

91. R. D. Martine and R. M. May, "Outward signs of breeding," *Nature* 293 (1981): 7–9. As to testicle size, which is considered the better indicator of promiscuity, the human testicles are small compared to the highly promiscuous chimpanzees but, as expected, larger than those of the gorilla.

92. T. H. Clutton-Brock, S. D. Albon and F. E. Guinness, "Parental investment in male and female offspring in polygynous mammals," *Nature* 289 (1981) 487–89; and R. L. Trivers and D. E. Willard, "Natural selection of parental ability to vary the sex ratio of offspring," *Science* 179 (1973): 90–92.

93. See note 5.

94. W. LaBarre, *The Human Animal* (University of Chicago Press, 1954).

95. For human polyandry, see note 77; as to the Tasmanian hen, con-

sult J. Maynard Smith and M. G. Ridpath, "Wife sharing in the Tasmanian native hen, *Tribonyx mortierii*: A case of kin selection?" *American Naturalist* 106 (1972): 447–52.

96. A. Jolly, *Lucy's Legacy: Sex and Intelligence in Human Evolution* (Harvard University Press, 1999).

97. Consult F. M. Mondimore, *A Natural History of Homosexuality* (Johns Hopkins University Press, 1996).

98. C. S. Ford and F. A. Beach, *Patterns of Sexual Behavior* (Harper & Row, 1951).

99. S. Hrdy, *The Woman that Never Evolved* (Harvard University Press, 1999)

Chapter 5. The Brain: Your Personal Necktop Computer

100. See note 87.

101. For an easy introduction to brain anatomy and function, consult S. Greenfield, *The Human Brain* (Basic books, 1998).

102. For an overview of neurotransmitters, I suggest M. Tohyama, K. Takatsjui, and S. S. Kathna, *Atlas of Neuroactive Substances and Their Receptors in the Rat* (Oxford University Press, 1998).

103. See note 32.

104. For a discussion on the "Swiss army knife" and "car motor" models of brain modules, I recommend R. M. Nesse, "Natural selection, mental modules and intelligence," *Novartis Foundation Symposium* 233 (2000): 96–121; and Nesse and Williams, under note 29.

105. S. Pinker, *How the Mind Works* (W. W. Norton & Co, 1999).

106. As to the increase of mental diseases, see E. F. Torrey and J. Miller, *The Invisible Plague: The Rise of Mental Illness from 1750 to the Present* (Rutgers University Press, 2002); theories on the cause of schizophrenia can be found in D. Horrobin, *The Madness of Adam and Eve—How Schizophrenia Shaped Humanity* (Bantam Press, 2001); or B. Furlow, "The making of a mind," *New Scientist* (21 July 2001): 38–41.

107. C. Gross et al., "Serotonin1A receptor acts during development to establish normal anxiety-like behaviour in the adult," *Nature* 416 (2002): 396–400.

108. For detailed information on psychoactive drugs, try C. Regan, *Intoxicating Minds* (Weidenfeld & Nicolson, 2001); or M. Robert and D. Julien, *A Primer of Drug Action: A Concise Nontechnical Guide to the Actions, Uses, and Side Effects of Psychoactive Drugs* (W. H. Freeman & Co, 2001). R. Rudgley, *An Encyclopaedia of Psychoactive Substances* (St. Martins Press, 1999), offers an overview of historical and social aspects of their use.

109. The terms "wanting" and "liking" were introduced by T. E. Robinson and K. C. Berridge, "The neural basis of drug craving: An incentive-sensitization theory of addiction," *Brain Research. Brain Research Reviews* 18 (1993): 247–91.

110. See note 21.

111. For a flavored discussion, see D. R. Ford and T. H. Mikuriya, *Marijuana: Not Guilty as Charged* (Good Press, 1997).

112. R. Kubey and M. Csikszentmihalyi, "Television addiction," *Scientific American* (February 2002): 62–68.

113. Consult note 38.

114. For a scholarly review, consult R. G. Pertwee, "Cannabinoid receptor ligands: Clinical and neuropharmacological considerations, relevant to future drug discovery and development," *Expert Opinion on Investigational Drugs* 9 (2000): 1553–71. For an alternative strategy to obtain a more specific effect, see also B. F. Cravatt et al., "Supersensitivity to anandamide and enhanced endogenous cannabinoid signaling in mice lacking fatty acid amide hydrolase," *Proceedings of the National Academy of Science USA* 98 (2001): 9371–76.

115. The phrase "cosmetic psychopharmacology" was coined by P. Kramer in his book, *Listening to Prozac* (Penguin, 1997). For an ethical discussion, see L. Sperry and H. Prosen, "Contemporary ethical dilemmas in psychotherapy: Cosmetic psychopharmacology and managed care," *American Journal of Psychotheraphy* 52 (1998): 54–63.

Chapter 6. Rewards: Use Your Head—That's What It's There For

116. For in depth, but easy to read, discussions of play behavior, I recommend: T. G. Power, *Play and Exploration in Children and Animals* (LEA, 1999); or M. Bekoff and J. Byers *Animal Play* (Cambridge Univer-

sity Press, 1998). A short treatise on the evolution of play can be found in B. Furlow, "Play's the thing," *New Scientist* (9 June 2001): 29–31.

117. G. M. Burghardt, *Play Behavior in Animals* (Chapman & Hall, 2000).

118. When discussing gender differences in behavior, it is important to keep in mind that we are talking about differences in average of two overlapping "Bell curves." Books, such as D. C. Geary, *Male, Female: The Evolution of Human Sex Differences* (APA, 1998); or the more popular book B. Pease and A. Pease, *Why Men Don't Listen & Women Can't Read Maps: How We're Different and What to do About it* (Welcome Rain, 2000), offer lots of relevant information pertaining to the issue.

119. J. Panksepp and J. Burgdorf, "50-kHz chirping (laughter?) in response to conditioned and unconditioned tickle-induced reward in rats: Effects of social housing and genetic variables," *Behavioural Brain Research* 115 (2000): 25–38.

120. See Panksepp's book, note 87.

121. See note 87.

122. See D. Morris, *Intimate Behavior* (Jonathan Cape, 1971); or, by the same author, *The Human Animal* (Crown Publications, 1994).

123. See either note 119 or note 87.

124. See J. Parvizi et al., "Pathological laughter and crying: A link to the cerebellum," *Brain* 124 (2001): 1708–19, or Panksepp's book, note 87.

125. See de Waal and Lanting, note 85.

126. M. Konner, "Seeking universals," *Nature* 415 (2002): 121.

127. J. W. Sturm, F. Andermann and S. F. Berkovic, "Pressure to laugh: An unusual epileptic symptom associated with small hypothalamic hamartomas," *Neurology* 54 (2000): 971–73; and I. Fried et al., "Electric current stimulates laughter," *Nature* 39 (1998): 650.

128. J. McCrone, "Comic relief," *New Scientist* (27 May 2000): 23–26.

129. R. R. Provine, *Laughter: A Scientific Investigation* (Viking Press, 2000).

130. See note 115.

131. For a discussion of leisure and the need to do something "useful," I suggest S. Parker, *The Sociology of Leisure* (Allan & Unwin Ltd, 1976).

132. See note 40.

133. For an excellent introduction, consult: J. H. Wilmore and D. L. Costill, *Physiology of Sport and Exercise* (Human Kinetics Publications, 1999); as to precision of movement, see T. J. Sejnowski, "Making smooth moves," *Nature* 394 (1998): 725–26.

134. For a discussion of the "biology of sport," I recommend D. Morris, *Manwatching: A Field Guide to Human Behavior* (Abrams, 1977).

135. A. H. Goldfarb and A. Z. Jamurtas, "Beta-endorphin response to exercise. An update," *Sports Medicine* 24 (1997): 8–16; or, for a more popular account, R. Yeung, "Racing to euphoria," *New Scientist* (23 November 1996): 28–31.

136. See Myers, under note 21.

137. If you want to learn more about our capacity for imagination, I suggest: P. L. Harris, *The Work of the Imagination* (Blackwell, 2000); or G. G. Scott, *Power of Fantasy: Illusion and Eroticism in Everyday Life* (Birch Lane Press, 1994).

Chapter 7. Consciousness and Emotions: On Burns and Blossoms

138. A more formal definition of consciousness is: "To be conscious of something is to have a flexible neuronal representation that can be used to drive many different behavioral outputs"—from *Nature* 381 (1996): 97. See also Gould and Gould under note 84 for a comparison of human and animal consciousness.

139. For an overview on sleep, I recommend S. Chokroverty and R. B. Daroff, *Sleep Disorders Medicine: Basic Science, Technical Considerations, and Clinical Aspects* (Butterworth-Henemann, 1999). For a short introduction to the question of consciousness, I suggest F. Crick and C. Koch, "The problem of consciousness," *Scientific American* (September 1992): 152–59; for a more thorough discourse, G. M. Edelman and G. Tononi, *A Universe of Consciousness: How Matter Becomes Imagination* (Basic Books, 2001). E. Cardena, S. J. Lynn, and S. Krippner (eds.), *Varieties of Anomalous Experience* (American Psychological Association, 2000), offers an interesting dis-

cussion on the state of consciousness associated with mystical experiences. Consult also note 87.

140. See note 87; or G. Aston-Jones et al., "A neural circuit for circadian regulation of arousal," *Nature Neuroscience* 4 (2001): 732–38.

141. J. Born et al., "Timing the end of nocturnal sleep," *Nature* 397 (1999): 29.

142. G. G. Gallup et al., "Further reflections on self-recognition in primates," *Animal Behavior* 50 (1995): 1525–32.

143. D. Reiss and L. Marino, "Mirror self-recognition in the bottlenose dolphin: A case of cognitive convergence," *Proceedings of the National Academy of Science USA* 98 (2001): 5937–42.

144. J. Kagan, *The Second Year: The Emergence of Self-Awareness* (Harvard University Press, 1986).

145. See D. J. Povinelli, *Folk Physics for Apes: The Chimpanzees Theory of How the World Works* (Oxford University Press, 2000); or K. Wright, "The Tarzan syndrome," *Discover* (November 1996): 88–98.

146. Spinney, "I had a hunch," *New Scientist* (5 September 1998): 42–47.

147. R. Carter, "Tune in, turn off," *New Scientist* (9 October 1999): 30–34.

148. J. D. Connolly and M. A. Goodale, "The role of visual feedback of hand position in the control of manual prehension," *Experimental Brain Research* 125 (1999): 281–86.

149. See: A. Motluk, "It's a wonderful lie," *New Scientist* (22/29 December 2001): 70–71; or D. Schacter, *The Seven Sins of Memory* (Houghton Mifflin, 2001). For more on hypnosis, M. R. Nash, "The truth and the hype of hypnosis," *Scientific American* (July 2001): 37–43.

150. Animals that cannot swim also appear to lack conscious control of breathing—they are unable to close the passage to the lungs. The conscious control of breathing observed in man may be a consequence of our period of living in close association with water. See note 62.

151. W. F. Hill, "Effects of mere exposure on preferences in nonhuman mammals," *Psychological Bulletin* 85 (1978): 1177–98.

152. For further discussion on free will, I recommend R. M. Restak, *The Modular Brain: How New Discoveries in Neuroscience are Answering Age-*

Old Questions About Memory, Free Will, Consciousness, and Personal Identity (Touchstone, 1994).

153. See note 34.

154. The categorization of feelings is reflected in typical introductory books in psychology, such as Atkinson et al. (see note 39). I also recommend D. Evans, *Emotion: The Science of Sentiment* (Oxford University Press, 2001) for an excellent introduction to the evolutionary perspective on emotions.

155. P. W. Halligan, "Inability to recognize disgust in Huntington's disease," *The Lancet* 351 (1998): 464.

156. J. J. Hallcrest, *Facial Expressions: Anatomy & Analysis* (ABBE Publications, 1992).

157. See note 34.

158. See Nesse and Williams, note 29.

159. See Kramer under note 115; see also R. M. Sapolsky, *The Trouble with Testosterone* (Simon & Schuster, 1997).

160. F. E. Andre, "The future of vaccines, immunization concepts and practice," *Vaccine* 19 (2001): 2206–9.

161. G. Hamilton, "Let them eat dirt," *New Scientist* (18 July 1998): 26–31; see also M. Yazdanbakhsh, P. G. Kremsner, and R. V. Ree, "Allergy, parasites and the hygiene hypothesis," *Science* 296 (2002): 490–94.

162. T. K. Hensch, "Whisking away space in the brain," *Neuron* 24 (1999): 623–37.

163. See for example G. R. Lubach et al., "Effects of early rearing environment on immune responses of infant rhesus monkeys," *Brain, Behavior, and Immunity* 9 (1995): 31–46, and references therein.

164. D. Liu et al., "Maternal care, hippocampal glucocorticoid receptors, and hypothalamic-pituitary-adrenal responses to stress," *Science* 277 (1997): 1659–62.

165. R. M. Post et al., "Neural plasticity and emotional memory," *Development and Psychopathology* 10 (1998): 829–55.

166. See note 87 for an excellent review.

167. E. M. Hallowell, *Worry: Hope and Help for a Common Condition* (Ballantine Books, 1998).

168. For an excellent treatise on these emotions, see J. LeDoux, *The Emotional Brain: The Mysterious Underpinnings of Emotional Life* (Simon & Schuster, 1997).

169. C. B. Nemeroff, "The neurobiology of depression," *Scientific American* (June 1998): 28–35.

170. D. Hamer and P. Copeland, *Living With Our Genes* (Doubleday, 1998).

171. P. Brown, "A mind under siege," *New Scientist* (16 June 2001): 34–37.

172. See note 168; also the recent book by N. E. Rosenthal, *The Emotional Revolution: How the New Science of Feelings Can Transform Your Life* (Citadel Press, 2002), discusses how an understanding of emotions can help us alleviate mental suffering.

173. See note 168; or K. A. Maubach et al., "Novel strategies for pharmacotherapy of depression," *Current Opinion in Chemical Biology* 3 (1999): 481–88.

174. C. Mlot, "Probing the biology of emotion," *Science* 280 (1998): 1005–7.

175. F. Strack, L. L. Martin, and S. Stepper, "Inhibiting and facilitating conditions of the human smile: A nonobtrusive test of the facial feedback," *Journal of Personality and Social Psychology* 54 (1988): 768–77.

Chapter 8. Sex: The Most Important and Most Difficult Task

176. See note 87; or P. E. Micevych and R. P. Hammer (eds.), *Neurobiological Effects of Sex Steroid Hormones* (Cambridge University Press, 1995).

177. For example, a recent authoritative study on sex in the United States concluded that 43 percent of women have sexual problems: E. O. Laumann, A. Paik and R. C. Rosen, "Sexual dysfunction in the United States: Prevalence and predictors," *JAMA* 281 (1999): 537–44.

178. Lisa Stowers et al., "Loss of sex discrimination and male-male aggression in mice deficient for TRP2," *Science* 295 (2002): 1493–500.

179. For discussions of the biological function of sex: M. Ridley "Is sex good for anything?" *New Scientist* (4 December 1993): 36–40; or, by

the same author, *The Red Queen: Sex and the Evolution of Human Nature* (Penguin, 1995). For those interested in scholarly discussions, the vol. 3 (no. 4) issue of *Nature Reviews* (2002) is dedicated to the question.

180. For a comprehensive treatise, I recommend C. S. Ford and F. A. Beach, *Patterns of Sexual Behavior* (Harper & Row, 1951). This book was written half a century ago, by an anthropologist and a psychologist, respectively, at a time when the zeitgeist of the social sciences allowed for both an openness toward sex and toward the utilization of an evolutionary perspective to behavior. There are a number of more recent books on sexual behavior, but it seems as though some of the research referred to in this book has later been forgotten.

181. For more on mate selection and strange courtship strategies, see: H. Freedman, *Sex-Link* (Bantam, 1977); or D. P. Barash, *Sociobiology and Behavior* (Hodder and Stoughton, 1982). I also recommend D. P. Barash and J. E. Lipton, *The Myth of Monogamy: Fidelity and Infidelity in Animals and People* (Freeman, 2001).

182. P. Verrell, "When males are choosy," *New Scientist* (20 January 1990): 46–51.

183. R. Dunbar, "Are you lonesome tonight," *New Scientist* (11 February 1995): 26–31.

184. R. Dunbar, "What's in a baboon's behind?" *Nature* 410 (2001): 158.

185. For pictures of these monkeys, and a delightful discussion of sexual characteristics, I recommend D. Morris, *Manwatching: A Field Guide to Human Behavior* (Abrams, 1977).

186. J. R. MacKinnon, *The Ape Within Us* (Holt & Co, 1978).

187. D. Fox, "Gentle persuasion," *New Scientist* (9 February 2002): 32–35.

188. For an excellent discussion of the sexual life of bonobos, see de Waal and Lanting (under note 85). For a short review, I suggest T. Kano, "The social behavior of chimpanzees and bonobos: Empirical evidence and shifting assumptions," *Current Anthropology* 39 (1998): 410–11.

189. D. Hamer and P. Copeland, *The Science of Desire: The Search for the Gay Gene and the Biology of Behavior* (Touchstone, 1996).

190. B. Bagemihl, *Biological Exuberance: Animal Homosexuality and Natural Diversity* (St. Martin's Press, 1999).

191. G. Vines, "Obscure origins of desire," *New Scientist* (28 November 1992): 2–8.

192. D. Bem, "Exotic becomes erotic: A developmental theory of sexual orientation," *Psychological Reviews* 103 (1996): 320–59.

193. C. J. Cole and C. R. Townsend, "Parthenogenetic lizards as vertebrate systems," *Journal of Experimental Zoology. Supplement* 4 (1990): 174–76.

194. For more on sex in creepy things, see notes 5 and 181.

195. See Barash, note 181.

Chapter 9. Mating Behavior: What Has Love Got to Do with It?

196. R. Dunbar, "The ecology of monogamy," *New Scientist* (30 August 1984): 12–15; or, for a more in depth discussion, see Barash and Lipton, under note 181.

197. For more on mating strategies, see note 181; or J. F. Wittenberger and R. L. Tilson, "The evolution of monogamy: Hypotheses and evidence," *Annual Review of Ecological System* 11 (1980): 197–211.

198. For more information on hormones and bonding, I suggest T. L. Crenshaw, *The Alchemy of Love and Lust: How Our Sex Hormones Influence Our Relationships* (Pocket Books, 1997).

199. See note 87.

200. C. S. Carter and L. L. Getz, "Monogamy and the prairie vole," *Scientific American* (June 1993): 70–76.

201. See note 87.

202. C. Wedekind and S. Furi, "Body odour preferences in men and women: Do they aim for specific MHC combinations or simply heterozygosity?" *Proceedings of the Royal Society of London. Series B. Biological Sciences* 264 (1997): 1471–79; and the experiment with perfume: N. L. McCoy and L. Pitino, "Pheromonal influences on sociosexual behavior in young women," *Physiology & Behavior* 75 (2002): 367–75.

203. For more on aphrodisiacs and love portions, I suggest note 198; and T. Crenshaw and J. P. Goldberg, *Sexual Pharmacology: Drugs that Affect Sexual Functioning* (Norton, 1996). For MSH, see D. Martindale, "Hot on the scent," *New Scientist* (3 November 2001): 11.

204. See note 87.

205. S. P Mendoza and W. A. Mason, "Attachment relationships in

new world primates," *Annals of the New York Academy of Sciences* 807 (1997): 203–18.

206. K. Hawkes et al., "Grandmothering, menopause, and the evolution of human life histories," *Proceedings of the National Academy of Science USA* 95 (1998): 1336–39.

207. R. D. Alexander, *The Biology of Moral Systems* (Aldine, 1987).

208. D. Marazziti et al., "Alteration of the platelet serotonin transporter in romantic love," *Psychological Medicine* 29 (1999): 741–45.

209. L. Pitkow et al., "Facilitation of affiliation and pair-bond formation by vasopressin receptor gene transfer into the ventral forebrain of a monogamous vole," *Journal of Neuroscience* 21 (2001): 7392–96.

210. See note 77.

211. D. Morris, *The Human Sexes* (St. Martin's Press, 1997).

212. D. M. Buss, "Human mate selection," *American Scientist* 73 (1985): 47–51.

213. G. Miller, *The Mating Mind* (Doubleday, 2000).

214. For more background on the theory of kissing, I suggest note 122.

215. For a not so serious account, see 'E. Petting,' "Keep a stiff upper lip," *New Scientist* (21/28 December 1991): 32–33.

216. C. R. Freeman-Gallant, "DNA fingerprinting reveals female preference for male parental care in savannah sparrows," *Proceedings of the Royal Society of London. Series B. Biological Sciences* 263 (1996): 157–60; or R. Dunbar, "Your cheatin' heart," *New Scientist* (21 November 1998): 29–32.

217. J. Gray, *Men Are from Mars, Women Are from Venus* (HarperCollins, 1992). For additional literature on the differences between men and women, I can recommend notes 105 and 170.

218. D. M. Buss, *The Dangerous Passion: Why Jealousy is as Necessary as Love and Sex* (Free Press, 2000).

219. J. T. Winslow et al., "A role for central vasopressin in pair bonding in monogamous prairie voles," *Nature* 365 (1993): 544–48.

220. See D. Symons, *The Evolution of Human Sexuality* (Oxford University Press, 1979).

221. See note 5.

222. See note 217 for relevant literature.

223. F. de Waal, *Chimpanzee Politics: Power and Sex Among Apes* (Johns Hopkins University Press, 2000).

224. J. Knight, "Meet the Herod bug," *Nature* 412 (2001): 12–14.

225. For hormonal regulation of sexual development, see note 176.

226. J. Imperato-McGinley et al., "Androgens and the evolution of male-gender identity among male pseudohermaphrodites with 5-alpha-reductase deficiency," *New England Journal of Medicine* 300 (1979): 1233–37.

227. The fate of the male seahorse is described by Barash, see note 5.

Chapter 10. Good and Evil: The Pleasure of Compassion

228. See: A. Jolly, *The Evolution of Primate Behavior* (Macmillan, 1972); but try also note 12; or F. de Waal (ed.), *Tree of Origin: What Primate Behavior Can Tell Us About Human Social Evolution* (Harvard University Press, 2001).

229. See note 11.

230. See note 46.

231. For more on the importance of social life for human evolution, I suggest R. Dunbar et al. (eds.), *The Evolution of Culture* (Rutgers University Press, 1999).

232. W. D. Hamilton, *Narrow Roads of Gene Land: The Collected Papers of WD Hamilton* (Freeman, 1996).

233. I recommend Dawkins for a discussion of the relationship between genes, cells, individuals, and groups of individuals, see note 12.

234. For more comprehensive coverage of the evolution of social behavior, I suggest: E. Sober and D. S. Wilson, *Unto Others: The Evolution and Psychology of Unselfish Behavior* (Harvard University Press, 1999); or note 18.

235. On reputation: M. Milinski, D. Semmann, and H.-J. Krambeck, "Reputation helps solve the 'tragedy of the commons'," *Nature* 415 (2002) 424-26; on docility: H. A. Simon, "A mechanism for social selection and successful altruism," *Science* 250 (1990) 1665-68; and on punishment: E. Fehr and S. Gächter, "Altruistic punishment in humans," *Nature* 415 (2002): 137–40.

236. The evolutionary rationale for human morality has recently been discussed in several books, such as: R. Wright, *The Moral Animal* (Vin-

tage Books, 1995); M. Ridley, *The Origin of Virtue* (Penguin, 1998); and the primatologist F. de Waal, *Good Natured: The Origin of Right and Wrong in Humans and other Animals* (Harvard University Press, 1997).

237. The discussion is based on Panksepp's book, see note 87.

238. M. P. Bouvard et al., "Low-dose naltrexone effect on plasma chemistries and clinical symptoms in autism: A double-blind placebo-controlled study," *Psychiatry Research* 58 (1995): 191–201.

239. See note 87.

240. K. E. Barnard and T. B. Brazelton, *Touch: The Foundation of Experience* (International University Press, 1990).

241. M. Daly and M. Wilson, *Homicide* (Aldine de Gruyter, 1988).

242. For information on child rearing in these and other animals, see N. A. Krasnegor and R. S. Bridges (eds.), *Mammalian Parenting* (Oxford University Press, 1990).

243. See note 21.

244. B. Rimland, "The altruism paradox," *The Southern Psychologist* 2 (1982): 8–9.

245. R. M. Sapolsky, *Why Zebras Don't Get Ulcers: An Updated Guide to Stress, Stress Related Diseases, and Coping* (Freeman & Co, 1998).

246. See note 87 for more information on the evolution and neurology of circuits related to rage or anger; for an evolutionary perspective, see also Evans under note 154.

247. If you really want to dip into human weaknesses, I suggest a collection of articles with the common title, "Destination hell," *New Scientist* (28 March 1998): 24–43.

248. T. H. Clutton-Brock and G. A. Parker, "Punishment in animal societies," *Nature* 373 (1995): 209–16.

249. For those interested in Norse mythology, I can recommend H. A. Guerber, *Myths of the Norsemen: From the Eddas and Sagas* (Dover Publications, 1992).

250. The main biblical reference is Numbers 31, verses 17 and 18; Barash (note 5) and Pinker (note 105) have both discussed Jewish genocides with reference to the Bible.

251. See note 135.

252. See D. L. Horowitz, *The Deadly Ethnic Riot* (University of Cali-

fornia Press, 2001), for a description of one of the worst type of curses to befall modern societies.

Chapter 11. Community: Making the Most of Our Social Instincts

253. N. A. Chagnon, *Yanomamö: The Last Days of Eden* (Harvest Books, 1992).

254. A. B. Weiner, *The Trobrianders of Papua New Guinea* (International Thomson Publishing, 1988).

255. K. Douglas, "Playing fair," *New Scientist* (10 March 2001): 38–42.

256. See Dugatkin under note 18.

257. G. Hardin, "The tragedy of the commons," *Science* 162 (1968): 1243–48.

258. For more background on Japanese culture, and the ideas I put forth, I recommend: G. Clark, *Understanding the Japanese* (Kinseido, 1983); and P. Varley, *Japanese Culture* (University of Hawaii Press, 2000).

259. R. M. Keesing, *Cultural Anthropology* (Holt, Rinehart and Winston, 1981).

260. See note 21.

261. A. Alland, *To Be Human* (Wiley, 1980).

262. A. Ballard, "Modern hunter-gatherers and early symbolic culture," in R. Dunbar et al. (eds.), *The Evolution of Culture* (Rutgers University Press, 1999), p. 50–68.

263. M. Newton, *Savage Girls and Wild Boys* (Faber and Faber, 2002).

264. For more on the question of boredom and organization of work, I suggest: M. Csikszentmihalyi, *Beyond Boredom and Anxiety: Experiencing Flow in Work and Play* (Jossey-Bass, 2000); or C. Shilling, *The Body and Social Theory* (Sage Publications, 1993).

265. For an introduction to the concept of time: A. Gell, *The Anthropology of Time: Cultural Constructs of Temporal Maps and Images* (Berg, 1992); but see also Csikszentmihalyi (under note 264).

266. If you want to read more on social contracts, try B. Skyrms, *Evolution of the Social Contract* (Cambridge University Press, 1996).

267. C. A. Bramblett, *The Patterns of Primate Behavior* (Waveland Press, 1993); and E. B. Keverne, N. D. Martensz, and B. Tuite, "Beta-

endorphin concentrations in cerebrospinal fluid of monkeys are influenced by grooming relationships," *Psychoneuroendocrinology* 14 (1989): 155–61.

268. R. Dunbar, "Why gossip is good for you," *New Scientist* (21 November 1992): 28–31.

269. J. A. Hostetler, *Hutterite Society* (Johns Hopkins University Press, 1997).

270. For more on rational choice, or the lack of it, I recommend J. Elster, *Nuts and Bolts for the Social Sciences* (Cambridge University Press, 1989).

271. V. L. Nimgaonkar et al., "Low prevalence of psychoses among the Hutterites, an isolated religious community," *American Journal of Psychiatry* 157 (2000): 1065–70. For a broader view, see C. McLaughlin and G. Davidson, *Builders of the Dawn: Community Lifestyles in a Changing World* (Book Publication Company, 1990).

272. See note 75.

273. See note 5; or S. D. Singh, "Urban monkeys," *Scientific American* 221 (1969): 108–15.

274. R. N. Cardinal et al., "Impulsive choice induced in rats by lesions of the nucleus accumbens core," *Science* 292 (2001): 2499–501.

275. See note 255.

276. J. Lovelock, *Gaia: A New Look at Life on Earth* (Oxford University Press, 2000).

277. For further discussion, see J. P. Lovell (ed.), *Insights from Film into Violence and Oppression* (Praeger Publications, 1998).

278. A. Huxley's book, *Brave New World*, has not exactly boosted the popularity of this idea.

Chapter 12. Religion: If God Is in Your Genes

279. E. J. Larson and L. Witham, "Scientists and religion in America," *Scientific American* (September 1999): 78–83; and G. Easterbrook, "Science and God: A warming trend," *Science* 277 (1997): 890–93.

280. I have previously discussed this idea in B. Grinde, "The biology of religion: A Darwinian gospel," *Journal of Social and Evolutionary Systems* 21 (1998): 19–28. For other authors with related ideas, see: B. D. Josephson, "Religion in the genes," *Nature* 362 (1993): 583; L. B. Steadman and C. T. Palmer, "Religion as an identifiable traditional behavior subject to

natural selection," *Journal of Social and Evolutionary Systems* 18 (1995): 149–64; or A. Newberg, E. G. D'Aquili, and V. Rause, *Why God Won't Go Away: Brain Science and the Biology of Belief* (Ballantine Books, 2001).

281. R. A. Solecki, "Shandidar IV, a Neanderthal flower burial in northern Iraq," *Science* 190 (1975): 880–81; see also Lewin (under note 44).

282. J. L. Arsuaga et al., "Three new human skulls from the Sima de los Huesos middle pleistocene site in Sierra," *Nature* 362 (1993): 534–37; and note 59.

283. A. F. C. Wallace, *Religion: An Anthropological View* (Random House, 1966); see also note 77.

284. R. A. Rappaport, "The sacred in human evolution," *Annual Review of Ecology and Systematics* (1971): 23–44; or, for a more comprehensive treatise on religions, read N. Smart, *The World's Religions* (Cambridge University Press, 1998).

285. M. Vaneechoutte, "The memetic basis of religion," *Nature* 365 (1993): 290.

286. See: Newberg, D'Aquili and Rause under note 280; B. Holmes, "In search of God," *New Scientist* (April 21 2001): 24–28; or A. Motluk, "Touched by the Word of God," *New Scientist* (November 8 1997) 7.

287. For comments on the various advantages of religion, see for example: C. D. Bateson, "Sociobiology and the role of religion in promoting prosocial behavior: An alternative view," *Journal of Personality and Social Psychology* 45 (1983): 1380–85; P. Hefner, "Myth and morality: The love command," *Zygon* 2 (1991): 115–36; as well as Wallace (note 283) and Rappaport (note 284).

288. See: H. G. Koenig and H. J. Cohen, *The Link Between Religion and Health: Psychoneuroimmunology and the Faith Factor* (Oxford University Press, 2002); C. G. Ellison, "Are religious people nice people? Evidence from the National Survey of Black Americans," *Social Forces* 71 (1992): 411–30; or note 21.

289. J. M. Diamond, "The language steamrollers," *Nature* 389 (1997): 544–46.

290. M. Wertheim, "God of the quantum vacuum," *New Scientist* (October 4 1997): 28–31.

Chapter 13. The Art of Seeing: Visual Delight

291. Some of the ideas I present in this chapter also appear in B. Grinde, "The biology of visual aesthetics," *Journal of Social and Evolutionary Systems* 19 (1996): 31–40.

292. See note 77; or J. R. Benton and R. Diyanni, *Arts and Culture: An Introduction to the Humanities* (Prentice Hall, 1998).

293. For documentation on early decorative behavior see: J. Halverson, "Art for art's sake in the Paleolithic," *Current Anthropology* 28 (1987): 63–87; and K. Coe, "Art: The replicable unit – An inquiry into the possible origin of art as a social behavior," *Journal of Social and Evolutionary Systems* 15 (1992) 217-34. The red ochre stones are described by C. S. Henshilwood et al., "Emergence of modern human behavior: Middle Stone Age engravings from South Africa," *Science* 295 (2002): 1278–80.

294. For further information, consult N. W. Daw, *Visual Development* (Plenum Publications, 1995).

295. G. H. Jacobs, "Primate photopigments and primate color vision," *Proceedings of the National Academy of Science USA* 93 (1996): 577–81.

296. M. S. Livingstone, "Art, illusion and the visual system," *Scientific American* (January 1988): 68–75.

297. R. S. Woodworth, *Experimental Psychology* (Holt, 1938).

298. E. Wreschner, "Red ochre and human evolution: A case for discussion," *Current Anthropology* 21 (1980): 631–44.

299. See note 184.

300. T. A. Wehr, "Manipulations of sleep and phototherapy: Non-pharmacological alternatives in the treatment of depression," *Clinical Neuropharmacology* 13 (1990): S54–65.

301. Consult K. E. Orrin, *Overload and Boredom* (Greenwood Press, 1986) for a discussion on sensory overload.

302. See note 105.

303. A. P. Møller, "Female swallow preference for symmetrical male sexual ornaments," *Nature* 357 (1992): 238–40; R. A. Johnstone, "Female preferences for symmetrical males as a by-product of selection for mate recognition," *Nature* 372 (1994): 172–75; and D. Concar, "Sex and the symmetrical body," *New Scientist* (April 22 1995): 40–44.

304. For more on various schools of art, see H. Osborne, *Aesthetics and Art Theory* (Dutton, 1970).

305. For more information, consult W. F. Allman, *The Stone Age Present* (Touchstone, 1995).

306. A presentation of the hedonist school can be found in E. Dissanayake, *What is Art for?* (University of Washington Press, 1989).

307. D. Morris, *The Human Animal* (Crown Publications, 1994).

Chapter 14. Sounds and Song: Musical Satisfaction

308. The explanation I suggest in this chapter has previously been published in B. Grinde, "A biological perspective on musical appreciation," *Nordic Journal of Music Therapy* 9 (2000): 18–27. In this journal, and on its Internet site, http://www.njmt.no/, there are also comments made by other scientists.

309. A. P. Merriam, *The Anthropology of Music* (Northwestern University Press, 1964). See also note 77.

310. J. Zhang et al., "Oldest playable musical instruments found at Jiahu early Neolithic site in China," *Nature* 401 (1999): 366–68.

311. I. Turk, J. Dirjec and B. Kavur, "Was the oldest musical instrument in Europe found in Slovenia," *Anthropologie* 101 (1997): 531–40.

312. M. R. Zetner and J. Kagan, "Perception of music by infants," *Nature* 383 (1996): 29.

313. J. A. Sloboda, "Music structure and emotional response: Some empirical findings," *Psychology of Music* 19 (1991): 110–20; A. Storr, *Music and the Mind* (Ballantine Books, 1992); and A. C. North and D. J. Hargreaves (eds.), *The Psychology of Music* (Oxford University Press, 1997).

314. See, for example: K. Uetake, J. F. Hurnik, and L. Johnson, "Effect of music on voluntary approach of dairy cows to an automatic milking system," *Applied Animal Behaviour Science* 53 (1997): 175–82.

315. S. Young, "Blues for beaky," *New Scientist* (24/31 December 1994): 44–7.

316. H. Preuschoft, *The Lesser Apes: Evolutionary and Behavioral Biology* (Edinburgh University Press, 1985).

317. For more information on the physiology of hearing, I suggest R. M. Warren, *Auditory Perception: A New Analysis and Synthesis* (Cambridge University Press, 1999).

318. For more background, see G. F. Ball and S. H. Hulse, "Birdsong," *The American Psychologist* 53 (1998): 37–58.

319. Pinker (see note 53) offers an excellent introduction to language acquisition in children.

320. For discussions on the relationship between music and language, see: A. T. Downing, *Music and the Origins of Language* (Cambridge University Press, 1995); or note 105. Recently it has been shown that the processing of musical input in the brain involves much the same area used to process spoken words: B. Maess et al., "Musical syntax is processed in Broca's area: An MEG study," *Nature Neuroscience* 4 (2001): 540–45.

321. H. M. Lenhoff et al., "Williams syndrome and the brain," *Scientific American* (December 1997): 42–47.

322. S. P. Springer and G. Deutsch, *Left Brain, Right Brain: Perspective from Cognitive Neuroscience* (Freeman & Co, 1997).

323. For sound production in whales and birds, P. M. Gray et al., "The music of nature and the nature of music," *Science* 291 (2001): 52–54.

324. See note 53; and H. Nishimura et al., "Sign language 'heard' in the auditory cortex," *Nature* 397 (1999): 116.

325. M. R. Zentner and J. Kagan, "Perception of music by infants," *Nature* 383 (1996): 29; and J. G. Roederer, *The Physics and Psychophysics of Music* (Springer, 1995).

326. K. Brown, "Striking the right note," *New Scientist* (December 4 1999): 38–41.

327. L. Finnas, "How can musical preferences be modified? A research review," *Bulletin of the Council for Research in Music Education* 102 (1989): 1–58.

328. K. Hevner, "Experimental studies of the elements of expression in music," *American Journal of Psychology* 48 (1936): 246–68; or Sloboda, under note 313.

329. A. Goldstein, "Thrills in response to music listening," *Physiological Psychology* 8 (1980) 126-29); J. Panksepp, "The emotional sources of 'chills' induced by music," *Music Perception* 13 (1995): 171–207; A. Motluk, "The big chill," *New Scientist* (April 27 1996): S17–19; and Sloboda (under note 313).

330. See Panksepp under note 329 or 87.

331. C. L. Krumhansl, "Rhythm and pitch in music cognition," *Psychological Bulletin* 126 (2000): 159–79.

332. A. J. DeCasper and A. D. Sigafoos, "The intrauterine heartbeat: A potent reinforcer for newborns," *Infant Behavior and Development* 6 (1983): 19–25.

333. P. S. G. Stein et al., *Neurons, Networks and Motor Behavior* (MIT Press, 1997); E. Marder, "Moving rhythms," *Nature* 410 (2001): 755; or T. Gura, "Rhythm of life," *New Scientist* (4 August 2001): 32–35.

334. For the cultural role of music, see for example: I. Deliege and J. Sloboda, *Perception and Cognition of Music* (Psychology Press, 1997); or W. Benzon, *Beethoven's Anvil: Music in Mind and Culture* (Basic Books, 2001).

335. See Miller under note 9.

336. The suggestion is discussed by S. Brown, "The 'musilanguage' model of music evolution," in B. Merker, N. L. Wallin, and S. Brown (eds.), *The Origins of Music* (MIT Press, 2000), p. 271–300.

337. T. Grim and M. Honza, "Does supernormal stimulus influence parental behaviour of the cuckoo's host?" *Behavioral Ecology and Sociobiology* 49 (2001), 322–29.

338. M. Florentine, W. Hunter, and S. Buus, "On the behavioral characteristics of loud-music listening," *Ear and Hearing* 19 (1998): 420–28.

339. See note 78.

Chapter 15. Is the Future Just History?

340. S. J. Olshansky, B. A. Carnes and R. N. Butler, "If humans were built to last," *Scientific American* (March 2001): 42–47.

341. For more on the evolution of life, and the creative events, see: S. J. Gould, "The evolution of life on the Earth," *Scientific American* (October 1994): 63–9; and R. Fortey, *Life: A Natural History of the First Four Billion Years of Life on Earth* (Vintage Books, 1999).

342. M. McLeod, "One small step for fish, one giant leap for us," *New Scientist* (19 August 2000): 28–32.

343. See note 11.

344. H. Gee, "Return to the planet of the apes," *Nature* 412 (2001): 131–32.

345. For a critical introduction to eugenics, see: D. B. Paul, *Controlling Human Heredity: 1865 to the Present* (Humanity Books, 1995); or, for a more positive view, R. Lynn, *Eugenics: A Reassessment* (Praeger, 2001). For more genetically based discussions: P. Kitcher, *The Lives to Come: The Genetic Revolution and Human Possibilities* (Simon and Schuster, 1996); and J. F. Crow, "The odds of losing at genetic roulette," *Nature* 397 (1999): 293–94.

346. M. Ward, "End of the road for brain evolution," *New Scientist* (25 January 1997): 14.

347. If you want to read about the importance of having a meaning, or purpose, to life, I recommend V. E. Frankl, *Man's Search for Meaning* (Washington Square Press, 1998).

348. F. de Waal, F. Aureli, and P. G. Judge, "Coping with crowding," *Scientific American* (May 2000): 54–59.

GLOSSARY

The following list includes technical terms that are either repeatedly used or deserve a more detailed explanation than the one given in the text.

Adaptation. The evolutionary process that causes an organism to adapt to the environment. Changes in any structure, biochemical process or behavioral pattern that makes an organism more fit to survive and to reproduce.

Altruism. True altruism occurs when an individual helps another at a personal cost—for example, when the mother spends time and energy helping her infant. The evolutionary explanation for this behavior is that it benefits the genes shared between mother and infant. Altruistic acts benefiting more distant kin are based on the same principle. Altruism, or preferably "apparent altruism," is also occasionally used in cases where the individual actually does reap a personal benefit. For example, when chimpanzees help each other there is a good chance the aid will be returned, since these animals do form alliances. Such behavior is referred to as reciprocity, or, in cases where the return is given by a third party, as indirect reciprocity. Some scientists believe altruism may also be a result of group selection; in other words, that evolution can favor groups where the individuals help each other.

Biomass. The total weight of all the living organisms, typically either of a particular species or of some group of species found in a given area.

Cells. Cells are the units, or the building blocks, of life. Some organisms consist of a single cell, such as bacteria, while a human body contains approximately 10^{14} cells with various functions. Our thoughts, behavior, and feelings depend on the performance of the nerve cells in the brain.

Chromosomes. The main component of each chromosome is an extremely long chain of a DNA molecule. The genes comprise segments of this chain. When a cell divides, the chromosomes become organized (with the help of proteins), and are then visible in a microscope. Each human cell contains 23 pairs of chromosomes, of which one pair is the sex chromosomes.

Default good mood. The state of mind that evolution designed for us to be in as long as troublesome situations are avoided or dealt with. The idea is that we are designed to be in an optimistic and cheerful mode because this serves the genes best. Discord conditions have a tendency to mess up our default mood.

Discord. Short for discord between environment and genes. The present conditions of life are obviously different from those our genes are adapted to, which roughly speaking corresponds to the Stone Age environment. While some of the mismatches do not matter, others are likely to constitute a strain or stress factor. I refer to the more unfortunate mismatches as Discords.

DNA. The core of life, and the most famous acronym in biology. It stands for the chemical name Deoxyribonucleic Acid. A DNA molecule is made up of two complementary chains that are twirled together in a double helix. The "pearls" on each chain are the four different nucleotide molecules: A, T, C, and G (adenine, thymine, cytosine, and guanine). The fact that the two chains are complementary facilitates replication.

Environment of Evolutionary Adaptation (EEA). EEA is the condition of living to which our genes are adapted. Since our genes were shaped over millions of years by the ever-compromising process of evolution, an exact EEA may have never existed; moreover, humans are presently adapted to different physical environments—for example, to either cold or warm climates. Yet EEA is a useful concept. Our innate behavioral propensities are presumably much the same around the globe, and it is particularly important to try to understand the EEA of social life.

Fitness. The fitness of an individual is a measure of one's capacity to raise offspring. In principle, individuals with the better genes send more genes into the next generation. As evolution cares primarily about genes, not individuals, the fitness of your genes will improve if you help other individuals who carry the same genes. This is referred to as *inclusive fitness*. Fitness "summarizes," rather than explains, the ability of a genotype to survive and reproduce. The word *success* can be used to describe an individual, or a species, with a high fitness.

Genes. Genes are the unit of inheritance by which hereditary characteristics are transmitted from parent to offspring. In principle, each gene is the blueprint for the design of one protein, and it is the proteins that carry out the various tasks required for living. Moreover, a gene is a segment of the DNA molecules that are harbored in the chromosomes. Yet, when you take a closer look, it becomes rather difficult to define, or count, genes. For example, one particular segment of DNA can give rise to several distinct proteins, and segments from different parts of the chromosome can combine to form novel proteins.

Genome. The genetic complement of organisms. Each cell harbors a complete genome, in the form of the DNA molecules enclosed in the chromosomes. The human genome includes some 40,000 or more genes. Surprisingly, these genes constitute only a small percentage of the total DNA; the rest is either "parasitic," also referred to as selfish (or "junk") DNA, or has other functions.

Habitat. The kind of environment, or locality, in which a plant or animal thrives. To use a metaphor from human life: The habitat is the address of the organism, while the niche is its occupation.

Happiness. In research on quality of life, it is common to distinguish between conditions required for happiness (food, shelter, health, and so on) and the actual sensation of well-being, typically referred to as "subjective appreciation of life." Both components may be included when one tries to compute a score for what is referred to as quality of life or happiness. In this book, the term "happiness" is restricted to how people actually feel, more in the sense of "the average mood." The term may, however, cover a wider range of moods than what is easily included in the well-being of research on happiness. For example, I argue that feelings such as grief and sorrow can add to the score; and so can a deeper peacefulness that may reflect satisfaction, but not nessecarily joy.

Hominids. The hominid lineage includes present humans and all our ancestors from the time we split from the chimpanzees five or six million years ago. *Hominoid* is a larger category that also embraces the other living great apes and their ancestors.

Human behavioral biology. A field of science that tries to understand our innate tendencies of behavior. In this book human behavioral biology is intended to include both social behavior and behavior carried out in solitude—in fact, all mental processes. It is about the role of the brain in the life of humans.

Mutations. Mutations are changes in the genes, more specifically in the DNA. Most mutations have no impact on the organism, and those that do have an impact are most likely destructive. Only rarely is there a mutation that actually leads to an improvement; yet, without mutations, evolution would cease. The rare, beneficial mutations are selected for, and will over time spread in a population, thus helping the species adapt to a changing world.

Neurotransmitters. These are required to transfer the nerve signals from one cell to the next. As a gross approximation I differentiate between two groups: The smaller ones, such as glutamate, GABA (gamma-aminobutyric acid), acetylcholine, dopamine, serotonin, and norepinephrine, are generally widespread in the brain and serve many functions. Yet it is possible to intervene specifically in particular circuits that use these transmitters because the various circuits may employ different receptors and different modulators designed to regulate the activity of the transmitters. Thus, drugs that interact with the appropriate receptors and modulators may specifically influence particular brain functions. Drugs can act either like agonists (stimulators of transmitter action) or antagonists (inhibitors). The second group of transmitters consists of neuropeptides, such as endorphins (which are part of the opioid system), oxytocin, and vasopressin. These are typically designed for particular functions and thus act on more limited parts of the brain. Since peptides are large molecules, it is more difficult to design agonists and antagonists that have pharmaceutically useful properties, but to the extent that we are able to design such effector molecules, they have the potential of acting specifically on important brain modules.

Niches. The roles of organisms in an ecological community. Each species has certain interactions with other species and a certain impact on the environment. For example, a partial description of the niche of the giraffe would be that giraffes eat the leaves of particular trees, are occasionally killed by big cats, and their decaying bodies are the home of a variety of microorganisms.

Selection. The process whereby evolution is able to improve the characteristics of a species. In principle it implies that the more fit members, those with the better genes, obtain more children. The two main forces of selection are, briefly: *natural selection*, which improves survival skills, and *sexual* selection, which improves the chances of finding a partner for procreation.

Species. This is the lower unit of classification in biological systematics. A species is typically defined as a type, or population, of organisms where all the members are capable of interbreeding with each other. However, it is not always easy to decide whether individuals can interbreed—for example, when they are separated in time. Thus, a species is often defined just in terms of particular characteristics. For example, those who study the evolution of hominids tend to name new species based solely on features of bone remnants, such as *Homo erectus* and *Homo habilis*. If these hominids had lived today, we would probably be able to breed with them.

Variation. When we talk about variation in an evolutionary sense, we mean the dissimilarities between individuals that are due to the combination of genetic and environmental differences. With the exception of identical twins, no two humans are genetically identical.

Finding the way in difficult terrain.

INDEX

as mammalian invention, 117
rough and tumble, 117, 118
signals, 120
play–face, 118
Playboy, 187
playful behavior, 160
"playless society," 116
pleasure, 55, 105, 141
drives, 48
of play, 118
Plotkin, Henry, 81
plumage, 23
police, 251, 253
pollution, 79
polyandry, 88
polygyny, 88
popular music stars, status of, 259
population, 86
density, 80
growth curves, 334
pornography, 53, 88, 187
industry, 177
"social," 187
positive brain circuits, 158
"positive psychology," 35
positive sensations, 42
possessiveness, 210
postmenopausaol, 199
postpartum depression, 155
Povinelli, Daniel, 134
predators, 23, 29, 31, 71, 221
prevailing conditions, 25
priests, 35
Catholic, 283
primate ancestors, 64
primates, 64, 66
primitive traits, 76
procreation, 105, 165, 210
progeny, 23, 36, 55
prokaryotes, 331
promiscuity, 87–89, 90, 180, 210
prosopagnosia, 102

proteins, 71
Provine, Robert, 122
Prozac, 108, 109, 148
psilocybin mushroom, 104
psychiatry, 83
psychoactive drugs, 103, 110
psychoactive substances, 106, 108
psychology, 83
pubic hair, 177
punishment, 48
puppets, 18,
puppies, 198
pure sounds, 317
purpose in life, 344
pursuit of happiness, 52
pygmy chimpanzee. *See* bonobos

Q

quality of life, 11, 36, 44

R

rage, 236–42, 236, 271
buttons, 240, 245
circuit, 239, 241
module, 237
Rain Man, 136
rank, 259
rape, 52, 184, 186
rapid eye movement (REM), 131
rats, 86, 262
laughing, 120
mothers, 262
pups, 262
and rough and tumble play, 118
whiskers of, 148, 150
receptor molecules, 97
reciprocity, 226
reconciliation, in children's play, 262
red, 300, 308
red ochre, stone, 294
Reflections on Poetry (Baumgarten), 304
regurgitation, 206